SIXTH EDITION

THE NEW APPLIED MATHEMATICS

SIXTH EDITION

THE
NEW APPLIED
MATHEMATICS

SIDNEY J. LASLEY

MYRTLE F. MUDD

PAUL V. ROGLER

Chairman of Secondary
Mathematics for Public Schools,
Wilmington, Delaware

WITHHOLDING TAX S1

ORMATION

$ 48.00

leral Income Tax withheld,
any

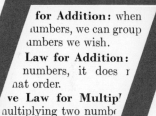

for Addition: when
numbers, we can group
umbers we wish.
Law for Addition:
numbers, it does r
nat order.
ve Law for Multip'
multiplying two numbe
matter in what ord

PRENTICE-HALL, INC.   Englewood Cliffs, N. J.

PREFACE

We today realize that a mastery of the basic processes of mathematics is most essential. The demands of the Space Age bring to light the importance of the fundamentals skills of mathematics and the ability to apply mathematical knowledge.

Governmental and industrial surveys have revealed an urgent need for courses in mathematics that will develop a higher degree of facility in the fundamentals of arithmetic, in the use of formulas and equations, and in the development of spatial concepts and mensuration. Many different groups have worked on suggestions for ways of modernizing mathematics instruction and, consequently, high schools are offering courses that place increased emphasis on the understanding of basic principles of arithmetic, algebra, and geometry.

The sixth edition of THE NEW APPLIED MATHEMATICS is designed to equip high-school students with mathematical abilities, knowledges, and experiences that will meet their everyday mathematical requirements.

Many of the suggestions of the School Mathematics Study Group have been incorporated into the new edition. Attention is given to illustrating ways in which the axioms of our number system are used in computations; the structure of our number system is given meaning by means of the study of numeration systems that use bases other than the familiar base ten; and many new problems dealing with sports records, newly designed articles, and space probe data have been added.

In general, the book offers:

a. A maximum course for one year's work in general mathematics. The large amount of material included provides for a selection of topics in accordance with class needs.

b. Provision for individual differences: (1) by grading the exercises, by means of stars, into three grades of difficulty; (2) by suggesting "Play off" activities at the close of each chapter.

c. A vocabulary study at the beginning of each chapter and a *Glossary of Mathematical Terms* in the *Appendix* to enable students to read the content more intelligently.

d. A plan of procedure to improve skill in the fundamentals of arithmetic and percentage. There are class *Inventory Tests* with individual follow-up *Practice Exercises* designed to overcome any weakness. For maintenance and improvement of the skills attained, there are *Check-Up Exercises* and *Review Exercises* supplemented by *Achievement Tests*.

e. Many topics which provide knowledges of value to a consumer in the home or in business. In these chapters there is an abundance of exercises which afford application of mathematical processes.

f. Geometry that is intuitive in nature. The students are made familiar with important geometric forms, mensuration, and constructions.

g. Formulas, equations, graphs, and signed numbers, which are the most usable topics of algebra.

The exercises encourage self-activity by the student, increase interest, and produce greater effort.

Such a program appeals to students and at the same time prepares them to meet everyday mathematical situations.

The Authors

CONTENTS

CHAPTER II   **ADDITION, SUBTRACTION, MULTIPLI-CATION, AND DIVISION OF COMMON FRACTIONS WITH APPLICATIONS**

CHAPTER III   **ADDITION, SUBTRACTION, MULTIPLI-CATION, AND DIVISION OF DECIMAL FRACTIONS WITH APPLICATIONS**

CHAPTER IV   PERCENTAGE AND PROBLEM SOLVING

CHAPTER V   DENOMINATE NUMBERS; RATIO AND PROPORTION

CHAPTER VI   **DIRECT MEASUREMENT OF LINES AND ANGLES**

CHAPTER VII   **GRAPHS**

CHAPTER XI   LOCAL, STATE, AND FEDERAL TAXES

CHAPTER XII   POSITION AND FORM OF OBJECTS

CHAPTER XVI THE FORMULA

CHAPTER XVII THE EQUATION

CHAPTER XVIII SIGNED NUMBERS

INTRODUCTION

1. The beginnings of arithmetic. Arithmetic had its beginning when man first began to count. It served to answer the everpresent question: "How many?"

Our number system has been in the process of development for hundreds of centuries. It is difficult for us to realize that at one time there were no names for numbers. Primitive man showed how many sheep he owned by placing as many rocks in a pile, or sticks in a row, as he had sheep.

After the number *one* came into being, primitive man could say, "I have *one* sheep." If he had two or more sheep, he could say, "I have *many* sheep." Later when the word *two* came along, he could express himself as having *one* sheep, *two* sheep, or *many* sheep.

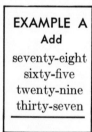

EXAMPLE A
Add
seventy-eight
sixty-five
twenty-nine
thirty-seven

After the names for numbers came into existence it was a long, long time before any symbols were written to represent those names. How well do you think you would succeed in adding a column of numbers expressed as words as in example A? Today we often have more than one name, or symbol, for the same number. We can write the number "ten" as 10, as 5×2, or as $30 \div 3$, as $\sqrt{100}$, and in many other ways. The various ways of writing a number help us use it in many different problems.

Fig. 1

Fig. 2. Best things in a boy's life

All of our numbers are combinations of the ten digits: 0, 1, 2, 3, 4, 5, 6, 7, 8, and 9. For example, the number 728 is made up of the digits 7, 2, and 8. These same three digits may be combined to make other whole numbers, such as 782, 278, 287, 827, and 872. What whole numbers can you form by combining the digits 1, 4, 8, and 5?

Numbers may be whole numbers, called *integers*, or parts of whole numbers, called *fractions*.

2. The importance of mathematics. Huckleberry Finn once said, "I have been to school most all the time and could say the multiplication table up to six times seven is thirty-five, and I don't reckon I could ever get any further than that if I was to live forever. I don't take no stock in mathematics anyway."

Huck Finn did not live in an age of planes, cars, spaceships, radios, television, and atomic bombs. He could never have studied aviation, calculated the flight of a bullet, measured an engine part to a thousandth of an inch, squared a number, solved an equation, or read a blueprint. Huck's lack of mathematical knowledge would have made such problems impossible for him.

The days of Huck Finn are past. New problems call for increased mathematical skill. The world demands speed and accuracy. The businessman of today is no longer satisfied with the speed of yesterday, nor will he tolerate any inaccuracy in his records. He knows that inaccuracy may cost him customers and money.

You and I must make a special effort to eliminate all our errors and to speed our work to meet the demands of the times. The first step is to improve our skills in the *fundamentals of arithmetic*.

3. Plan of procedure to improve the fundamentals of arithmetic. Each of you will need to continue your practice in the fundamentals of arithmetic. Some of you will practice in order that you may maintain the high skill that is already yours. Others of you, who have not yet reached a satisfactory score in one or more of the computations, will need to practice in order to improve your skill.

In this book you will find four types of exercises to aid you in mastering the fundamentals of arithmetic.

The first five chapters contain *Inventory Tests* designed to show you any weak spots in your computations. The follow-up *Practice Exercises* in the Appendix are there to help you overcome those weaknesses.

You will find a series of *Review Exercises* and *Check-up Exercises* which are planned to help you maintain and improve the skills that you have mastered. The *Review Exercises* are supplemented by *Achievement Tests*. A chart at the back of this book may be used to tabulate the results of the *Achievement Tests*. The results of these tests will show you how well you are maintaining and improving your skills in the fundamentals of arithmetic.

You will learn more about the *Achievement Tests* and *Review* and *Check-up Exercises* later on. Let us now concern ourselves with the *Inventory Tests* and *Practice Exercises*.

The *Inventory Tests* are for all members of the class. Each of these tests covers one phase of computation. The first test covers addition of integers.

It is possible to make one of three ratings on these tests—an A, B, or C rating. An A rating indicates that the person making it is well prepared on this particular computation. The C rating indicates that the person making it is not well prepared on this particular computation. He needs to do the *Practice Exercises* for this computation and then take the *Inventory Test* again.

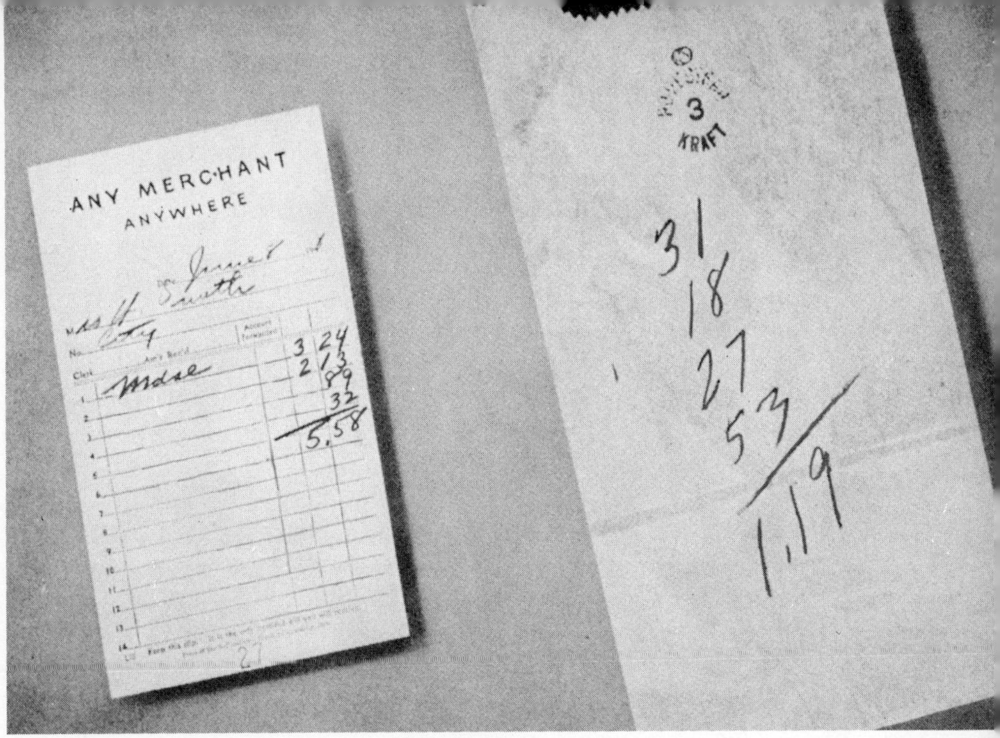

Fig. 3. Mistakes in Arithmetic Are Costly in Business

The B rating indicates a lack of top accuracy. Many will wish to improve their accuracy by doing the *Practice Exercises* and then repeating the *Inventory Test*. Others may prefer to go directly to the next *Inventory Test*.

The *Practice Exercises* provide remedial work on the type of computation covered by the *Inventory Tests*. The *Practice Exercises* are found in the Appendix.

──────────────── EXERCISES ────────────────

What are the correct totals in Fig. 3?

What numbers must be supplied to make the answers to the following exercises correct?

(1)	28	(2)	678	(3)	7264	(5)	468
	63		235		− ?		× ?
	79		154		3307		3744
	23		22	(4)	92863	(6)	816
+ ?		+ ?			− ?		× ?
	298		1135		50704		7344

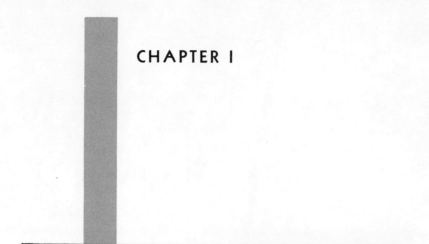

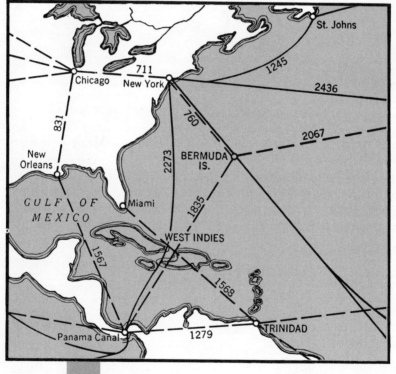

CHAPTER 1

ADDITION, MULTIPLICATION,

SUBTRACTION, AND DIVISION OF

INTEGERS WITH APPLICATIONS

VOCABULARY

1. arithmetic	4. integer	7. computation	10. perimeter
2. mathematics	5. digit	8. addend	11. length
3. fundamentals	6. addition	9. sum	12. width

4. Terms used in addition. The numbers to be added are called *addends*. The result obtained by addition is called the *sum*.

```
28 addend
61 addend
─────────
89 sum
```

──────────────── PROOF ────────────────

5. Proving addition by adding in the opposite direction. After adding a column of figures from the bottom up, add them from the top down; or first add from the top down, and then add from the bottom up. The two answers in either case should be the same.

The use of this proof or check, as it is also called, comes from a basic rule that can be used in adding numbers. This rule states that when we are adding two or more numbers together it does not matter in what order we add them. That is, 7 + 9 is the same as 9 + 7, or 11 + 2 + 8 is the same as 8 + 2 + 11. This rule is often called the Law of Order for Addition.*

EXERCISES

Add the following numbers, and prove the answer in each case:

1. 7	**2.** 8	**3.** 24	**4.** 27	**5.** 412
3	5	35	13	127
4	2	26	36	328
5	5	83	18	425
2	3	72	52	519
3	9	28	84	296

6. Simplifying addition by grouping. A second rule that can help simplify our addition states that we can group together any numbers we wish when we are adding. Thus to add 11 + 2 + 8 we can add 11 + 2 and then add 8, or we can add to 11 the sum of 2 + 8. As one is less likely to make a mistake when adding a ten, and since 2 + 8 = 10, we choose to add 11 + 10 and we get 21. A good way to add a long list of numbers is to look for groups of numbers that add ten in this way.

EXAMPLES

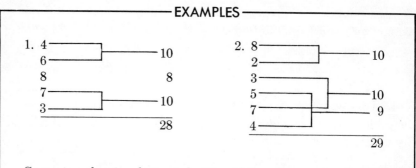

Group together 4 and 6 to make 10; add 8; and group together 7 and 3 to make 10. This gives 10 + 8 + 10 = 28.

Group together the 8 and the 2 to make 10, group together the 3 and the 7 to make 10; then add 5 + 4. This gives 10 + 10 + 9, or 29.

---

* This rule is also called The Commutative Law for Addition.

ADDITION OF INTEGERS

Add the following numbers, and check the answers in each case:

1. 7	2. 7	3. 84	4. 25	5. 748
3	6	46	77	341
5	3	68	83	153
5	4	13	15	751
4	5	72	78	926
2	2	45	66	524

This second rule that we use in addition is called The Law of Grouping for Addition.* Another use of this Law of Grouping can be a help in adding long columns of numbers. Where the adding of two numbers causes you to jump a multiple of ten, (10, 20, 30, 40, etc.), separate the second addend into two parts, one of which will make up the difference between the first number and the "ten-number." The other part of the second addend is then added to the "ten-number" to give the sum. For example, when adding 38 and 5, you see that it takes 2 added to 38 to give 40; then there are 3 left from the 5, so you say 40 and 3, or 43 is the sum. When adding 56 and 7, you first say 60, thinking, "I have used 4 from the 7; now there are 3 left." Then say the 3; thus you are saying 63, which is the sum. When you are adding a long column of numbers, just say each sum to yourself as you go down the column.

Add the following numbers, and check the answers in each case:

1. $ 649	2. $ 72	3. $ 427	4. $9167	5. $35108
76	870	3690	8605	347
3457	598	685	1084	8677
416	16745	486	5837	67
539	6308	5679	8755	4672
7683	69188	219	3196	86438
241	7569	2010	7468	2194

Although these rules help you with your addition, you must first be able to add all of the basic combinations. You must memorize the basic number facts. Turn to page 403 to review these if you need practice.

---

* This rule is also called The Associative Law for Addition.

7. Finding the distance between places. The development of the automobile has brought paved highways, and the development of paved highways has caused people to travel more and more in automobiles—some on business trips and others on tours for pleasure. Such trips make it rather necessary for the traveler to be able to read maps and to find distances between places.

—————————————— *EXERCISES* ——————————————

Distances on maps are expressed in miles. Prove the sums obtained in each case.

1. In figure 1, find the distance from A to E, from C to F, from B to E, and from A to F.

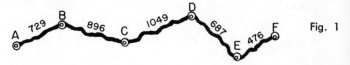
Fig. 1

2. In figure 2, what are the distances from A to F, from B to H, from C to I, and from A to I?

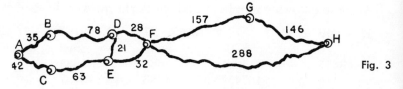
Fig. 2

3. In figure 3, what are the shortest distances from A to D, from A to F, from D to H, and from C to G?

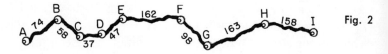
Fig. 3

4. Calculate these distances on the map shown on page 6:
(a) From Chicago to St. Johns.
(b) From the Panama Canal to St. Johns via Bermuda.
(c) From Chicago to the Panama Canal via New Orleans.
(d) From Miami to New Orleans via Trinidad.
(e) From Chicago to Trinidad via New Orleans.
(f) From New York to Panama via Chicago.
*(g) From New Orleans to Bermuda by the shortest distance pictured.
*(h) From the Panama Canal to New York by shortest route.

**(i) From Chicago to Bermuda via New York is how much shorter than via New Orleans and the Panama Canal?

**(j) How many miles longer is it from Chicago to New York via New Orleans, Panama Canal, and Bermuda than by the shortest route to New York?

8. Finding perimeters. The *perimeter* of an object is the distance around the object. You may find the perimeter by adding the lengths of all the sides.

————————————— *SHOP EXERCISES* —————————————

All distances are in feet. Prove the sum in each case.

1. Find the distance around the lot shown in figure 4.

*2. Find the perimeter of the flat surface, figure 5. A = 160', B = 55', C = 19', D = 23', E = 16', F = 39', G = 36', H = 47', I = 19'.

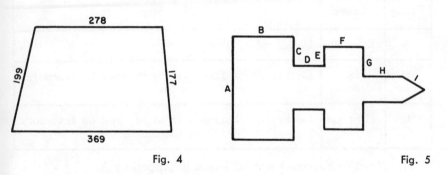

Fig. 4   Fig. 5

*3. What is the perimeter of each of the lots in figure 6?

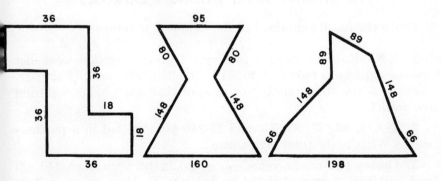

Fig. 6

Write your answers on folded paper. Add:

8	7	8	9	9	7	7	5	8	4	
6	9	3	8	5	0	6	7	8	7	**(10)**

$36 + 8 =$ $47 + 6 =$ $59 + 8 =$ $46 + 7 =$ $28 + 9 =$ **(15)**

4	23	623	7214	1721	
9	48	245	1806	6805	
8	16	985	385	328	
3	56	646	2738	1482	**(20)**
5	21	546			

Rating	Correct	Next Step
A	19 or 20	Do Inventory Test 2.
B	18	Do Inventory Test 2 or do Practice Exercises 1a to 1d.
C	17 or less	Do Practice Exercises 1a to 1d; then do Inventory Test 1 again.

The *Practice Exercises* will be found in Appendix A.

———— ADDITIONAL APPLICATIONS — EXERCISES ————

Prove the results obtained in the following exercises:

1. Ruth Ross works in a factory. During a certain week her production was as follows: 266, 318, 293, 310, 308, and 154 articles. What was the total number of articles that she produced during the week?

2. $8,678, $6,483, $3,675, and $3,946 are invested in a partnership. What is the total investment?

3. During two recent years college graduates were: men 240,990 and 252,960; women 121,564 and 128,963. How many college graduates were there during the two years?

4. In a recent year, visitors to a city park spent $122,655.95 for soft drinks, ice cream, and other food. They spent $26,015.78 for miniature train rides. What was the total amount spent for these items?

5. The weights of five planes are: 3,160 lb., 3,450 lb., 4,520 lb., 5,680 lb., and 4,860 lb. Find the total weight.

6. In three recent years the output of television sets was (1) 4,920,000 (2) 6,349,000 and (3) 5,708,000. How many sets were manufactured during these years?

*7. The daily sales for one week were $105.75, $214.34, $197.67, $268.45, $245.96, $297.58. What was the total for the week?

*8. In one year the railroads hauled the following carloads of livestock: cattle and calves, 311,589 carloads; hogs, 218,950; sheep and lambs, 95,828; horses and mules, 11,824; other live animals, 186. Find the total carloads of animals.

**9. The land area and population of the different parts of the world are shown in the table. Find the total land area and the total number of people.

Regions	Square Miles	Population
Africa	11,710,424	244,270,000
Asia	10,347,491	1,665,000,000
Europe	2,092,664	427,000,000
U.S.S.R.	8,176,061	214,490,000
North America	8,664,864	265,000,000
South America	6,937,551	139,980,000
Oceania	3,301,158	16,460,000

**10. In a recent year the following arrests were made in cities with populations of 2,500 or more:

Age	Arrests
15	86,642
16	110,446
17	113,942
18	106,795
19	98,839
20	90,321

Find the total number of arrests for ages 15–20 inclusive.

How do you account for the increase of arrests from age 15 to age 17?

How do you account for the decrease of arrests from age 17 through age 20?

9. Terms used in multiplication. The number that is to be multiplied is called the *multiplicand*. The

```
 72 multiplicand
  8 multiplier
576 product
```

number by which the multiplicand is multiplied is called the *multiplier*. The result obtained by multiplication is called the *product*. Either the multiplicand or the multiplier can also be called a *factor*. A *factor* is any one of two or more numbers being multiplied.

10. Proving multiplication by interchanging the multiplier and the multiplicand. To multiply a second time in the same order as the first time is not a good proof, for the same mistake is likely to be made the second time. A basic rule that can be used in multiplying numbers states that when we are multiplying two or more factors together it does not matter in what order we multiply them. This rule is called The Law of Order for Multiplication.* It tells us that we can interchange the multiplicand and the multiplier and obtain the same product. If the multiplier and the multiplicand are interchanged and the same product is obtained, the work is probably correct.

——————————— EXAMPLES ———————————

1. Multiply 487 by 39; prove.

```
              39
   487       487
    39       273
  4383       312
  1461       156
 18993  ←Proof→  18993
```

2. Multiply 597 by 27; prove.

```
              27
   597       597
    27       189
  4179       243
  1194       135
 16119  ←Proof→  16119
```

* This rule is also called The Commutative Law for Multiplication.

Multiply each of the following exercises, and prove each answer by interchanging the multiplicand and the multiplier.

1. 478
  96
	2. 779
	  84
		3. 670
		357

4. 5797
  82
	5. 974
	  59
		6. 508
		  94

7. 544 108	8. 959 68	9. 843 480

10. 567
  570
	11. 638
	  359
		12. 8557
		  406

13. 329 508	14. 700 800	15. 609 808

11. Proving multiplication by dividing the product by the multiplier or the multiplicand.

──────── EXAMPLE ────────

$$
\begin{array}{ccc}
 & & 487 \\
487 & \text{Proofs: } 39\overline{)18993} & \\
39 & 156 & \\
\hline
4383 & \overline{339} & \\
1461 & 312 & \\
\hline
18993 & \overline{273} & \\
 & 273 & \\
\end{array}
$$

Proofs: 39)18993
487
156
339
312
273
273

or: 487)18993
39
1461
4383
4383

487
39
4383
1461
18993

Multiply in each of the following exercises, and prove each answer by the preceding method:

1. $823 \times 74 =$	3. $726 \times 481 =$	5. $1582 \times 26 =$
2. $318 \times 58 =$	4. $514 \times 188 =$	6. $4105 \times 31 =$

Multiply: (Write your answers on a folded paper.)

8	7	8	9	9	7	7	
6	9	3	8	5	0	6	(7)

8	4	0	9	5	7	0	
8	7	5	4	6	8	2	(14)

6	2	8	9	9	8	7	
9	9	4	6	9	5	7	(21)

608	300	405	807	107	
40	700	708	79	108	(26)

Rating	Correct	Next Step
A	25 or 26	Do Inventory Test 3.
B	24	Do Inventory Test 3 or do Practice Exercises 2a to 2d.
C	23 or less	Do Practice Exercises 2a to 2d; then do Inventory Test 2 again.

─────────────── SUBTRACTION ───────────────

VOCABULARY

1. subtraction   2. minuend   3. subtrahend   4. remainder
5. difference

12. Terms used in subtraction. The number from which another number is to be subtracted is called the *minuend*. The number that is to be subtracted from another number is called the *subtrahend*. The result obtained by subtraction is called the *remainder* or the *difference*.

```
176 minuend
 23 subtrahend
153 remainder
```

13. Proving subtraction. To prove or check subtraction, add the subtrahend and the remainder. If their sum is equal to the minuend, the subtraction is correct.

EXAMPLE

9,287 minuend	*Proof:* 2,988 subtrahend
2,988 subtrahend	6,299 remainder
6,299 remainder	9,287 minuend

EXERCISES

Subtract each of the following, and prove each answer:

1.	8,648	2.	4,050	3.	$6,015	4.	$68,067
	2,939		3,987		4,695		8,988

5.	549,213	6.	7,807	7.	6,008	8.	2,637
	526,785		3,954		5,163		1,798

9.	574,731	10.	36,643	11.	8,950	12.	7,856
	93,689		8,557		984		5,687

INVENTORY TEST 3   Subtraction of Integers

(Write your answers on a folded paper.)

Subtract:

25	44	36	54	23	7	35	
9	9	7	6	5	0	7	(7)

20	40	12	6	31	17	24	
8	7	8	6	2	9	5	(14)

48	305	423	916	208	
28	74	58	208	23	(19)

500	800	700	1,000	
68	235	189	407	(23)

12,789	27,845	122,044	131,721	
4,593	7,689	63,078	48,608	(27)

Rating	Correct	Next Step
A	26 or 27	Do Inventory Test 4.
B	25	Do Inventory Test 4 or do Practice Exercises 3a to 3d.
C	24 or less	Do Practice Exercises 3a to 3d; then do Inventory Test 3 again.

Practice Exercises will be found in Appendix A.

Solve and prove the following exercises:

1. Mt. McKinley in Alaska has a height of 20,320 ft. Mt. Evans in Colorado is 14,260 feet high. What is the difference in their heights?

2. The Pacific Ocean has an area of 63,801,700 sq. mi. The Atlantic Ocean has an area of 31,830,800 sq. mi. How much larger is the Pacific Ocean than the Atlantic Ocean?

3. In a recent election California ballots totaled 4,021,538 and Illinois had 3,984,046 ballots. How many more votes were cast in California than in Illinois?

4. The same year that Canada had 35,961 schools Mexico had 32,437 schools. At that time Canada's schools outnumbered the Mexico schools by how many?

5. In a year when the population of New York City was 7,781,984 Chicago's population numbered 3,550,404. How much larger was the population of New York than that of Chicago?

6. The total customs collections for one year were $388,773,987. The next year the collections were $346,505,321. Find the decrease.

7. How much more is earned by a motion picture company during a six months' period when $2,769,190 is earned than during the previous six months' period when $1,355,781 was earned?

8. A Texas newspaper had a morning circulation of 1,238,880. The evening circulation was 1,692,366. Find the difference between the evening and morning newspaper circulation.

9. The school enrollment in the United States from 14 to 17 years of age one year was 9,067,000. Three years later for the same age group the number was 10,242,000. How much was the increase in enrollment for this age group?

10. At a time when the home economics classes number 1,588,109 students the trades and industry classes numbered 938,490. The home economics students outnumbered the trades and industry classes by how many?

11. The population of Hawaii in 1950 was 499,794 and in 1960 was 632,772. What was the ten year increase in population?

12. The United States population in a recent year was male, 88,331,494; female, 90,991,681. How many more females than males were there in the population of the U. S. at that time?

13. How many more were in attendance at the National League baseball games when the attendance was 8,016,575 than when it was 7,419,721?

14. How many more were in attendance at the American League baseball games when the attendance was 7,928,592 than when it was 6,964,076?

*15. The members of a class had $6 to buy food for a picnic. If they bought 36 oranges at 4 for 25¢, how much did they have left for other food?

*16. Mr. Jones has $12,500 with which to build a home. The lot cost $2,475. The house cost $14,700. The garage cost $1,785. If the other expenses amounted to $287, how much money must he borrow to complete the home?

——————————— DIVISION ———————————

VOCABULARY

1. division   2. dividend   3. divisor   4. quotient

14. Terms used in division. The number that is to be divided is called the *dividend*. The number by which the dividend is divided is called the *divisor*.* The result obtained by division is called the *quotient*.

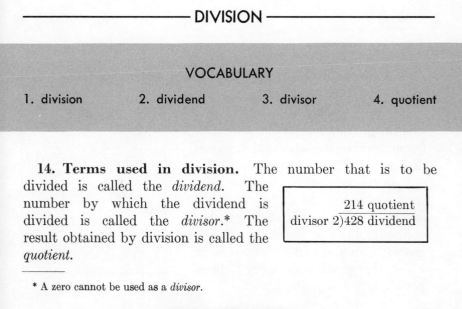

214 quotient
divisor 2)428 dividend

——————

* A zero cannot be used as a *divisor*.

15. Proving division by multiplying the quotient and the divisor and adding the remainder to the product.

```
                                EXAMPLE
             197 quotient
divisor 48)9467 dividend        Proof:  197 quotient
           48                            48 divisor
           466                          1576
           432                           788
           347                          9456
           336                          +11 remainder
            11                          9467 dividend
```

EXERCISES

Divide in each of the following exercises, and prove each answer by the preceding method:

1. 5091 by 35   2. 7283 by 42   3. 45,724 by 63

4. 4003 by 17   5. 4500 by 18   6. 19,336 by 82

16. Proving division by using the quotient as the divisor.

If the quotient is used as the divisor, the quotient of the proof frequently will be the same as the original divisor.

If in the original division the quotient contains a remainder, as in the example, use only the whole number of the quotient as the divisor in the proof. Can you make an exercise in which this proof does apply? Does not apply?

```
      EXAMPLE

     352          24
24)8463     352)8463
   72           704
  126          1423
  120          1408
   63            15
   48
   15
```

Complete each of the following exercises, and prove by the preceding method:

1. 910 ÷ 35	**5.** 1812 ÷ 28	**9.** 2400 ÷ 64
2. 2436 ÷ 42	**6.** 2124 ÷ 18	**10.** 3243 ÷ 92
3. 888 ÷ 37	**7.** 3710 ÷ 82	**11.** 10,001 ÷ 34
4. 4514 ÷ 74	**8.** 1537 ÷ 53	**12.** 212,121 ÷ 21

INVENTORY TEST 4   **Division of Integers**

Express any fraction in the quotient in its lowest terms.

Divide:

$8\overline{)48}$	$9\overline{)27}$	$7\overline{)49}$	$9\overline{)63}$	$6\overline{)42}$	
$4\overline{)32}$	$7\overline{)56}$	$8\overline{)72}$	$2\overline{)0}$	$3\overline{)27}$	**(10)**
$9\overline{)36}$	$7\overline{)28}$	$9\overline{)81}$	$5\overline{)0}$	$8\overline{)64}$	**(15)**
$7\overline{)357}$	$9\overline{)621}$	$8\overline{)768}$	$6\overline{)3006}$	$9\overline{)5040}$	
$24\overline{)1752}$	$42\overline{)4326}$	$14\overline{)3663}$	$56\overline{)2058}$		**(24)**

Rating	Correct	Next Step
A	23 or 24	Do Inventory Test 5.
B	22	Do Inventory Test 5 or do Practice Exercises 4a to 4d.
C	21 or less	Do Practice Exercises 4a to 4d; then do Inventory Test 4 again.

Practice Exercises will be found in Appendix A.

17. Averages. To find the average of numbers, divide their sum by the number of addends.

Using letters,* the rule is shortened to read:

$$a \text{ (average)} = \frac{s \text{ (sum)}}{n \text{ (number of addends)}}$$

That is,
$$a = \frac{s}{n}$$

Ray made the following grades in mathematics one week: 80, 72, 88, 94, and 95. Find his average grade for the week.

The sum (s) of his grades is 429.

The number of grades—addends (n)—is 5.

The average (a) is $85\frac{4}{5}$.

EXAMPLE

$a = \dfrac{s}{n}$ $s = 80 + 72 + 88 + 94 + 95 = 429$

$n = 5$

$a = \frac{429}{5}$

$a = 85\frac{4}{5}$

Therefore, the average grade for the week was $85\frac{4}{5}$.

EXERCISES

1. Find the average of the following temperatures recorded at 7 A. M. for one week: 68°, 62°, 70°, 64°, 79°, 86°, and 82°.

2. What is the average horsepower (H.P.) of six engines having the following H.P. ratings: 320, 290, 375, 400, 340, and 360?

3. Find the average speed of five airplanes whose speeds are: 240 m. p. h., 286 m. p. h., 318 m. p. h., 253 m. p. h., and 320 m. p. h.

***4.** In a recent year the United States government paid rent amounting to $193,400,000. Of this amount $160,200,000 was for property within the United States, $700,000 for property in outlying areas. What was the average monthly expenditure for rental property in foreign lands?

5. The attendance at school in a certain class for one week was: Monday, 40; Tuesday, 39; Wednesday, 38; Thursday, 40; Friday, 37. What was the average daily attendance?

---
* A rule in which letters are used to represent numerical values is called a *formula*.

6. A man's yearly salary for the past six years has been: $4,200, $5,000, $5,450, $6,500, $7,000, and $7,800. Find his average salary.

7. A plane that travels 2,000 mi. between 1 P. M. and 9 P. M. has an average speed of how many miles per hour?

8. The average temperature for a certain city is, month by month, as follows:

January .....28°	April ....56°	July ....80°	October .....60°
February ....30°	May ....65°	August .....82°	November ...48°
March ......43°	June ....74°	September ...75°	December ...30°

Determine the yearly average temperature of the city.

*9. A car travels 15 mi. in 1 hour over a rough road, and later travels 60 mi. in 2 hours over a better road. What was the average speed of the car?

Solution: The average speed (u) equals the *total* distance (d) divided by the *total* time. (Always use *totals* when solving for an average.)

$$a = \frac{d}{t} \qquad d = 15 \text{ mi.} + 60 \text{ mi.} = 75 \text{ mi.}$$

$$t = 1 \text{ hr.} + 2 \text{ hr.} = 3 \text{ hr.}$$

$$a = \frac{?}{?}$$

$$a = ? \qquad \text{average speed (m. p. h.)}$$

*10. A train traveled 360 mi. in 6 hours; then traveled 640 mi. in 8 hours. Find the average speed of the train.

*11. Mrs. Case spent $9.00 for 50 bars of soap and $16.00 for 80 bars. What was the average price per bar for the soap?

**12. A plane travels 600 m. p. h. for 2 hr., and then 320 m. p. h. for ½ hr. What is the plane's average speed per hour?

**13. A plane flying between Chicago and Salt Lake City, approximately 1,260 miles, travels at an average speed of 350 m. p. h. to Salt Lake City and 300 m. p. h. on the return trip. What was the average speed for the whole trip?

**14. In a class of 30 pupils, the following scores were made on a test: 5 pupils made 100% each, 6 made 90% each, 12 made 80%, 2 made 70%, 2 made 60%, 2 made 40%, and 1 made 0%. What was the average score per pupil? (Hint: The total score of the five who made 100% each was 500%.)

1. Mr. Clark paid $282 for three rugs. Find the average cost per rug.

2. Jerry's school had an enrollment of 1,824 pupils. 735 pupils were boys. How many girls were enrolled?

3. Ross sold 14 cupboards that he learned to make at school. He received $7 each for them. How much did Ross earn by his sales?

4. Carl plans to save $50 by Christmas, which is 16 weeks away. His average savings per week must be how much?

5. In 1950 Los Angeles had a population of 1,970,358. By 1960 the population had increased to 2,479,015. How great was the increase?

6. How long can a plane remain in the air if it carries 140 gal. of gasoline and uses 18 gal. per hour?

7. Jack and Mary, of teen age, went on a vacation to a ranch. They made the following purchases of western garments for the trip:

Jack		Mary	
1 hat	$3.98	1 hat	$3.98
1 belt	2.48	1 belt	2.75
1 shirt	2.87	1 pr. jeans	2.98
2 shirts @*	2.04	1 sweater	4.98
2 pr. denim pants @	3.27	1 outfit	6.75
1 pr. shoes	6.98	2 shirts @	2.10
1 outfit @	6.75	1 pr. shoes	7.95
3 pr. socks @	.79	4 pr. socks @	.65

* @ means that the cost is for 1 unit, as for 1 hat or 1 pair of shoes.

a. How much did Jack spend for all his western garments?

b. How much did Mary spend for her garments?

c. Find the total spent by both on the clothes.

8. If Mary and Jack were given $250 each for the ranch trip, how much money did each have left after paying for the special clothing?

9. It is estimated that the adults in our country use an average of 143 books of matches a year. How many such books would be used in an office of 18 adults?

10. Mrs. Craft keeps roomers at $54 per month. How much will she receive per year from 3 roomers?

11. Recently there were approximately 1,410,000 classroom teachers in elementary and secondary public schools and 36,300,000 pupils. What was the approximate average number of pupils per teacher?

12. Nancy's grades in mathematics for one week were 96, 84, 90, 78, and 88. What was Nancy's average for the week?

*13. Joe bought a $800 used car, paying $80 down. At $40 per month, how many payments will it take to pay for the car?

*14. During a vacation season each of the 2,000,000,000 visitors to United States National Parks left an average of 2 pounds of litter. For removal of the litter and improved sanitation the Government spent more than $2,000,000. Approximately how many pounds of litter were removed during the summer? At $10,000 per recreational feature, how many amusement places could be added to the parks with the money paid for the litter removal and for sanitation improvement?

**15. The most weight that plane B can carry is 12,400 lb. The plane's empty weight is 7,000 lb. It carries 220 gal. of gasoline which weighs 6 lb. per gallon, 13 qt. of oil which weighs 7 lb. per gallon, 2 pilots and a hostess weighing 168 lb., 140 lb., and 120 lb., respectively. What weight remains for the passengers, baggage, and any other shipment?

16. If you know the cost of one chair, how do you find the cost of eight such chairs?

17. If you know the cost of four pounds of sugar, how do you find the cost of one pound of sugar?

18. How would you find the total ages of all the members of your class?

19. How would you find how much taller the tallest pupil in your class is than the shortest pupil?

*20. How would you find the average temperature in September?

**21. How would you find the average speed of a plane that flies at two different speeds if you knew the time that it flies at each speed?

**22. How would you find the average grade of all the pupils in your class?

**23. How would you find the difference between the average heights of 14-year-old American boys of the present time and of 14-year-old boys of fifty years ago?

Draw Table I. Solve the following exercises and put the answers in the proper squares.

TABLE 1

Vertical

1. $8 \times 7 = 56$ (Put the 5 in square 1 and 6 in square 7.)
2. $38 \times 6 =$
3. $258 \div 129 =$
4. $800 - 282 =$
5. $45 + 17 =$
6. $140 - 60 =$
9. Perimeter of rectangle $15''$ by $10'' =$
10. $13 \times 13 =$
11. Average of 32, 28, and 9.
12. $181 - 179 =$
13. $17 \times 17 =$
14. Perimeter of a square $18''$ on a side.
16. $1542 - 1018 =$
18. $2296 \div 7 =$
19. Perimeter of a square $19''$ on a side.
22. $7 \times 8 =$
23. $9 \times 9 =$
24. $2000 \div 40 =$

Horizontal (across page)

1. $18 + 34 = 52$ (Put the 5 in the square marked 1 and the 2 in the square marked 2.)
3. $384 - 128 =$ (Put the answer in squares 3, 4, and 5.)
6. $4 \times 2 =$
7. $25 \times 25 =$
8. $25 \times 50 =$
10. $29 + 14 - 25 =$

12. $208 \div 8 =$
15. $67 - 32 =$
17. $21,865 + 28,319 + 43,688 =$
20. $9 + 14 =$
21. $91 + 88 + 117 =$
22. $3 \times 3 \times 3 \times 2 =$
23. $26 + 33 + 45 - 16 =$
25. $1000 - 909 =$
26. $10,800 \div 15 =$

CHAPTER II

ADDITION, SUBTRACTION, MULTIPLI-

CATION, AND DIVISION OF COMMON

FRACTIONS WITH APPLICATIONS

VOCABULARY

1. fraction
2. common fraction
3. proper fraction
4. improper fraction

5. mixed number
6. numerator
7. denominator
8. least common denominator

18. Common fractions. Henry had a board which he divided into three equal parts as shown below. He used one of the three equal parts to make a table top. This part of the board is indicated by the fraction $\frac{1}{3}$. The 1 is the *numerator* and 3 is the *denominator*. The remaining portion, made up of two of the three equal parts, is $\frac{2}{3}$ of the whole board. In this fraction, 2 is the _____ and 3 is the _____.

A fraction that is written with a numerator and a denominator, such as $\frac{5}{9}$, is called a *common fraction*.

If the numerator is less than the denominator, as in $\frac{5}{9}$ or $\frac{2}{3}$, the fraction is called a *proper fraction*.

If the numerator is larger than the denominator, as in $\frac{5}{2}$, the fraction is an *improper fraction*.

A number made up of a whole number and a fraction, such as $4\frac{1}{2}$, is called a *mixed number*.

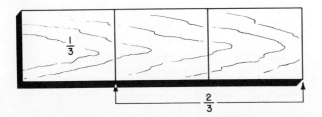

29

19. Changing the form of a fraction. In order to succeed with fractions, you must be able to do these four things:

(a) To change a fraction to lower or higher terms:

$$\tfrac{2}{4} = \tfrac{1}{2} \quad \tfrac{1}{4} = \tfrac{3}{12}.$$

(b) To change improper fractions to whole or mixed numbers:

$$\tfrac{8}{4} = 2 \quad \tfrac{5}{4} = 1\tfrac{1}{4}.$$

(c) To change mixed numbers to improper fractions:

$$2\tfrac{1}{2} = \tfrac{5}{2}.$$

(d) To change two or more fractions to fractions having the same denominator:

$$\tfrac{1}{3} \text{ and } \tfrac{1}{2} = \tfrac{2}{6} \text{ and } \tfrac{3}{6}.$$

──────────────── EXERCISES ────────────────

1. Change each of the following fractions to its lowest terms by dividing the numerator and the denominator by the largest number that is contained exactly in both of them.

┌──── EXAMPLE ────┐

$$\frac{10}{12} = \frac{10 \div 2}{12 \div 2} = \frac{5}{6}$$

If both the numerator and the denominator of a fraction are divided by the same number, the value of the fraction remains the same.

$\frac{12}{33}$	$\frac{9}{27}$	$\frac{8}{18}$	$\frac{10}{22}$	$\frac{18}{26}$	$\frac{24}{60}$
$\frac{48}{60}$	$\frac{46}{69}$	$\frac{20}{90}$	$\frac{24}{64}$	$\frac{12}{15}$	$\frac{15}{18}$ **(12)**
$\frac{124}{200}$	$\frac{5}{1000}$	$\frac{40}{640}$	$\frac{70}{2000}$	$\frac{36}{72}$	$\frac{18}{24}$
$\frac{27}{33}$	$\frac{25}{45}$	$\frac{56}{63}$	$\frac{27}{36}$	$\frac{42}{48}$	$\frac{35}{40}$ **(24)**

2. Write each of the following improper fractions as a mixed number or as a whole number. Each fraction should be reduced to its lowest terms:

┌── EXAMPLE ──┐

$$\tfrac{18}{4} = 4\tfrac{2}{4} = 4\tfrac{1}{2}$$

$\frac{11}{3}$	$\frac{9}{2}$	$\frac{7}{3}$	$\frac{24}{5}$	$\frac{8}{3}$	$\frac{20}{8}$	$\frac{34}{16}$	$\frac{25}{3}$ **(8)**
$\frac{34}{2}$	$\frac{25}{4}$	$\frac{10}{8}$	$\frac{32}{5}$	$\frac{9}{4}$	$\frac{17}{6}$	$\frac{6}{5}$	$\frac{8}{5}$
$\frac{2}{2}$	$\frac{6}{3}$	$\frac{33}{15}$	$\frac{7}{5}$	$\frac{11}{6}$	$\frac{21}{4}$	$\frac{48}{3}$	$\frac{35}{7}$ **(24)**
$\frac{9}{8}$	$\frac{17}{4}$	$\frac{44}{10}$	$\frac{16}{5}$	$\frac{43}{6}$	$\frac{15}{10}$	$\frac{60}{8}$	$\frac{27}{5}$
$\frac{7}{3}$	$\frac{42}{6}$	$\frac{18}{8}$	$\frac{12}{9}$	$\frac{35}{10}$	$\frac{16}{3}$	$\frac{54}{6}$	$\frac{40}{12}$ **(40)**

3. Write each of the following mixed numbers as improper fractions:

$$\boxed{\text{EXAMPLE} \quad 3\tfrac{2}{5} = \tfrac{17}{5}}$$

$8\dfrac{3}{5} = \dfrac{}{5}$ $3\dfrac{1}{16} =$ $4\dfrac{3}{4} =$ $4\dfrac{1}{5}$ $7\dfrac{2}{9} =$ $3 = \dfrac{}{4}$

$4\dfrac{3}{4} = \dfrac{}{4}$ $5\dfrac{1}{3} =$ $7\dfrac{2}{3} =$ $8\dfrac{1}{6} =$ $7\dfrac{1}{4} =$ $12 = \dfrac{}{2}$ **(12)**

$12\dfrac{1}{2} = \dfrac{}{2}$ $2\dfrac{3}{16} =$ $2\dfrac{5}{6} =$ $1\dfrac{3}{4} =$ $6\dfrac{3}{4} =$ $9\dfrac{2}{3} =$

$2\dfrac{7}{8} = \dfrac{}{8}$ $9\dfrac{1}{3} =$ $10\dfrac{3}{5} =$ $3\dfrac{1}{7} =$ $8\dfrac{2}{3} =$ $16\dfrac{2}{3} =$ **(24)**

$$\boxed{\begin{array}{l}\text{EXAMPLE} \\[4pt] \dfrac{1}{3} = \dfrac{1\times 4}{3\times 4} = \dfrac{4}{12} \\[6pt] \dfrac{1}{4} = \dfrac{1\times 3}{4\times 3} = \dfrac{3}{12} \\[6pt] \dfrac{5}{6} = \dfrac{5\times 2}{6\times 2} = \dfrac{10}{12}\end{array}}$$

When two or more fractions are changed to the least *like* denominators possible, they are changed to the *least common denominator*.

If both the numerator and the denominator of a fraction are multiplied by the same number, the value of the fraction remains the same.

4. Change the following groups of fractions to least common denominators.

1. $\frac{1}{2} = ?/6$
$\frac{2}{3} = ?/6$

2. $\frac{3}{4} = ?/12$
$\frac{5}{6} = ?/12$

3. $\frac{1}{4} = ?/20$
$\frac{3}{5} = ?/20$

4. $\frac{2}{5} = ?/15$
$\frac{2}{3} = ?/15$

5. $\frac{9}{8} = ?/24$
$\frac{5}{6} = ?/24$

6. $\frac{1}{2} =$
$\frac{4}{5} =$

7. $\frac{7}{12} =$
$\frac{2}{3} =$

8. $\frac{3}{10} =$
$\frac{4}{15} =$

9. $\frac{1}{6} =$
$\frac{3}{8} =$

10. $\frac{3}{16} =$
$\frac{2}{3} =$

11. $\frac{4}{5}$
$\frac{1}{4}$

12. $\frac{5}{12}$
$\frac{5}{8}$

13. $\frac{11}{12}$
$\frac{3}{5}$

14. $\frac{7}{8}$
$\frac{5}{6}$

15. $\frac{3}{7}$
$\frac{1}{2}$

16. $\frac{3}{4}$
$\frac{2}{3}$

17. $\frac{5}{6}$
$\frac{7}{9}$

18. $\frac{3}{4}$
$\frac{7}{8}$

19. $\frac{1}{2}$
$\frac{5}{12}$

20. $\frac{5}{12}$
$\frac{1}{3}$

21. $\frac{3}{4}$
$\frac{3}{8}$

22. $\frac{11}{12}$
$\frac{1}{4}$

23. $\frac{2}{5}$
$\frac{4}{5}$

24. $\frac{2}{5}$
$\frac{3}{8}$

25. $\frac{5}{6}$
$\frac{7}{10}$

26. $\frac{1}{2}$ 27. $\frac{1}{4}$ 28. $\frac{2}{3}$ 29. $\frac{2}{5}$ 30. $\frac{2}{3}$
$\frac{2}{3}$ $\frac{1}{3}$ $\frac{1}{4}$ $\frac{1}{2}$ $\frac{3}{4}$
$\frac{1}{8}$ $\frac{3}{8}$ $\frac{5}{6}$ $\frac{7}{10}$ $\frac{7}{8}$

INVENTORY TEST 5   Addition of Common Fractions

Add; then reduce each sum to its lowest terms:

$\frac{5}{8} + \frac{2}{3}$ $\frac{3}{16} + \frac{7}{8}$ $\frac{5}{12} + \frac{1}{3} + \frac{5}{6}$

$12\frac{1}{4} + 37\frac{2}{3}$ $27\frac{1}{3} + 34\frac{4}{5}$ $18\frac{1}{3} + 25\frac{7}{8}$ **(6)**

$\frac{1}{8}$ $\frac{2}{5}$ $\frac{1}{2}$ $\frac{7}{8}$ $\frac{3}{4}$

$\frac{1}{5}$ $\frac{7}{10}$ $\frac{1}{3}$ $\frac{4}{5}$ $\frac{1}{6}$ **(11)**

$8\frac{8}{9}$ $24\frac{3}{16}$ $172\frac{1}{2}$ $181\frac{2}{7}$

$6\frac{1}{3}$ $18\frac{3}{8}$ $256\frac{2}{3}$ $156\frac{2}{3}$ **(15)**

Rating	Correct	Next Step
A	14 or 15	Do Inventory Test 6.
B	12 or 13	Do Inventory Test 6 or Practice Exercises 5a to 5e.
C	11 or less	Do Practice Exercises 5a to 5e; then do Inventory Test 5 again.

——————————————— *SHOP EXERCISES* ———————————————

20. Addition of ruler fractions.   The inch on an ordinary ruler is usually marked off into halves, fourths, eighths, and sixteenths.   A steel rule, called a *scale*, is further graduated into 32nds and 64ths.   It is most essential to a mechanic to be able to make use of these very small divisons.

A mechanic must be able to calculate total lengths of objects shown in shop drawings.

Find the total (over-all) length of the object shown in this shop drawing.

Total length $= \frac{7}{8}'' + \frac{7}{8}'' + 1\frac{3}{32}'' = ?$

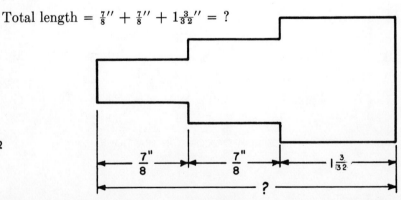

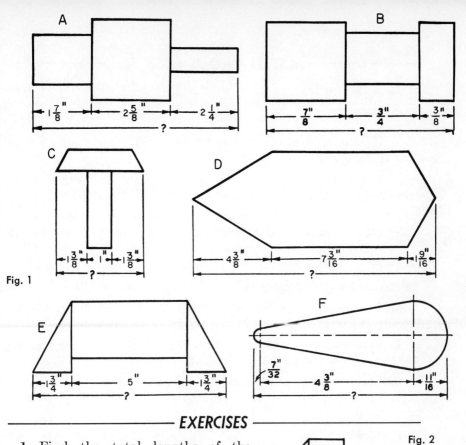

Fig. 1

Fig. 2

EXERCISES

1. Find the total lengths of the objects in figure 1.

2. Find the total length of the lathe chuck, figure 2.

3. A drawing board is built of three plies: $\frac{5}{8}$ in., $\frac{3}{16}$ in., and $\frac{9}{32}$ in. What is the total thickness of the board?

4. A carpenter lays floors in three layers: first the rough sheathing, $\frac{7}{8}$ in. thick; then the furring strips, $\frac{7}{8}$ in. thick; and on top the finished flooring, $\frac{13}{16}$ in. thick. How thick is the floor?

5. When Jim was building a cabinet, he glued together five boards, $8\frac{3}{4}$ in., $6\frac{7}{8}$ in., $7\frac{5}{16}$ in., $5\frac{1}{2}$ in., and $6\frac{5}{8}$ in. wide. What was the combined width of the boards?

6. A panel was built up of five plies $\frac{1}{4}$ in., $\frac{1}{8}$ in., $\frac{3}{16}$ in., $\frac{5}{16}$ in., and $\frac{5}{32}$ in. thick, respectively. How thick was the panel?

21. Addition of non-ruler fractions. Many fractions that are not found on a ruler are in common use. These include fractions such as $\frac{1}{3}$, $\frac{1}{5}$, $\frac{1}{6}$, $\frac{1}{10}$, their multiples, and many others.

MISCELLANEOUS EXERCISES

1. A farm is divided as follows: $14\frac{3}{4}$ acres in one field, $9\frac{2}{3}$ acres in another, and $17\frac{1}{2}$ acres in the third.   Find the total number of acres.

2. How many feet of molding are required to go around a room $14\frac{3}{4}$ ft. long and $23\frac{5}{6}$ ft. wide?

3. Betty traveled $18\frac{7}{10}$ miles by automobile and $124\frac{3}{5}$ miles by airplane.   How many miles did she travel on the trip?

4. On an automobile trip, $326\frac{6}{10}$ miles were traveled the first day, $197\frac{3}{10}$ the second day, $388\frac{7}{10}$ the third, and $467\frac{9}{10}$ the fourth. How many miles were traveled?

5. Find the perimeter of a five-sided figure if its sides are the following lengths: $8\frac{7}{12}$ in., $4\frac{2}{3}$ in., $5\frac{5}{6}$ in., $7\frac{3}{4}$ in., and $6\frac{1}{2}$ in.

6. A salesgirl made five sales from one bolt of linen: $4\frac{3}{4}$ yd., $7\frac{2}{3}$ yd., $18\frac{1}{4}$ yd., $9\frac{1}{6}$ yd., and $7\frac{3}{4}$ yd.   How many yards did she sell?

7. Five bolts of gingham contain $68\frac{2}{3}$ yd,. $47\frac{3}{4}$ yd., $55\frac{5}{6}$ yd., $49\frac{1}{2}$ yd., and $58\frac{11}{12}$ yd.   What is the total yardage?

8. Mr. North bought material for four cases that took $1\frac{1}{3}$ yd., $1\frac{5}{9}$ yd., $1\frac{5}{6}$ yd., and $1\frac{1}{2}$ yd.   How many yards did he buy for all the cases?

INVENTORY TEST 6   Subtraction of Common Fractions

$\frac{1}{2}$	$\frac{5}{6}$	$\frac{7}{8}$	$\frac{9}{10}$	$\frac{11}{12}$
$\frac{1}{3}$	$\frac{2}{3}$	$\frac{1}{4}$	$\frac{4}{5}$	$\frac{3}{4}$ **(5)**

$\frac{7}{12} - \frac{1}{3}$		$\frac{5}{6} - \frac{3}{4}$	$\frac{7}{8} - \frac{3}{16}$ **(8)**
$9\frac{2}{3}$	$5\frac{1}{2}$	$7\frac{5}{6}$	$9\frac{3}{5}$
$3\frac{1}{2}$	$1\frac{3}{4}$	3	4 **(12)**

48	$72\frac{5}{8}$	43
$24\frac{3}{4}$	$16\frac{1}{2}$	$10\frac{3}{8}$ **(15)**

Rating	Correct	Next Step
A	14 or 15	Do Inventory Test 7.
B	12 or 13	Do Inventory Test 7 or do Practice Exercises 6a to 6d.
C	11 or less	Do Practice Exercises 6a to 6d; then do Inventory Test 6 again.

A. Ruler fractions.

1. A board was reduced from $3\frac{1}{4}$ in. in thickness to $2\frac{5}{8}$ in. by being run through a planer. How much was taken off the board?

2. David knows the total bottom and top lengths of this box that he is making. He wishes to know how much longer the top is than the bottom of the box (figure 3). Can you tell him?

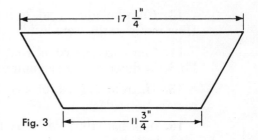

Fig. 3

3. If a plank $8\frac{3}{16}$ in. thick must be cut down to $5\frac{3}{4}$ in., how thick is the piece cut off by the saw?

4. The length of this box (figure 4) is how much more than the width?

5. Find the difference between the length of the top and the bottom of the scale drawing of a hog house, figure 5.

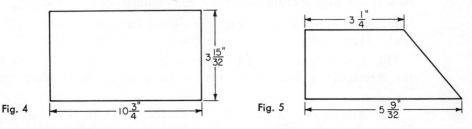

Fig. 4   Fig. 5

6. How much must a $1\frac{1}{16}$-in. board be planed to make it the required thickness of $\frac{29}{32}$ in.?

7. A rough casting weighed $72\frac{1}{16}$ lb. After being finished in a lathe, it weighed $68\frac{1}{4}$ lb. How much was the loss in finishing?

8. One steel strip is $\frac{5}{8}$ in. thick and another is $\frac{17}{32}$ in. thick. What is the difference in thickness?

9. A taper is reduced gradually from $2\frac{19}{32}$ in. at one end to $1\frac{7}{16}$ in. at the other. How much is the reduction?

*10. How many feet of baseboard will be required to go around a room $12\frac{1}{4}$ ft. wide and $14\frac{1}{6}$ ft. long, allowing $3\frac{1}{2}$ ft. for a door?

**11. Two circular holes are cut in a steel plate. The distance from the outside of one hole to the outside of the other across the diameters is $5\frac{1}{4}$ in. Their diameters are $1\frac{3}{16}$ in. and $1\frac{3}{4}$ in. What is the length of the metal between the holes? (Make a sketch of the metal plate.)

B. Non-ruler fractions.

12. Grace bought $4\frac{1}{3}$ yd. of ribbon to make a pillow top. She found that she needed $5\frac{2}{3}$ yd. How many more yards did she need to buy?

13. Cora bought $6\frac{1}{3}$ yd. of lace and used $4\frac{2}{3}$ yd. of it on a dress. How many yards were left?

14. Clara used $4\frac{2}{3}$ yd. of cloth to make a skirt. Jane used $5\frac{1}{9}$ yd. Find the difference in the number of yards used by the girls.

15. If, from $21\frac{1}{6}$ yd. of lace $19\frac{5}{9}$ yd. are used, how many yards remain unused?

16. Alta had $106\frac{1}{3}$ yd. of ribbon and used $78\frac{1}{6}$ yd. How many yards had she left?

17. Mrs. Allen had 100 lb. of sugar. She used $75\frac{4}{9}$ lb. How many pounds remain unused?

18. Mary canned 86 lb. of tomatoes and Nora canned $93\frac{2}{3}$ lb. How many more pounds did Nora can than Mary?

19. A jar that holds $3\frac{1}{3}$ gal. when filled has $\frac{5}{6}$ of a gallon in it now. How many more gallons are needed to fill the jar?

*20. A boat travels $\frac{1}{6}$ of its journey in rain, $\frac{2}{3}$ in sunshine, and the remainder in fog. What part of its journey did it travel in fog?

*21. A load of coal was driven on the scales to be weighed. The truck weighed $3750\frac{3}{10}$ lb.; the shovel, $3\frac{2}{5}$ lb.; the chute, $27\frac{1}{10}$ lb. What is the weight of the coal, if the total weight is 8527 lb.?

*22. From a pile of $34\frac{4}{5}$ tons of coal, a dealer sold $6\frac{3}{10}$ tons to one customer, $8\frac{1}{5}$ tons to another, and $6\frac{7}{10}$ tons to the third customer. How many tons of coal were left?

INVENTORY TEST 7 Multiplication of Common Fractions

Multiply; then reduce all products to lowest terms:

$\frac{3}{4} \times \frac{2}{5}$	$\frac{7}{8} \times \frac{6}{7}$	$6 \times 3\frac{1}{3}$	$\frac{1}{3} \times \frac{1}{3}$	**(4)**
$8 \times \frac{3}{4}$	$\frac{4}{15} \times 25$	$3\frac{1}{5} \times 10$	$2\frac{1}{2} \times 6$	**(8)**
$3\frac{1}{7} \times 14$	$3\frac{3}{4} \times 1\frac{3}{5}$	$\frac{2}{3} \times \frac{3}{7} \times \frac{7}{8}$	$8\frac{1}{3} \times 2\frac{2}{5}$	**(12)**
$7 \times \frac{1}{3}$	$12\frac{1}{2} \times \frac{1}{15}$	$180 \times \frac{5}{6}$	$20 \times \frac{1}{3}$	**(16)**

Rating	Correct	Next Step
A	15 or 16	Do Inventory Test 8.
B	13 or 14	Do Inventory Test 8 or do Practice Exercises 7a to 7c.
C	12 or less	Do Practice Exercises 7a to 7c; then do Inventory Test 7.

22. Changing the amount of a recipe. It is often necessary to make either more or less of a given food than the recipe provides for.

————————————— *HOME EXERCISES* —————————————

1. Fruit whip recipe (four servings):

$\frac{2}{3}$ cup fruit pulp   3 tablespoons sugar
2 egg whites   1 tablespoon lemon juice
      $\frac{1}{4}$ teaspoon salt

Determine the amount of each ingredient to serve (a) 8 persons; (b) 2 persons; *(c) 12 persons.

2. To make baked custard (4 servings):

$\frac{1}{4}$ cup sugar   3 eggs, beaten
$\frac{1}{4}$ teaspoon salt   2 cups hot milk
      1 teaspoon vanilla

Find the amount of the ingredients needed to serve (a) 8 people; *(b) 6 people; **(c) 9 people.

3. Crystallized walnuts:

4 cups walnut meats $\frac{3}{4}$ cup water
$1\frac{1}{2}$ cups sugar $\frac{1}{2}$ teaspoon cream of tartar
      1 tablespoon honey or syrup

Mix sugar, water, honey, and cream of tartar and boil to 242° F, or a medium-soft ball. Add nuts and stir.

Find the amount of ingredients to make:

(a) Double the recipe.   *(c) One-fourth the recipe.
*(b) One-half the recipe.   **(d) One and one-half times the recipe.

4. Clara uses $\frac{1}{3}$ yd. of velvet to cover a jewel box. How many yards of velvet will she need to cover 8 such boxes?

5. How much ribbon must Sally buy to make 6 hair ornaments if each ornament contains $\frac{3}{8}$ yd. of ribbon?

6. If 12 strips of $\frac{5}{8}$-in. steel are stacked on top of each other, how high a stack will they make?

7. How high a stack will 18 bricks, each $2\frac{1}{2}$ in. thick, make?

8. A purchase of $26\frac{1}{2}$ yd. of fencing is how many feet of fencing?

9. What is the weight of 120 boxes if each weighs $23\frac{3}{4}$ oz.?

10. Find the weight of 36 boxes of hose weighing $6\frac{1}{2}$ oz. each.

11. A house valued at $12,600 is insured for $\frac{4}{5}$ of its value. For what sum of money is it insured?

*12. Sound travels at the rate of 1,087 ft. per second in air. How far away is a train whose whistle is heard $3\frac{3}{10}$ seconds after the smoke is seen?

**13. A garden plot $48\frac{1}{2}$ ft. by $60\frac{1}{2}$ ft. contains how many square feet?

23. A special type of multiplication. In multiplying a mixed number (a) by an integer or (b) by another mixed number, it is sometimes better to arrange the work in a vertical column.

┌─── **EXAMPLE 1** ───┐

$$
\begin{array}{r}
72 \\
8\frac{2}{3} \\
\hline
48 \\
576 \\
\hline
624
\end{array}
$$

┌─── **EXAMPLE 2** ───┐

$$
\begin{array}{r}
76\frac{1}{3} \\
84\frac{1}{2} \\
\hline
28\frac{1}{6} \\
38 \\
304 \\
608 \\
\hline
6450\frac{1}{6}
\end{array}
$$

In example 1:

$72 \times \frac{2}{3} = 48$

$72 \times 8 = 576$

$72 \times 8\frac{2}{3} = 624$ product.

In example 2:

$\frac{1}{2} \times \frac{1}{3} = \frac{1}{6}$

$84 \times \frac{1}{3} = 28$

$76 \times \frac{1}{2} = 38$

$76 \times 4 = 304$

$76 \times 8 = 608$

$76\frac{1}{3} \times 84\frac{1}{2} = 6450\frac{1}{6}$ product.

Multiply vertically:

1. $27\frac{1}{4}$
   $28\frac{1}{3}$

2. $35\frac{1}{3}$
   $18\frac{2}{7}$

3. $64\frac{3}{5}$
   75

4. $205\frac{1}{3}$
   $78\frac{2}{5}$

5. $72\frac{2}{3}$
   $84\frac{5}{6}$

6. $87\frac{1}{2}$
   $44\frac{1}{3}$

7. $45\frac{3}{4}$
   $48\frac{3}{5}$

8. $21\frac{5}{6}$
   $18\frac{3}{7}$

9. $104\frac{3}{8}$
   $48\frac{1}{2}$

10. $72\frac{4}{5}$
    $65\frac{5}{6}$

11. 69
    $84\frac{2}{3}$

12. $93\frac{3}{4}$
    88

13. $81\frac{1}{3}$
    $27\frac{4}{9}$

14. $56\frac{1}{2}$
    $78\frac{1}{4}$

15. $52\frac{1}{6}$
    $36\frac{1}{4}$

INVENTORY TEST 8   Division of Common Fractions

Divide; then reduce all fractions in quotients to lowest terms:

$\frac{4}{5} \div \frac{2}{3}$	$\frac{7}{8} \div \frac{1}{2}$	$\frac{1}{2} \div \frac{1}{4}$	$\frac{1}{2} \div \frac{2}{3}$	(4)
$\frac{7}{9} \div \frac{2}{3}$	$\frac{9}{4} \div \frac{1}{3}$	$6 \div \frac{2}{3}$	$\frac{2}{3} \div 12$	(8)
$9 \div \frac{3}{4}$	$8 \div \frac{1}{2}$	$\frac{7}{8} \div 2$	$\frac{8}{9} \div 16$	(12)
$\frac{4}{5} \div 8$	$3\frac{1}{3} \div 2$	$3\frac{3}{4} \div 2\frac{1}{2}$	$4\frac{4}{5} \div 2\frac{2}{3}$	(16)

Rating	Correct	Next Step
A	15 or 16	Do Inventory Test 9.
B	13 or 14	Do Inventory Test 9 or do Practice Exercises 8a to 8c.
C	12 or less	Do Practice Exercises 8a to 8c; then do Inventory Test 8 again.

—————————— SHOP EXERCISES ——————————

1. Find the number of shelf boards $2\frac{1}{3}$ ft. long that can be cut from a 14-ft. board.

2. How many strips of steel each $\frac{5}{16}$ in. thick will it take to make a pile $7\frac{1}{2}$ in. high?

3. Clyde wishes to rip a board $4\frac{7}{8}$ in. wide down the middle. How far from the edge must he lay out the line where he is to saw?

4. How many strips of brass each $\frac{5}{16}$ in. thick will it take to build up a piece for a motor to a thickness of $1\frac{9}{16}$ in.?

*5. The leg of a stool tapers from $2\frac{1}{4}$ in. across one end to $1\frac{1}{2}$ in. at the other end. If the length of the leg is 8 in., how much is the reduction per inch?

*6. Mrs. Flagg bought a chicken weighing $4\frac{1}{4}$ lb. for $1.80. What was the cost per pound?

*7. How many clown costumes can be made from a bolt of cloth containing $38\frac{1}{2}$ yd., if each costume requires $5\frac{1}{2}$ yd.?

*8. A scarf is to be made $\frac{1}{4}$ as wide as it is long. What is the required length if the width is to be 9 in.?

**9. A remnant of cloth $\frac{7}{8}$ yd. long sold for $3.50. Another piece of like material $\frac{5}{6}$ yd. long sold for $3. Which was the better price per yard and how much better?

**10. Mary is to cut crosswise, from 32-in. cloth, 6 yd. of banding 4 in. wide. How much cloth must she buy, and how much waste will there be?

**11. A dress measures $2\frac{1}{3}$ yd. around the lower edge. An 8-in. ruffle is to be made one-fourth fuller. How much cloth 30 in. wide must be allowed for it?

――――――――― MISCELLANEOUS EXERCISES ―――――――――

12. How long will it take Sam and Joe to walk to camp, a distance of 10 mi., if they walk at the rate of $3\frac{1}{3}$ m. p. h.?

13. A certain job requires 45 hours. If a man works at it $2\frac{1}{2}$ hours per day, how many days will it take him to complete the job?

14. Find the average speed of a train that travels 125 mi. in $3\frac{1}{8}$ hours.

15. How many sacks containing $2\frac{1}{4}$ bushels each can be filled from a bin of oats containing 270 bushels?

――――――――― REVIEW OF CHAPTER II ―――――――――

1. How many more cups of pineapple in a #2 XT can of $2\frac{3}{4}$ cups than in a #1$\frac{1}{4}$ can of $1\frac{1}{2}$ cups?

2. A #1 Tall can holds 2 cups. A #2 Tall can holds $3\frac{1}{4}$ cups. The #2 Tall can holds how many times as much as the #1 Tall can?

3. Henry's class sold 424 tickets to the school play. If Henry sold $\frac{1}{8}$ of the tickets, how many did he sell?

4. Bob played 18 games of chess, winning $\frac{2}{3}$ of the games. How many games did he win?

5. Mark's room is $10\frac{1}{2}$ ft. long, and Sam's room is $12\frac{1}{6}$ ft. long. Sam's room is how much longer than Mark's room?

6. How high a stack will 10 books, each $\frac{7}{8}$ in. thick, make?

7. How many books $\frac{7}{8}$ in. thick would make a stack 14 in. high?

8. June gathered up scraps of lace in the sewing box. She found pieces of these lengths: $2\frac{1}{3}$ yd., $3\frac{1}{4}$ yd., $\frac{7}{8}$ yd., and $2\frac{5}{6}$ yd. Find the total yards of lace.

9. Albert helped his father take inventory in their grocery store. He weighed potatoes in four different sacks. Their weights were: $47\frac{1}{2}$ lb., $63\frac{7}{8}$ lb., $56\frac{3}{4}$ lb., and $74\frac{5}{8}$ lb. Find their total weight.

10. John's weight is $102\frac{3}{4}$ lb. and Joe's weight is $95\frac{1}{2}$ lb. (a) Find the total weight of the boys. (b) What is their average weight? (c) How much is the difference in their weights?

11. This recipe makes four large corn waffles:

2 c. sifted flour $\frac{1}{2}$ tsp. salt $\frac{1}{2}$ c. melted shortening
$2\frac{1}{2}$ tsp. baking powder   2 eggs   1 c. cream-style corn
                    $1\frac{1}{2}$ c. milk

Rewrite the recipe: (a) for three times the amount; (b) to make two such waffles;* (c) to make three such waffles.

12. A new lawn fertilizer feeds $12\frac{1}{2}$ sq. ft. for only a penny. If one bag feeds 5,000 sq. ft., what is the cost of a bag?

13. How do you find how much more the heaviest pupil in your class weighs than the lightest pupil in your class?

14. If you know the distance between two towns and the rate at which you can travel, how do you find the time required to travel this distance?

*15. A recipe is written to serve 12 people. (a) How do you change the recipe to serve 18 people? (b) 8 people? (c) 9 people?

**16. You can travel a known fraction of the distance between two places by air, and another known fraction by water. How do you find the fraction of the distance required to complete the trip?

──────────── *PLAYOFF FOR CHAPTER II* ────────────

In Magic Square 1:

1. Add each row.
2. Add each column.
3. Add each diagonal.

Do you get the idea?

Magic Square 1.

8	1	6
3	5	7
4	9	2

In Magic Square 2:

Make each row, each column, and each diagonal total 15.

Magic Square 2.

		$2\frac{1}{2}$
2	5	8

41

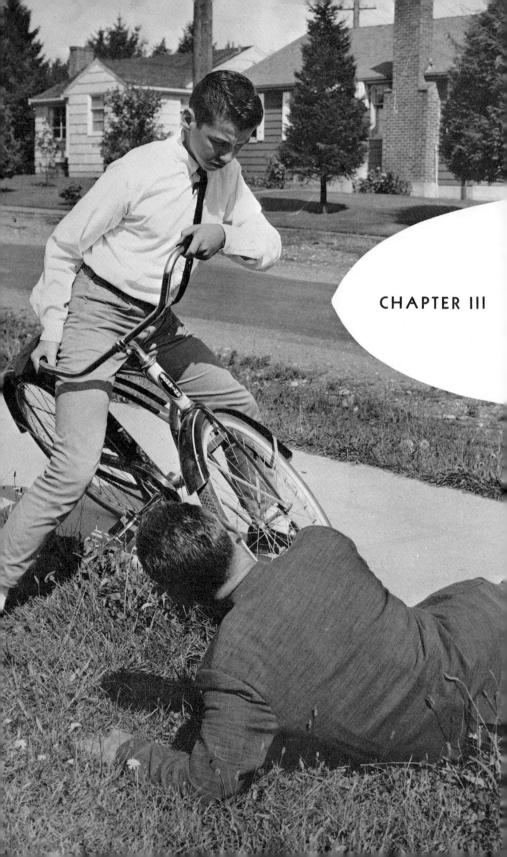

CHAPTER III

ADDITION, SUBTRACTION, MULTIPLI-

CATION, AND DIVISION OF DECIMAL

FRACTIONS WITH APPLICATIONS

VOCABULARY

1. decimal fraction   2. measurement   3. estimate

24. Reading and writing decimal fractions. Decimal fractions, commonly called *decimals*, are being used more and more in the place of common fractions in industry.

A decimal fraction is a fraction whose denominator is 10, or 100, or 1,000, and so on. However, the denominator is not so written. Instead of the 10, 100, and so on, being written as a denominator, it is written with a decimal point to indicate the size of the denominator. For example:

$\frac{3}{10}$ (There is one zero in 10; point off one decimal place.) = .3

$\frac{4}{100}$ (There are two zeros in 100; point off two decimal places.) = .04.

$\frac{7}{1000}$ (There are three zeros in 1,000; point off three decimal places.) = .007

Write these common fractions as decimal fractions:

(a) $\frac{9}{10}$ (b) $\frac{3}{100}$ (c) $\frac{7}{1000}$ (d) 1/10,000   (e) $\frac{47}{1000}$ (f) $\frac{51}{100}$

(g) 21/10,000   (h) 17/100,000   (i) 33/1,000,000   (j) $\frac{73}{10}$ (k) $\frac{467}{1000}$

In reading a number that is a combination of a whole number and a decimal, use the word "*and*" to indicate the decimal point. For example, 324.678 is read "three hundred twenty-four and six hundred seventy-eight thousandths." (*Note.* Use the word *and* at no other place in reading decimals.)

Read these decimal fractions aloud:

(a) .6   (b) .5   (c) .64   (d) .26   (e) 1.24
(f) 4.36   (g) .301   (h) 2.282   (i) 5.1767   (j) .365
(k) 3.9   (l) 2.509   (m) 1.1786   (n) 8.1345   (o) 2.27486

Write the following numbers as decimal fractions:

(a) 18 hundredths   (b) twelve and 4 tenths
(c) 27 thousandths   (d) 5 and 3 tenths
(e) six thousandths   (f) 12 ten-thousandths
(g) two and 3 thousandths   (h) 9 hundred-thousandths
(i) one and 7 ten-thousandths (j) fifty and sixty-six thousandths

25. Changing common fractions to decimal fractions. In a common fraction, the line between the numerator and the denominator indicates division. For instance, the common fraction $\frac{5}{7}$ means $5 \div 7$. To change the common fraction $\frac{5}{7}$ to a decimal fraction, place a decimal point after the 5, annex as many zeros as needed (usually two), and then divide 5.00 by 7. The quotient must have as many decimal places as there are decimal places in the dividend.

┌─ **EXAMPLE** ─┐

$$\frac{5}{7} = 7\overline{)5.00}^{\,.71\frac{3}{7}}$$

Express as decimal fractions:

(a) $\frac{6}{7}$ (b) $\frac{4}{9}$ (c) $\frac{8}{25}$ (d) $\frac{3}{50}$ (e) $\frac{3}{20}$ (f) $\frac{5}{16}$

(g) $\frac{7}{12}$ (h) $\frac{8}{15}$ (i) $\frac{5}{6}$ (j) $\frac{3}{200}$ (k) $\frac{11}{25}$ (l) $\frac{1}{100}$

26. Changing decimal fractions to common fractions.

To write a decimal as a common fraction, write the decimal, leaving off the decimal point, as the numerator of the fraction; then write the appropriate denominator. Usually, reduce the fraction to lowest terms.

```
┌──────── EXAMPLES ────────┐
│ (a) .65 = 65/100 = 13/20 │
│                          │
│ (b) .005 = 5/1,000 = 1/200 │
└──────────────────────────┘
```

$$\text{(a) } .65 = \frac{65}{100} = \frac{13}{20}$$
$$\text{(b) } .005 = \frac{5}{1,000} = \frac{1}{200}$$

──────────────── EXERCISES ────────────────

Express as common fractions in lowest terms:

(a) .85	(b) .72	(c) .7	(d) .8	(e) .006	(f) .004
(g) .18	(h) .015	(i) .62	(j) .45	(k) .125	(l) .625
(m) .0012	(n) 1.5	(o) 3.45	(p) 2.125	(q) .0008	(r) .00125

27. Arranging a series of numbers according to size.

In a series of numbers, it is not always easy to decide which is the highest or the lowest in value. If the numbers are common fractions, it is sometimes better to change them to decimal fractions.

Which is the largest fraction in the series $\frac{2}{5}$, $\frac{3}{8}$, $\frac{4}{9}$, $\frac{3}{7}$? Change each fraction to a decimal. Then, by looking at the first decimal place (tenths), we can easily select $\frac{3}{8}$ ($.37\frac{1}{2}$) as the smallest number. For the remaining three numbers, we must look to the first two decimal places (hundredths). Arranged in order from largest to smallest, the series is: $.44\frac{4}{9}$, $.42\frac{6}{7}$, $.40$, $.37\frac{1}{2}$, or $\frac{4}{9}$, $\frac{3}{7}$, $\frac{2}{5}$, $\frac{3}{8}$.

```
┌─ EXAMPLES ─┐
│ 2/5 = .40  │
│ 3/8 = .37½ │
│ 4/9 = .44⁴⁄₉ │
│ 3/7 = .42⁶⁄₇ │
└────────────┘
```

$$\frac{2}{5} = .40$$
$$\frac{3}{8} = .37\frac{1}{2}$$
$$\frac{4}{9} = .44\frac{4}{9}$$
$$\frac{3}{7} = .42\frac{6}{7}$$

Within some groups of numbers, it is necessary to change the numbers to thousandths or even a lower denomination before determining the order of size.

──────────────── EXERCISES ────────────────

1. Recite orally the numbers in each series in the order of their size.

Largest first:

(a)	.20	.03	.16
(b)	.60	.59	.71
(c)	.3	.04	.18
(d)	.125	.15	.2
(e)	.608	.6	.06
(f)	.167	.30	.28

Smallest first:

(g)	.05	.45	.005
(h)	.06	.66	6.6
(i)	1	.18	1.8
(j)	.33	3	.03
(k)	.8	.88	.08
(l)	.375	3.75	.07

2. Write the numbers in each series in the order of their size.

Largest first: Smallest first:

(a)	$.42\frac{1}{2}$	$.42$	$.82\frac{1}{8}$	(i)	$\frac{1}{16}$	$\frac{1}{12}$	$\frac{1}{15}$
(b)	$.23$	$.2\frac{1}{2}$	$.2\frac{3}{4}$	(j)	$\frac{3}{8}$	$\frac{3}{7}$	$\frac{2}{5}$
(c)	$.9$	$.89$	$.9\frac{1}{4}$	(k)	$1\frac{1}{4}$	$1\frac{1}{3}$	$1\frac{1}{8}$
(d)	$\frac{3}{4}$	$.77$	$.07\frac{1}{2}$	(l)	$\frac{1}{2}$	$\frac{3}{4}$	$\frac{5}{8}$
(e)	$\frac{7}{8}$	$\frac{5}{6}$	$.85$	(m)	2.0	$2\frac{1}{2}$	2.35
(f)	$\frac{5}{8}$	$\frac{3}{5}$	$.6\frac{1}{2}$	(n)	$.895$	$.807$	$.8594$
(g)	$\frac{1}{4}$	$\frac{2}{9}$	$\frac{2}{7}$	(o)	$.678$	2	$.7$
(h)	$\frac{3}{16}$	$\frac{1}{8}$	$\frac{1}{7}$	(p)	3.6	$3\frac{5}{8}$	$3.60\frac{1}{2}$

28. Addition and subtraction of decimal fractions. Arrange the numbers to be added or subtracted in a vertical column with the decimal points directly below each other so that tenths will be under tenths, hundredths under hundredths, and so on. In any integer, the decimal point belongs at the right of the last digit.

┌─ EXAMPLE A ─┐

Addition

3.17	3.17
2.8	2.80
12.	12.00
17.97	17.97

┌─ EXAMPLE B ─┐

Subtraction

24.6	24.600
-18.452	-18.452
6.148	6.148

Zeros may be filled in after the decimals to prevent a ragged appearance. The decimal point in the sum (or in the remainder) is placed directly below the decimal points in the column.

If a common fraction and a decimal fraction are to be added or subtracted, either express the decimal as a common fraction or the common fraction as a decimal; then proceed as usual.

┌─ EXAMPLE C ─┐

$3.2 + 1\frac{1}{4}$	3.20
	$+1.25$
	4.45

┌─ EXAMPLE D ─┐

$5\frac{1}{2} - 2.37\frac{1}{2}$	$5\frac{1}{2}$
	$-2\frac{3}{8}$
	$3\frac{1}{8}$

──────── *EXERCISES* ────────

Add:

	1.	2.	3.	4.	5.
	.2	1.4	4.56	12.200	$1.2\frac{1}{2}$
	.5	3.5	2.10	1.760	.8
	.7	1.2	1.18	.138	$4.3\frac{3}{4}$
	.6	2.7	.45	8.000	$2.\frac{1}{2}$

6. $3.8 + 2.65 + 4 + 1.2$ **7.** $2.16 + .4 + 2 + 1\frac{1}{2}$

Subtract:

8. .97	**9.** 5.6	**10.** 3.3	**11.** 6.	**12.** $8\frac{1}{2}$
.13	1.4	1.17	.14	1.7

13. $24.18 - 6.09$ **14.** $42.2 - 8.2\frac{1}{4}$ **15.** $35 - 18.7$

INVENTORY TEST 9   Addition and Subtraction of
                                         Decimal Fractions

Add:

1. 7.3	**2.** 5.85	**3.** 18.61	**4.** 15.03
1.8	.72	1.896	22.88
3.0	2.	$16\frac{1}{4}$	30.21

5. $1.2 + 3.45 + 8 + 3.4$ **6.** $32.6 + 7.14 + .8 + 14$

Subtract:

7. 2.8	**8.** .63	**9.** 7.9	**10.** $47\frac{1}{2}$
1.2	.08	.82	2.64

           11. $256.34 - 27.1$ **12.** $78 - 2.71$

Rating	Correct	Next Step
A	11 or 12	Do Inventory Test 10.
B	9 or 10	Either do Inventory Test 10 or do Practice Exercises 9a to 9d.
C	8 or less	Do Practice Exercises 9a to 9d; then do Inventory Test 9 again.

--- **EXERCISES** ---

1. The receipts from a football game were $1,456.40. The expenses were $268.55. Find the profit.

2. A broker received $1,128 to invest in bonds. If his commission is $25.80, how much remains to invest?

3. One quart dry measure contains 67.200625 cu. in., and one quart liquid measure contains 57.75 cu. in. How many more cubic inches are there in a dry quart than in a liquid quart?

4. If a contractor is awarded a construction job on a bid of $28,-452.75, what is his net profit if he estimates the cost at $25,594.49?

5. Jack had $7½ and paid a debt of $3.86. How much did he have left?

6. A carpenter agrees to build a cabinet for $25.00. The lumber cost him $8.20 and the hardware $2.28. How much was his profit?

7. Shipments of 1,845.9 lb., 2,384.72 lb., 1,694.2 lb., and 2,897.8 lb. of coal are placed in a bin. Find the total number of pounds of coal in the bin.

8. Joe's balance in the bank was $64.79 before depositing $26.43, $38.79, $17.65, and $29.48. Find his balance after he made the deposits.

9. A grocer's sales for Monday amounted to $267.63; Tuesday, $198.56; Wednesday, $367.98; Thursday, $406.45; Friday, $419.59; and Saturday, $438.36. What were the total sales for the week?

10. Find the total cost of a cement walk if the foreman was paid $88.75, laborers were paid $75.80, and cement cost $172.

*11. Harold made six trays to sell. His expenses were: wood $12.80, glue $1.65, varnish $4.55. He sold the trays for $28.60. How much was his profit on one tray?

*12. A merchant's balance in the bank on May 31 was $697.75. During June he deposited $37.44, $86.79, and $97.68 and withdrew $219.49, $59.95, and $197.38. What was his balance on June 30?

*13. Scott and Company had a bank balance on April 1 of $1,812.23. During April, deposits of $68.14, $25.87, $75, and $197.55 and withdrawals of $225, $98.46, $328.78, and $263.79 were made. What is the balance on April 30?

**14. In the following table, find the total sales for (a) each clerk, and (b) each day of the week:

TABLE 1

Clerk	Monday	Tuesday	Wednesday	Thursday	Friday	Saturday
A	$85.26	$93.07	$88.95	$82.76	$92.16	$86.45
B	68.34	82.72	76.23	75.24	87.33	88.72
C	96.28	75.29	48.39	67.35	86.38	95.24
D	92.75	84.56	64.75	59.28	93.25	83.76

———————— *SHOP EXERCISES* ————————

29. Decimal fractions in shop measurements. Many measurements in the shop require such a high degree of accuracy that a special tool that measures to the thousandth of an inch is used. Consequently, measurements expressed as decimals frequently appear on drawings.

EXAMPLES

A. In figure A, the total length of the object is:

$$1.5'' + 2.1'' + 1.2'' = 4.8''$$

B. In figure B, the missing dimension is:

$$2.374'' - 1.437'' - .625'' = .312''$$

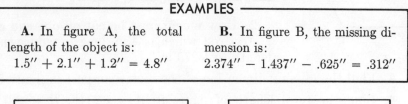

Fig. 1

EXERCISES

---

1. Find the missing dimensions in figures 2, 3, 4, 5, and 6 (all dimensions are in inches).

$A = .25 \quad D = .12 \quad G = .10$
$B = .27 \quad E = .10 \quad H = .12$
$C = .27 \quad F = .12 \quad I = .27$
$\qquad\quad J = .27 \quad K = .20$

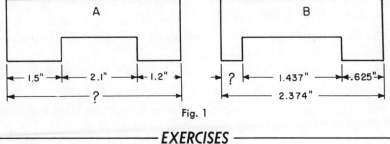

Fig. 2

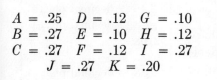

$A = 95.69$
$B = 32.93$
$C = 36.14$
$D = ?$

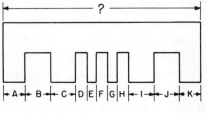

Fig. 3

Fig. 4

$A = .778$
$B = .389$
$C = .778$
$D = .389$
$E = .778$

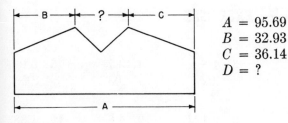

Fig. 5

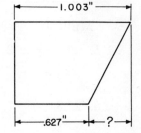

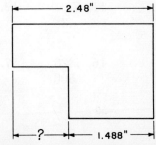

Fig. 6

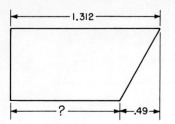

Fig. 7

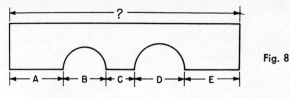

Fig. 8

2. How much must be cut off one end of a steel rod which is 4 in. long to reduce the length to 1.275 in.?

3. Find the missing dimension of the motor support in figure 7.

4. Find the total length of figure 8: $A = 1.234''$, $B = .887''$ $C = .491''$, $D = 1.196''$, $E = 1.234''$.

*5. How much should be cut off each end of a 3.25-ft. board to reduce its length to 2.5 ft.?

**6. A pipe has an outside diameter of 1.315 in. and an inside diameter of 1.04 in. What is the thickness of the pipe?

**7. How deep a cut must be made in a circular steel rod whose diameter is $2\frac{1}{8}$ in. to bring the diameter to 1.275 in.?

30. Multiplication of decimal fractions. Decimal fractions are multiplied exactly like integers. After multiplying, determine the location of the decimal point in the product as follows:

Beginning at the right-hand side of the product, point off as many decimal places as the sum of the number of decimal places in the multiplicand and the multiplier.

```
———— EXAMPLE ————

3.46 (2 decimal places)
 2.8 (1 decimal place)
————
2768
692
————
9.688 (3 decimal places)
```

——————— EXERCISES ———————

Multiply:

1. .26	2. 2.3	3. 4.8	4. 3.7	5. 6.9
.4	.6	.02	.03	.05

6. 22.3	7. 14.4	8. 2.124	9. 4.8	10. 1.38
.1	.07	.06	.08	.09

11. 7.21	12. .648	13. 3.89	14. 18.9	15. 3.04
.38	.46	.72	3.6	2.07

16. .326	17. .0345	18. 6.38	19. 6.53	20. 56.8
500	7.4	3.7	100	4.7

31. Multiplying a number by 10, 100, 1,000, and so on. To multiply a number by 10, 100, 1,000, and so on, move the decimal point as many places to the *right* as there are zeros in the multiplier. Annex zeros if necessary.

┌─────── EXAMPLES ───────┐
846 × 10 = 8,460
846 × 100 = 84,600
8.46 × 10 = 84.6
└────────────────────────┘

─────────────── EXERCISES—ORAL ───────────────

Multiply each of the following numbers by 10, 100, and 1,000:

1. 690	8. 33.3	15. 1298	22. 3.24	29. 7.2
2. 78	9. 200	16. 1.8	23. .526	30. 181
3. 4.78	10. 6.7	17. .35	24. 10	31. 666
4. 2344	11. 4.5	18. .07	25. .003	32. 3.45
5. 211	12. .8	19. 21.5	26. .6	33. .056
6. 21,800	13. 27.85	20. .4	27. 1	34. .1
7. 2.4	14. .139	21. 28	28. .5	35. 20

36. Mary Thomas makes bank deposits of $10 per month for 124 months. What is her total deposit in that period?

37. What is the total cost of 100 articles @ $4.06 each?

38. At $10 per month, how much does a telephone cost per year?

39. There are 1,760 yd. in a mile. How many yards are there in 100 mi?

40. A firm sold 7,685 washing machines @ $100 each. Find the amount of the total sales.

41. A cubic foot of water weighs 62.5 lb. What do 100 cu. ft. weigh?

42. A cubic foot of space holds 7.48 gal. of water. How many gallons will 1,000 cu. ft. hold?

43. An agent makes 5¢ commission on each Christmas card that he sells. What is his total commission on 1,000 cards?

INVENTORY TEST 10   Multiplication of Decimal Fractions

Multiply:

1. .3	2. .08	3. 524	4. 6.7
.8	7	.006	.08

5. 2.7×3 **6.** $3.6 \times .4$ **7.** $100 \times .08$ **8.** 7.92×10

9. 7.4   **10.** .32   **11.** 4.29   **12.** 5.63
$\underline{2.8}$ $\underline{.14}$ $\underline{.36}$ $\underline{6.07}$

Rating	Correct	Next Step
A	11 or 12	Do Inventory Test 11.
B	9 or 10	Do Inventory Test 11, or do Practice Exercises 10a and 10b.
C	8 or less	Do Practice Exercises 10a and 10b; then do Inventory Test 10 again.

SHOP EXERCISES

1. Forty-eight sheets of metal are stacked one on top of the other. If each sheet is .087 in. thick, what is the total height of the sheets?

2. At $1.84 per foot, what is the cost of 180 ft. of steel tubing?

3. If a $\frac{5}{8}$-in. rivet weighs .175 lb., what is the weight of (a) 1,000 such rivets? (b) Of 750 rivets? (c) Of 8,000 rivets?

4. A certain metal sheet with an area of 18.7 sq. ft. weighs .196 lb. per square foot. What is its total weight?

MISCELLANEOUS EXERCISES

5. If a plane which has a wing area of 386 sq. ft. can carry 20.8 lb. per square foot, how many pounds can the plane carry?

6. A steamer traveling 16.8 m. p. h. will go how far in 24 hours?

7. An aircraft traveling 228.6 m. p. h. will go how far in 2.8 hours?

8. The airline fare between New York and Los Angeles is $181.53 for an adult. How much passenger fare is received by the airline for a trip from New York to Los Angeles on which 18 adults are carried?

9. What is the weight of 10 aircraft engines whose average weight is 318.76 lb.?

10. If the flying cost of a certain plane is $.482 per mile, what will be the cost of a 780-mile flight?

11. If an average of 171.1 pupils per day enjoyed a playground, as seen in figure 9, during a summer vacation of 90 days, what was the attendance for the season?

32. Multiplying a number by a fractional part of 1. (See Appendix D for equivalent fractional parts of one.)

EXAMPLES

Multiply 128 by .12½.	Multiply 2.52 by .66⅔.	Multiply 324 by 1.33⅓.
$\dfrac{16}{\cancel{128}} \times \dfrac{1}{\cancel{8}} = 16$	$\dfrac{.84}{\cancel{2.52}} \times \dfrac{2}{\cancel{3}} = 1.68$	$\dfrac{108}{\cancel{324}} \times \dfrac{4}{\cancel{3}} = 432$

EXERCISES

1. $528 \times .25$
2. $756 \times .33\frac{1}{3}$
3. $4.59 \times .66\frac{2}{3}$
4. $65.6 \times .37\frac{1}{2}$
5. $16\frac{2}{3} \times 2.28$
6. $.12\frac{1}{2} \times 368$
7. $59.5 \times .14\frac{2}{7}$
8. $51.2 \times .87\frac{1}{2}$

9. $7.2 \times .83\frac{1}{3}$
10. $.08\frac{1}{3} \times 2.4$
11. $.28\frac{4}{7} \times 264.6$
12. $10.48 \times .62\frac{1}{2}$
13. $1.28 \times .06\frac{1}{4}$
14. $.66\frac{2}{3} \times .528$
15. $43.2 \times .37\frac{1}{2}$
16. $.62\frac{1}{2} \times 926.4$

17. $.87\frac{1}{2} \times 62.56$
*18. $.84 \times 1.33\frac{1}{3}$
*19. $33.6 \times 1.37\frac{1}{2}$
*20. $.968 \times 1.87\frac{1}{2}$
*21. $17.37 \times 2.33\frac{1}{3}$
*22. $1.66\frac{2}{3} \times 5.46$
*23. $2.12\frac{1}{2} \times .72$
*24. $1.62\frac{1}{2} \times 8.08$

Fig. 9. Playground

25. Find the cost of 96 yd. of lace @ 33⅓¢ per yard.

26. How much does a farmer's wife receive if she sells 64 doz. eggs at 50¢ per dozen?

27. Seventy bushels of potatoes at $1.20 per bushel cost how much?

28. Brokerage at 25¢ per share amounts to how much on 528 shares?

29. If 742 pupils of a certain school give 25¢ each to the Red Cross, how much is contributed?

30. At a bargain sale, 524 aprons were sold at 75¢ each; how much was collected from the sale?

31. If eggs are sold at a profit of 10¢ per dozen, what is the profit on a case (30 doz.)?

32. At 16⅔¢ per bulb, find the cost of 2 doz. electric light bulbs.

33. Find the total cost of 42 yd. of cloth at 25¢ per yard.

34. A gross (144) of marbles is sold at 10¢ per marble. What is the total amount of the sale?

*35. Find the cost of 88 yd. of cloth at $1.62½ per yd.

*36. Jerry's class of 32 pupils gave an average of $1.87½ per pupil to the "March of Dimes." How much did the class contribute?

*37. In April, Clark averaged $2.66⅔ per day for 18 days on an after-school job. How much did Clark earn in April?

*38. Don paid $48 for a bicycle and sold it for 0.87½ times as much as he paid for it. For how much did Don sell the bicycle?

*39. Dick lived 18 blocks from school. Tom lived 2.33⅓ times as far. How many blocks did Tom ride his bicycle on the way to school each morning?

*40. Food cost the Rapp family $164.24 in May. In June the food cost 1.37½ times as much. Find the cost of food in June for the Rapp family.

33. Division of decimals. The division of decimals may be performed in the same manner as the division of integers. Multiply the divisor by some multiple of 10 that will make the divisor an integer. The dividend must be multiplied by that same multiple of 10. Multiplying both the divisor and the dividend by the *same* number does not affect the value of the quotient.

Divide and place the decimal point in the quotient directly above the decimal point in the dividend.

EXAMPLE A		EXAMPLE B
.876 ÷ 2.8	The same result may be	.876 ÷ 2.8

┌─ EXAMPLE A ─┐
.876 ÷ 2.8
2.8 × 10 = 28
.876 × 10 = 8.76
$.31\frac{2}{7}$
28)8.76
8 4
36
28
$\frac{8}{28} = \frac{2}{7}$
└─────────────┘

The same result may be obtained as follows: Before beginning the process of division, (1) move the decimal point of the divisor to the right of the divisor; (2) move the decimal point of the dividend to the right the same number of places, adding any necessary zeros; (3) place the decimal point in the quotient directly above the point in the dividend.

┌─ EXAMPLE B ─┐
.876 ÷ 2.8
$.31\frac{2}{7}$
2 8.)8.76
8 4
36
28
$\frac{8}{28} = \frac{2}{7}$
└─────────────┘

EXERCISES

Estimate each quotient and then divide:

1. 3)6.9 2. .2)7.6 3. .02)6.6 4. .6)8.4

5. .03)2.4 6. .002).4 7. .005).06 8. 20).8

9. .4)8 10. 30).9 11. .7)4.2 12. .003).6

13. 4.2)2.94 14. .24)9.648 15. 2.8)168.84 16. .43).3913

17. .04)11.24 18. .003).9 19. .001).04 20. .18).7254

34. Dividing a number by 10, 100, 1,000, and so on. To divide a number by 10, 100, 1,000, and so on, move the decimal point as many places to the *left* as there are zeros in the divisor. (Prefix zeros if necessary.)

┌─── EXAMPLES ───┐
846 ÷ 10 = 84.6
846 ÷ 100 = 8.46
8.46 ÷ 100 = .0846
└────────────────┘

EXERCISES

A. Oral. Divide each of the following numbers by 10, 100, and 1,000:

1. 2 2. 1.8 3. .7 4. 30 5. .06
6. 52 7. 2.4 8. 24.5 9. 300 10. 6.75
11. .425 12. .007 13. 28.7 14. 1.11 15. 1267

16. 52.32	17. 3.724	18. 471.6	19. .6161	20. 3000
21. 24.65	22. 3.17	23. .8	24. 24	25. 500
26. 7.7	27. 5	28. .1	29. .18	30. 214
31. .07	32. 2000	33. .4	34. 1	35. 10

36. A $476 debt is paid in full in 100 equal payments. What is the amount of each payment?

37. An 8-in. space is divided into 100 equal parts. How long is each part?

B. Written

*38. What wages are paid for the completion of the following articles:

    (a)   150 articles @ $4.80 per 100
    (b)   400   "   @   2.50 " 100
    (c)   975   "   @   .96 " 100
    (b) 2,450   "   @   .75 " 100
    (e) 3,675   "   @   6.00 " 1,000
    (f) 2,693   "   @   1.63 " 1,000
    (g)   974   "   @   8.75 " 1,000
    (h)   543   "   @ 10.65 " 1,000

*39. At the rate of $2.75 for each 100 lb. of freight, what is the cost of shipping 29,000 lb?

*40. A freight car loaded with 86,400 lb. of wheat is shipped from Kansas City to St. Louis, Mo., at $19\frac{1}{2}$¢ per 100 lb. What is the total freight charge?

*41. Green & Co. shipped 30,580 pounds of freight at the rate of $1.96 per hundred pounds. What were the freight charges?

*42. At $63\frac{1}{4}$¢ per 100 lb., what are the freight charges on a shipment weighing 784 lb.?

*43. A lot shipment is a shipment containing two or more packages sent to the same address. Find the total weight in a lot shipment of 3 packages weighing 186 lb., 179 lb., and 256 lb.

*44. At $1.57 per 100 lb., what is the total cost of sending the lot shipment in exercise 43?

**45. What will be the cost of 11,000 cu. ft. of gas @ $1.37 per 1,000 cu. ft.?

1. $2\overline{)\,.66}$ 2. $.04\overline{)\,.68}$ 3. $.08\overline{)\,88}$ 4. $.05\overline{)84.5}$

5. $.002\overline{)16}$ 6. $3.2\overline{)1.155}$ 7. $.38\overline{)27.36}$ 8. $24\overline{)77.04}$

9. $2.4\overline{)\,.12096}$ 10. $.364\overline{)1.4014}$ 11. $72.65 \div 10$ 12. $5 \div 100$

13. $.08 \div 10$ 14. $2.75 \div 100$ 15. $68.4 \div 1000$ 16. $80 \div 100$

Rating	Correct	Next Step
A	15 or 16	Do Inventory Test 12.
B	13 or 14	Do Inventory Test 12, or do Practice Exercises 11a to 11c.
C	12 or less	Do Practice Exercises 11a to 11c; then do Inventory Test 11 again.

EXERCISES

1. Andy can pay off his debt of $1.62 in three equal payments. How much can he pay each payment?

2. How many shelves 11.6 in. long can be cut from a 92.8-in. board?

3. A 150-lb.-lot shipment consists of packages weighing 3.75 lb. each. How many packages are in the shipment?

4. At 5¢ each, how many stamps must be sold to add $325,256,865 to the Treasury of the United States?

5. A 216.75-acre farm can be divided into how many plots of 12.75 acres each?

6. At $.35 per yard, how many yards of lace can be bought for $26.25?

7. If gasoline costs $.345 per gallon, how many gallons can be bought for $1.16?

8. An agent sold belts and received a commission of $.24 a belt. His commission for one week was $126. How many belts did he sell?

*9. A ticket for a series of 5 football games costs $1.75. Single-game tickets cost $.50 each. How much is saved per ticket by purchasing the series ticket?

*10. Harold spent $64.61 for 182 school lunches last year. What was the average cost per lunch?

35. Rounding off numbers. The cost of merchandise is usually calculated to the nearest cent. As cents extend through the second decimal place, it is the third decimal place that determines the nearest cent. If the third decimal number is 5, or more than 5, add 1¢ to the cost. If the third decimal number is less than 5, disregard it and any numbers that may follow it.

Thus, when rounded off to the nearest cent, a cost of $1.535 becomes $1.54, while a cost of $1.534 becomes $1.53.

In amounts of money, the nearest hundredth is close enough for most purposes. However, there are times when a number must be written out to the thousandth or even to the millionth decimal place. For example, if the actual cost of certain articles is $.2455 each, and if 1,000 such articles are purchased, the total cost is $245.50. If the price per article had been rounded off to the nearest hundredth, which would be $.25 each, the cost of 1,000 would be calculated at $250, which is $4.50 more than the real cost per 1,000.

"About how many were at the concert today?" The answer, "About 3,000," might be near enough if by actual count 2,864 people were present. To the nearest thousand, 3,000 would be correct, while to the nearest hundred there were 2,900, and to the nearest ten there were 2,860 present. How close to round off a number, or whether to round it off at all, depends upon the use to be made of the number.

In writing a number correct to a required number of decimal places, look at the number in the decimal place that is one place beyond the decimal required. Do as you did in finding the nearest cent. That is, if the number in the first decimal place beyond the one required is 5 or more, add 1 to the last decimal required; if the number is less than 5, disregard it and any decimals to the right of it.

EXAMPLES

3.141592 to the nearest hundred-thousandth is 3.14159
    "   to the nearest ten-thousandth is 3.1416
    "   to the nearest hundredth is 3.14
    "   to the nearest tenth is 3.1.

---

1. Round off each decimal to the nearest hundredth:

(a)	.623	(b)	.8764	(c)	1.472	(d)	3.158	(e)	.7247
	.705		.2315		2.169		.297		.6666
	.816		.1798		1.083		1.604		.1666
	.341		.1505		4.032		2.309		.3333
	.722		.0637		7.192		5.001		.1717

2. Round off each decimal to the nearest thousandth:

(a)	.2348	(b)	.1086	(c)	3.1451	(d)	.7824	(e)	.0681
	.1726		.2007		7.0207		.4555		.0092
	.3549		.3198		6.3131		1.7232		.0796
	.1071		.1670		1.4999		5.6781		.0683

To round off a number ending in a common fraction of $\frac{1}{2}$ or greater, add 1 to the whole number. If the fraction is less than $\frac{1}{2}$, drop the fraction from the whole number.

EXAMPLES

$18\frac{1}{2}$ to the nearest whole number is 19.
$18\frac{3}{4}$ to the nearest whole number is 19.
$18\frac{1}{3}$ to the nearest whole number is 18.
$18\frac{3}{8}$ to the nearest whole number is 18.

---

3. Round off to the nearest whole number:

(a) $12\frac{1}{2}$	(b) $16\frac{2}{3}$	(c) $14\frac{3}{7}$
(d) $3\frac{1}{10}$	(e) $9\frac{5}{8}$	(f) $4\frac{7}{9}$
(g) $14\frac{1}{4}$	(h) $26\frac{5}{9}$	(i) $32\frac{2}{5}$

***4.** Find the cost of each of these novelties to the nearest cent:

(a) 2 for 5¢	(b) 6 for 24¢	(c) 8 for 25¢
3 for 10¢	8 for $1.00	2 for 7¢
4 for 15¢	12 for $1.25	4 for 27¢
3 for 13¢	12 for 50¢	12 for $1.15

***5.** Find the cost of each article to the nearest tenth of a cent:

(a) 3 for 7¢	(d) 7 for 25¢	(g) one dozen for 45¢
(b) 4 for 25¢	(e) 3 for 50¢	(h) one dozen for 50¢
(c) 3 for 8¢	(f) 4 for 75¢	(i) one dozen for 40¢

*6. Find each quotient to the nearest hundredth:

(a) $6\overline{)7.51}$ (c) $3\overline{)8.2}$ (e) $.08\overline{).0678}$ (g) $.5\overline{)7.126}$

(b) $.4\overline{).59}$ (d) $2\overline{).0678}$ (f) $.09\overline{).0978}$ (h) $7\overline{)6.585}$

――――――――――― EXERCISES ―――――――――――

Estimate and then find the average of each of these groups of numbers:

1. 9.3 in., 3.4 in., 1.7 in.

2. .6 ft., .5 ft., .8 ft., .9 ft.

3. 15.7 gal., 27.5 gal., 18.3 gal.

4. 7.7%, 9.4%, 6.2%, 3.9%.

5. $1.25; $2.72, $2.18.

6. .5, .25, .375.

7. .66, .5, .838.

8. 6.8, 4.6, 3.9.

9. 1.5, 2.2, 3.6.

10. .1, .7, .8.

11. The diameter of a rod was measured by four different employees. Their measurements of the diameter were: 1.68″, 1.67″, 1.69″, and 1.69″. Find the average diameter.

*12. Find Mr. Reed's average earnings per week if his earnings for 5 weeks were: $185, $178, $181, $187.50 and $182.50.

*13. A motorist traveled 180 mi. He used $13\frac{1}{2}$ gal. of gasoline. How many miles did he average per gallon?

*14. If Joan spent $1.50 for lunches the first week, $1.90 the second week, $1.10 the third week, and $1.95 the fourth week, what was the average cost of her lunches per week for the month?

―――――――――― REVIEW OF CHAPTER III ――――――――――

1. If the cost of 18 hammers is $47.50, what is the cost of 1 hammer?

2. Mr. Cooper drove 484.4 mi. and used 28 gal. of gasoline. What did he average in miles per gallon?

3. Tom has an after-school job that pays him $1.25 each day. Tom was ill for 6 days. How much did he lose in pay?

4. Beulah paid $1.70 for a chicken weighing $2\frac{1}{2}$ lb. Find the price per pound.

5. At 24¢ per gallon, how many gallons of gasoline can be bought for $17.28?

6. In a city, 5,289,000 Christmas seals were sold at 1¢ each. How much money was received from the sales?

7. Ed worked 18 hrs. at $1.25 per hr.   How much was earned?

8. How many 2.5 bu. bags will a bin of 1200 bu. of oats fill?

9. Find the cost of these school books and supplies for Myrna:

History $4.15	Paper $6.00	Note books $1.25
English 3.95	Mathematics ... 3.84	Miscellaneous ... 4.00

10. The first reading on A's car odometer was 2814.8 mi.   The second was 3272.2 mi.   How many miles did he drive?

11. The National Accidental Death Rates per 100,000 population in a recent year were:

Canada 54.1	Ireland 30.2	France 60.7
Egypt 49.7	Netherlands 35.9	Switzerland 58.4
England 38.1	Sweden 39.4	United States 52.2

(a) Which country had the highest accidental death rate?

(b) Which two countries were closest together?

(c) What was the difference between the rates for the U. S. and each of the following: England, Canada, and Switzerland?

(d) What is the difference between the highest and the lowest?

*12. The odometer on B's car registered 3567.3 mi. before he left on a trip.   Upon his return, it registered 4071.9 mi.   He used 28 gallons of gas.   What was his average mileage per gallon?

*13. A carload of cinders from Lock Haven, Pa. was moved to Luke, Md.   It weighed 93,400 lbs. and the freight cost was $186.80. What was the freight rate per hundred lbs.?

*14. A road rises 123.795 ft. in 4126.5 ft.   Find the average rise.

**15. A National Vehicle Safety-Check report listed the following numbers of defective items in 1,500,000 cars.   Round the numbers to the nearest thousand; to the nearest hundred.

Rear lights 112,547	Windshield wipers 20,579
Front lights 63,115	Steering 19,640
Brakes 49,476	Glass 13,324
Exhaust system 36,454	Horn 8,988
Tires 31,764	Rear-view mirror 4,203

──────────── *PLAYOFF FOR CHAPTER III* ────────────

Suppose that you were offered a job and the pay was one cent for the first day, double that amount for the second day, double that for the third day, etc. for every day.   Would you take the job?   What would be your wage for the thirty-first day?   What would be the total salary for the month?

CHAPTER IV

PERCENTAGE AND PROBLEM SOLVING

VOCABULARY

1. per cent   2. percentage

36. The meaning of per cent. A number written with the per cent sign (%) is a special kind of fraction. It is a fraction expressed as 100ths. The word *per cent* means *hundredths,* and a number written with the per cent sign may be written:

(a) as a common fraction:

$$3\% = \tfrac{3}{100}$$

or (b) as a decimal fraction:

$$3\% = .03$$

John Smith laid out a garden of 100 squares (5 squares wide, 20 squares long). He pictured his garden on squared paper as illustrated. John used 5 of the 100 squares for lettuce. That is, he used $\tfrac{5}{100}$ or 5% of the garden for lettuce. He used 20 of the squares for beans. That is, he used $\tfrac{20}{100}$ or 20% of the garden for beans. What per cent did he use for peas? for tomatoes? for corn?

What is the total of the 100ths? That is, how many 100ths represent all of the garden? What is the total of the per cents representing the vegetables planted? That is, what per cent represents all of the garden?

One hundred per cent of anything is all of that thing.

CORN

TOMATOES

PEAS

BEANS

LETTUCE

37. The use of per cent. Per cent is a convenient and easy way of making comparisons. For example, in September, Edna took an Inventory Test of 50 exercises in the fundamentals of arithmetic. She did 28 exercises correctly. This means that $\frac{28}{50} = \frac{56}{100}$ or 56% of the exercises were correct. After a few weeks' practice, Edna took a similar test but of 40 exercises (instead of 50) and made a score of 28 again. This was $\frac{28}{40}$ or .70 or 70% of the exercises correct. Thus, Edna could see that a few weeks' practice had raised her mark from 56% to 70%.

In an Inventory Test of 10 exercises in addition and 12 exercises in multiplication, Joe solved 7 correctly in addition and 10 correctly in multiplication. He made a comparison of these results in order to know in which process he needed the more practice. His addition score was $\frac{7}{10}$ or 70%. His multiplication score was $\frac{10}{12}$ ($\frac{5}{6}$) or $83\frac{1}{3}$%. Thus, he saw that, while he needed practice in each process, he needed more practice in addition.

Business firms use per cents to make comparisons of costs and of profits, and in budgeting money for various uses. The need for a knowledge of per cent in the business world is great. It is not uncommon for a businessman to advise young people in school to "learn how to use per cent."

In order to get the most use out of per cent, it is important to know four changes in the form of numbers.

(a) Changing a decimal to per cent. *Per cent* is merely another word for *hundredths*. To change a decimal to a per cent, express the decimal fraction as hundredths, omit the word *hundredths*, and write *per cent* to the right of the number. The following examples illustrate the process:

$$.35 = 35 \text{ hundredths} = 35 \text{ per cent} = 35\%$$
$$.09 = 9 \text{ hundredths} = 9 \text{ per cent} = 9\%$$
$$.1 = .10 = 10 \text{ hundredths} = 10 \text{ per cent} = 10\%$$
$$.375 = 37.5 \ (37\tfrac{1}{2}) \text{ hundredths} = 37\tfrac{1}{2} \text{ per cent} = 37\tfrac{1}{2}\%$$
$$.1125 = 11\tfrac{1}{4} \text{ hundredths} = 11\tfrac{1}{4} \text{ per cent} = 11\tfrac{1}{4}\%$$
$$1.7 = 1.70 = 170 \text{ hundredths} = 170 \text{ per cent} = 170\%$$

In which direction was the decimal point moved? A decimal can always be changed to per cent by moving the decimal point two places to the right and annexing the per cent sign.

Change to per cents:

(1) .15	(2) .045	(3) .6	(4) 1.375	(5) 2.
.08	.248	.2	$2.12\frac{1}{2}$	$.2\frac{1}{4}$
.52	.175	.5	3.5	.001

(b) Changing common fractions and mixed numbers to per cents. To change a common fraction or a mixed number to a per cent, first express the common fraction as hundredths in decimal form and then as per cent. For example:

$$\frac{1}{4} = .25 = 25\% \qquad \frac{4}{5} = .80 = 80\%$$
$$\frac{1}{16} = .06\frac{1}{4} = 6\frac{1}{4}\% \qquad \frac{5}{9} = .55\frac{5}{9} = 55\frac{5}{9}\%$$
$$1\frac{1}{2} = 1.50 = 150\%$$

Certain common fractions are used so frequently that it is important to memorize their equivalent per cents. See Appendix D for a rather full list. It is to your advantage to memorize the ones that are starred.

Change to per cents:

(1) $\frac{1}{5}$	(2) $\frac{1}{12}$	(3) $\frac{3}{20}$	(4) $\frac{2}{9}$	(5) $1\frac{1}{3}$
$\frac{3}{4}$	$\frac{1}{3}$	$\frac{4}{25}$	$\frac{9}{50}$	$2\frac{3}{8}$
$\frac{5}{8}$	$\frac{2}{15}$	$\frac{7}{100}$	$1\frac{1}{4}$	$1\frac{3}{16}$

(c) Changing per cents to decimals. To change a per cent to a decimal, think of the per cent as hundredths and then write it, using the decimal point to indicate hundredths.

$$65\% = 65 \text{ hundredths} = .65$$
$$5\% = 5 \text{ hundredths} = .05$$
$$.7\% = .7 \text{ hundredth} = .007$$
$$3\frac{1}{2}\% = 3\frac{1}{2} \text{ hundredths} = .03\frac{1}{2} = .035$$
$$150\% = 150 \text{ hundredths} = 1.50$$
$$\frac{1}{4}\% = \frac{1}{4} \text{ hundredth} = .00\frac{1}{4} = .0025$$

A fraction smaller than 1 per cent is often thought of as that fractional part of 1%:

$\frac{1}{2}\%$ is really $\frac{1}{2}$ of 1% $\qquad$ .8% is .8 of 1%
$1\% = .01$ $\qquad\qquad\qquad$ .8% = .8 of .01 = .008
$\frac{1}{2}\% = \frac{1}{2}$ of .01 = $.00\frac{1}{2}$ = .005

Look at the examples. In which direction was the decimal point moved? Past how many digits was it moved?

A per cent can be changed to a decimal by moving the decimal point two places left and removing the per cent sign.

Change to decimals:

(1) 35%	(5) 1%	(9) .4%	(13) 120%
(2) 60%	(6) 8%	(10) .5%	(14) 225%
(3) 16%	(7) 3%	(11) .1%	(15) $\frac{2}{3}\%$
(4) $12\frac{1}{2}\%$	(8) $4\frac{1}{2}\%$	(12) $\frac{1}{5}\%$	(16) $133\frac{1}{3}\%$

(d) Changing per cents to common fractions or mixed numbers. To change a per cent to a common fraction or a mixed number, first change the per cent to a decimal; then change the decimal to a common fraction and reduce it to the lowest terms.

$$35\% = .35 = \tfrac{35}{100} = \tfrac{7}{20}$$

$$3\% = .03 = \tfrac{3}{100}$$

$$7\tfrac{1}{2}\% = .07\tfrac{1}{2} = .075 = \tfrac{75}{1000} = \tfrac{3}{40}$$

$$.7\% = .007 = \tfrac{7}{1000}$$

$$\tfrac{1}{4}\% = .00\tfrac{1}{4} = .0025 = \frac{25}{10,000} = \frac{1}{400}$$

$$\tfrac{1}{3}\% = .00\tfrac{1}{3} = \frac{\tfrac{1}{3}}{100} = \frac{1}{3} \times \frac{1}{100} = \frac{1}{300}$$

$$1.5\% = .015 = \frac{15}{1,000} = \frac{3}{200}$$

$$240\% = 2.40 = 2\tfrac{40}{100} = 2\tfrac{2}{5}$$

Change to common fractions or mixed numbers:

(1) 40%	(5) 9%	(9) 120%	(13) .4%
(2) 25%	(6) 2%	(10) 230%	(14) .9%
(3) 18%	(7) $1\tfrac{1}{2}\%$	(11) 212%	(15) $\tfrac{3}{5}\%$
(4) 65%	(8) $2\tfrac{1}{4}\%$	(12) 3.5%	(16) $\tfrac{2}{3}\%$

INVENTORY TEST 12   **Per Cent**

Change these decimal fractions to per cents:

1. .16   **2.** .07   **3.** .125   **4.** 1.75   **5.** .005

Change these common fractions and mixed numbers to per cents:

6. $\tfrac{3}{100}$ **7.** $\tfrac{7}{50}$ **8.** $\tfrac{1}{10}$ **9.** $\tfrac{2}{7}$ **10.** $2\tfrac{3}{4}$

Change these per cents to decimals:

11. 18%   **12.** 4%   **13.** 120%   **14.** $\tfrac{1}{2}\%$ **15.** .2%

Change these per cents to common fractions in lowest terms:

16. 20%   **17.** 8%   **18.** 125%   **19.** 1.2%   **20.** $\tfrac{1}{4}\%$

Rating	Correct	Next Step
A	19 or 20	Do Inventory Test 13.
B	17 or 18	Do Inventory Test 13, or do Practice Exercises 12a to 12f.
C	16 or less	Do Practice Exercises 12a to 12f; then do Inventory Test 12 again.

38. Exercises using percentage. A *percentage* is a part of some quantity found by taking a certain per cent of the quantity. There are three types of exercises in which per cent is used.

(a) Finding a per cent of a number. This type of exercise is similar to the exercise $3 \times 4 = ?$ The 3 and 4 are called *factors*. Multiply the factors and get 12 as the result, called the *product*. The method of solving may be stated:

$$\text{Factor} \times \text{factor} = \text{product}$$

Similarly, 5% of $80 = ?$

$.05 \times 80 = 4$ (the product)

Factor × factor = product

EXAMPLES

6% of $24 = .06 \times 24 = 1.44$
140% of $60 = 1.4 \times 60 = 84$

Factor × factor = product

EXAMPLE

$16\frac{2}{3}\%$ of $72 = \frac{1}{6} \times \cancel{72}^{12} = 12$

Solve these exercises:

(1) 8% of 40

(2) 15% of 28

(3) $66\frac{2}{3}\%$ of 120

(4) 1% of 650

(5) $.5\%$ of 200

(6) $33\frac{1}{3}\%$ of 150

(7) 1.3% of 75

(8) $2\frac{1}{2}\%$ of 80

(9) 250% of 90

(10) $37\frac{1}{2}\%$ of 176

(11) $\frac{1}{2}\%$ of 300

(12) $\frac{3}{4}\%$ of 1200

(b) Finding what per cent one number is of another number. This type of exercise is similar to the exercise $? \times 4 = 20$. The product (20) and one factor (4) are known. One factor is missing. What is the missing factor? How did you find it? Yes, $20 \div 4 = 5$. That is,

$$\text{Product} \div \text{known factor} = \text{missing factor}$$

Similarly, $?\%$ of $16 = 4$

$4 \div 16 = .25$

$.25 = 25\%$ (the missing factor)

```
┌─────────────────── EXAMPLE ───────────────────┐
│                                                │
│              14 = ?% of 28                     │
│                                                │
│  The product (14) and one factor (28) are known.  The missing factor  │
│  can be found by this rule:                    │
│                                                │
│      Product ÷ known factor = missing factor   │
│  14 (product) ÷ 28 (known factor) = .50 or 50% (missing factor)  │
│                                                │
│  The division may be written: 14 (product) = 1 = .50 = 50%  │
│                               ───────────    ─              │
│                               28 (factor)    2              │
│                                                │
└────────────────────────────────────────────────┘
```

Solve:

(1) ?% of 12 = 3   (5) 4 = ?% of 14   (9) 24 = ?% of 16

(2) ?% of 50 = 20   (6) 9 = ?% of 25   (10) 1 = ?% of 100

(3) 12 = ?% of 60   (7) ?% of 8 = 20   (11) $\frac{1}{2}$ = ?% of 10

(4) 6 = ?% of 9   (8) ?% of 6 = 15   (12) ?% of 6 = $\frac{3}{4}$

(c) **Finding a number when a certain per cent of it is known.** This type exercise may be written: 3% of ? = 15 or 15 = 3% of ? What is known? What is to be found? What rule do you use to find the missing factor?

$$\text{Product} \div \text{known factor} = \text{missing factor}$$
$$15 \div .03 = 500, \text{ the missing factor}$$

```
┌─────────────────── EXAMPLE ───────────────────┐
│                                                │
│              (a) 25% of ? = 84                 │
│  84 (product) ÷ .25 (known factor) = 336 (missing factor)  │
│                                                │
│              (b) 62½ % of ? = 25               │
│                                    5           │
│                            5    2̶5̶   8         │
│  25 ÷ .62 1/2 = 25 ÷  ─  = ── × ── = 40 (missing factor)  │
│                       8    1    8̶             │
│                                                │
└────────────────────────────────────────────────┘
```

Solve:

(1) 40% of ? = 50   (5) 120% of ? = 84   (9) 48 = $\frac{3}{4}$% of ?

(2) 35% of ? = 14   (6) 2.5% of ? = 10   (10) 100% of ? = 9

(3) 8 = 32% of ?   (7) 4.2% of ? = 25.2   (11) 36 = 2% of ?

(4) 200% of ? = 12   (8) 18 = $\frac{1}{2}$% of ?   (12) .4% of ? = 2.4

Find the missing numbers:

(13) 7% of 180 = ?   (15) 4% of ? = 120

(14) 33$\frac{1}{3}$% of 192 = ?   (16) 2 = ?% of 6

(17) $12 = ?\%$ of 3   (19) $.2\%$ of $? = 30$
(18) 125% of $16 = ?$ (20) $\frac{1}{3}\%$ of $? = 24$
(21) $112\frac{1}{2}\%$ of $64 = ?$

Solve for the missing numbers:

1. 50% of $64 = ?$ 8. $12 = ?\%$ of 12   15. $?\%$ of $50 = 8$
2. $?\%$ of $24 = 6$ 9. 1.2% of $400 = ?$ 16. $66\frac{2}{3}\%$ of $18 = ?$
3. 20% of $? = 40$ 10. $?\%$ of $60 = 10$ 17. $\frac{1}{4} = ?\%$ of 1
4. 6% of $150 = ?$ 11. $8 = ?\%$ of 24   18. $5 = ?\%$ of 4
5. $33\frac{1}{3}\%$ of $120 = ?$ 12. $?\%$ of $80 = 8$ 19. 400% of $6 = ?$
6. 3% of $? = 9$ 13. 102% of $40 = ?$ 20. $37\frac{1}{2}\%$ of $88 = ?$
7. 150% of $200 = ?$ 14. $3 = ?\%$ of 15   21. $16\frac{2}{3}\%$ of $42 = ?$

Rating	Correct	Next Step
A	20 to 21	Do Inventory Test 14.
B	18 to 19	Do Inventory Test 14, or do Practice Exercises 13a to 13d.
C	17 or less	Do Practice Exercises 13a to 13d; then do Inventory Test 13 again.

39. Estimating reasonable products. To avoid getting absurd answers, near fractional equivalents of per cents are often used in estimating products in which per cents are a factor.

--- EXAMPLE ---

What is 19% of 724?
19% is close to 20%, or $\frac{1}{5}$.
724 is close to 700.
$\frac{1}{5}$ of $700 = 140$, the estimated product.
The exact product is 137.56.

--- *EXERCISES* ---

Estimate each product; then find the exact product:

1. 26% of \$440   6. 51% of \$84.50   11. 15% of \$7.20
2. 11% of \$690   7. 66% of \$39   12. 8% of \$120
3. 74% of \$480   8. 13% of \$88   13. 24% of \$16.80
4. 17% ot \$180   9. 34% of \$9.60   14. 62% of \$24.80
5. 19% of \$250   10. 21% of \$55.25   15. 87% of \$9.76

40. Problem solving. Do you feel "at ease" when you come face to face with a written problem? If not, you can gain confidence in your problem solving by following a few suggested steps. These steps will suggest that you think each problem through carefully, plan its solution, and be accurate in the use of the fundamental processes.

Steps in problem solving. The suggestions found in the following eight steps will help you become skillful at problem solving:

Step 1. *Read* the problem carefully and as many times as necessary to understand its meaning. Look in the dictionary for any word whose meaning is not clear.

Step 2. *Determine* what is to be found.

Step 3. *Select* which of the given facts will be helpful in finding the result.

Step 4. *Plan* your procedure. Will you add, subtract, multiply, or divide?

Step 5. *Estimate* the result in round numbers.

Step 6. *Solve* the problem, keeping the following suggestions in mind:

   (a) Put your work in systematic order.
   (b) Draw a sketch if it will help in the solution.
   (c) Write all numbers and decimal points legibly.
   (d) Label your result and any other important numbers.
   (e) Prove any sizable fundamental processes.

Step 7. *Compare* the result obtained with your estimated result.

Step 8. *Check*, if possible, working the problem backwards. That is, from the result you have found, work back to one of the given facts.

Each of the steps is important and should be used. However, in most problems the solution can be shortened by performing one or more of the steps mentally. *Learn* the eight steps and use them either mentally or in writing.

—————————————— *PROBLEMS* ——————————————

Solve these problems, following the suggestions on problem solving:

1. Mr. Sands used $8\frac{1}{4}$ gal. of gasoline for a trip of 165 mi. How many miles did he average per gallon?

2. The Girl Scouts of a certain troop sold 62 dozen doughnuts at 55¢ per dozen. If their expenses were $11.47, how much was their profit?

3. Henry is gathering up scrap metal to sell. He has three pieces weighing $15\frac{1}{2}$ lb., $12\frac{3}{8}$lb., and $14\frac{1}{8}$ lb. At 5¢ per pound, how much will he receive?

4. Nine tenants rented a garden space for $12.50. The plowing was $7.25; seeds and plants, $5.75; and fertilizer, $6.50. What was the average cost per tenant?

5. Which is cheaper, and how much: to buy 8 cans of frozen orange juice at $2.10 per dozen, or to buy 8 cans at 2 for 37¢?

6. Gene earned $6.25 per day for 25 days during July. His room and board for the time cost him $63.50. How much of his earnings did he have left?

7. Harold made a bread board and sold it for 65¢. If the lumber cost him 17¢, how much will he receive per hour for the 3 hours of labor that he spent on it?

8. Which is the better buy: (a) to pay $18.75 for a dress, or (b) to buy $3\frac{1}{4}$ yd. of material at $1.24 per yard, 9 buttons at 80¢ per dozen, and 8 yd. of braid at $7\frac{1}{2}$¢ per yard and pay a dressmaker $6.50? How much money would your choice save you?

9. Mr. Parker receives $480 per month, which he budgets as follows: $\frac{1}{3}$ for board and room, $\frac{1}{12}$ for clothing, $\frac{1}{10}$ for life insurance, $\frac{1}{15}$ for church and charity, $\frac{1}{20}$ for recreation, and $\frac{1}{30}$ for personal needs. He saves the remainder. How much does he save?

10. How much did it cost Mr. Adams to go on a 1,800-mi. trip if he got 15 mi. to the gallon of gasoline, which cost 32¢ per gallon?

11. A new 42 story building in New York has a 16 story base whose dimensions are 180 ft. by 380 ft. It has a 26 story tower whose dimensions are 180 ft. by 130 ft. What is the total number of square feet of floor space?

12. Twenty-eight music stands costing $18 each were priced to sell for $23.50. After the stands were sold, what was the total profit?

13. If dungarees costing $42 a dozen are sold at $4.25 each, what is the profit on each pair sold?

14. If TV tables that cost $45.60 per dozen are sold at $3.97 each, what is the profit on each table?

15. A 950-ft. fence with posts $8\frac{1}{3}$ ft. apart is to be built around a lot. How many posts will be needed?

16. Bert saved $\frac{1}{3}$ of his earnings. He then decided to invest $\frac{3}{4}$ of his savings in Government bonds. What part of his earnings did he invest in the bonds?

17. Bill is buying a car . He is to pay $500 down and $40 a month for 18 months. For cash he could buy the car for $1,075. How much would he save by paying cash?

*18. The members of a school concert sold $170 worth of tickets. If 200 pupil tickets were sold at 25¢ each, how many adult tickets were sold at 75¢ each?

*19. If the sun is 93,000,000 miles from the earth and light travels 186,000 miles per second, how many minutes are required for the sun's rays to reach the earth?

*20. A building valued at $6,400 is insured for $\frac{7}{8}$ of its value at the rate of $3.60 per $1,000. What is the cost of the insurance?

*21. John can do a certain piece of work in 48 hours, while Carl, his older brother, can do the same work in 32 hours. Which is it the cheaper to hire if John charges $33\frac{1}{3}$¢ per hour and Carl $37\frac{1}{2}$¢ per hour?

*22. Wesley has $20. This is $\frac{5}{6}$ of the money he needs to buy a bicycle. What is the cost of the bicycle?

**23. A plane flying from City A to City B uses $\frac{1}{3}$ of its fuel. Returning to City A, it uses $\frac{3}{10}$ of the original amount. There are 92 gallons left. How many gallons were in the tank at the start?

**24 A jet plane flying from City X to City Y used $\frac{3}{8}$ of its fuel. On the return trip it used $\frac{2}{3}$ of the amount left in the tank. When the plane returned to City X, there were 75 gallons left. How many gallons were in the tank at first?

**25. The windows in a house extend 6'6" above the floor and are 30 in. wide. How many yards of drapery material 36 in. wide are needed for each window? (One strip of material makes one drape, and the drapes are to extend from the top of the window to the floor. Allow 3 in. to turn under at the top and bottom of each drape. Two drapes to each window.)

"Hound dog" USAF

26. A hotel served 108,000 cups of coffee in a year. If $1\frac{1}{2}$ tons of coffee were used, determine the average number of cups obtained from one pound of coffee.

27. A printing press averages 2,500 impressions an hour and prints 64 pages at each impression. At \$4 per hour, what will it cost to print 15,000 catalogues containing 384 pages each?

28. A tank full of water has 2 pipes opening from it, one of which will empty one-sixth of it in 1 hour and the other one-fourth of it in 1 hour. If both pipes are open for 1 hour, what part will remain in the tank? What part will be emptied?

41. Percentage problems. Percentage problems are of three different types:

(a) To find a certain per cent of a number.
(b) To find what per cent one number is of another number.
(c) To find a number when a certain per cent of it is known.

42. Finding a certain per cent of a number. Jack spelled 40 words, of which 85% were correct. How many of the words were correctly spelled? You need to find a per cent (85%) of a number (40).

Step 1. Read the problem carefully.
Step 2. Find: Number of words correctly spelled.
Step 3. Known facts:

$$40 = \text{total number of words spelled.}$$
$$85\% = \text{per cent of words correctly spelled.}$$

Step 4. Procedure:

$$85\% \text{ of } 40 = \text{number correctly spelled.}$$
$$\text{Factor} \times \text{factor} = \text{product.}$$

Step 5. Estimate:

Use 80% in place of 85%.

$$80\% \text{ of } 40 = 32.$$

Step 6. Solution:

$$85\% \text{ of } 40 = 34.$$

Hence, 34 words were correctly spelled.

Step 7. Compare results with estimate: 34 words is near to 32.
Step 8. Check:

$$\tfrac{34}{40} = \tfrac{17}{20} = .85 = 85\%, \text{ per cent of words correct.}$$

1. John's lesson consisted of 15 problems. He got 80% correct. How many were correct?

2. Mary made a grade of 75% on 24 exercises. How many did she have right?

3. Harold won 20% of the 35 events in an athletic contest. How many events did he win?

4. Rudolph earns $28 per month working after school hours. He saves 15% of his earnings. How much does he save?

5. On a trip of 275 mi., Edward drove 60% of the distance. How many miles did he drive?

6. A radio that cost $42 was sold for 85% of its cost. For how much was it sold?

7. Jane received $8.50 on her birthday. She saved 40% of the money. How much did she save? How much did she spend?

8. Donald bought a wagon for $6.50. He sold it for 120% of the cost. For how much did he sell the wagon?

9. Last year Sam won 12 events in a contest. This year he won 125% as many as last year. How many events did he win this year?

10. In September, Bonnie read 180 words per minute. By the following March, she read 130% of her September rate. How many words did she read per minute in March?

43. Finding what per cent one number is of another number. In a class of 36 pupils, 33 were present. What per cent were present?

You need to find what per cent one number (33) is of another number (36).

Step 1. Read the problem carefully.
Step 2. Find: Per cent of pupils present.
Step 3. Known facts:

$$36 = \text{total pupils in the class.}$$
$$33 = \text{pupils present.}$$

Step 4. Procedure:

$$33 = ?\% \text{ of } 36.$$
$$\tfrac{33}{36} = ?\%.$$

Step 5. Estimate:

33 is slightly less than 100% of 36—say, 90%.

Step 6. Solution:

$$33 = \text{what } \% \text{ of } 36.$$
(Product ÷ known factor = missing factor.)
$$33 \div 36 = .91\tfrac{2}{3} \text{ or } 91\tfrac{2}{3}\%.$$

Hence, $91\tfrac{2}{3}\%$ of the pupils were present.

Step 7. Comparison:

$91\tfrac{2}{3}\%$ is slightly less than 100%—near 90%.

Step 8. Check:

$91\tfrac{2}{3}\%$ of $36 = 33$, pupils present.

──────────────── *EXERCISES* ────────────────

1. In an exercise of 32 sentences, Dora had 27 correct. What per cent did she have correct? What was her grade?

2. Clara has answered 18 out of 25 history questions correctly. What is her grade?

3. Harvey was given 18 lines of poetry to memorize. He learned all 18 of the lines. What is his grade?

4. Out of 30 points in a science lesson, Gerald had 25 correct. Calculate his grade.

5. Jerry missed 4 out of 32 problems. What per cent of the problems did he have correct?

, **6.** Ray worked 9 of the 14 weeks of his vacation. What per cent of his vacation did he work?

7. Charles was in school 180 of the 200 school days. What was his per cent of attendance?

*****8.** A coat priced to sell for $60 was put on sale and sold for $48. (a) How much was the discount? (b) What per cent?

*****9.** A wholesale firm reduced rugs from $72 to $64. What was the per cent reduction on the final selling price?

*****10.** In a study of fatal accidents occurring on a recent Fourth of July holiday, of 96 drivers who were speeding or drinking, 49 drivers had previous accidents. What per cent of the drivers had previous accidents (nearest whole per cent)?

******11.** Soup in a #2 can contains $2\tfrac{1}{2}$ cups while a #$2\tfrac{1}{2}$ can contains $3\tfrac{1}{4}$ cups. What per cent more soup is in the #$2\tfrac{1}{2}$ can?

12. The enrollment in a school increased from 750 students to 810 students in one year. What was the per cent of increase?

Solution: The per cent of increase is a comparison of the amount some quantity has increased with the quantity as it was before the increase. We find what per cent of the original quantity the amount of increase is. This is the per cent of increase.
The amount of increase in enrollment is 60 students.

$$60 \text{ is what per cent of } 750?$$
$$60 \div 750 = .08 = 8\%$$
The per cent of increase was 8%.

13. In five years the value of an acre of land increased from $4000 to $5200. What was the per cent of increase?

14. In one year Mr. Smith's salary increased from $12,000 to $13,440 while Mr. Jones' salary increased from $4,800 to $5,520. Which man had the greater per cent of increase in his salary?

15. In one year recently, fire losses in the United States increased from $1,047,000,000 to $1,108,000,000. What was the per cent of increase (to the nearest whole per cent)?

16. In a record-making depth dive in the water of a Swiss lake, a diver descended 728 ft. The previous record was 600 ft. The new dive was an increase of what per cent over the old dive?

17. A new model TV set increased the screen size from 175 sq. in. to 287 sq. in. What was the per cent of increase?

18. A new design in a refrigerator increased the freezing unit volume from 9.9 cu. ft. to 10.3 cu. ft. This is an increase of what per cent (nearest whole per cent)?

19. The price of chicken dropped from 35¢ per pound to 28¢ per pound. What was the per cent of decrease?

Solution: The amount of decrease was 7¢.

The original cost was 35¢
$$.07 \div .35 = .20 = 20\%$$
The per cent of decrease was 20%.

20. When a safety program was begun in a local assembly plant, the number of accidents in a month dropped from 464 to 348. What was the per cent of decrease?

21. From 1946 to 1961 the number of caribou decreased from 1,750,000 to 250,000. What was the per cent of decrease?

44. Finding a number when a certain per cent of it is known.

Mary's class sold 156 tickets for a school play. This was 12% of the tickets sold. How many tickets were sold?

You need to find a number (?) when a certain per cent (12%) is known (156).

Step 1. Think as you read the problem.

Step 2. Find: Total tickets sold.

Step 3. Known facts:

156 = tickets sold by Mary's class.

12% = per cent of tickets sold by Mary's class.

Step 4. Procedure:

$$12\% \text{ of all tickets} = 156.$$
$$12\% \text{ of } ? = 156.$$
$$156 \div .12 = ?$$

Step 5. Estimate:

$$150 \div .10 = 1500.$$

Step 6. Solution:

Method A

12% of tickets = 156.

1% of tickets = 156 ÷ 12 = 13.

100% of tickets = 100 × 13 = 1300.

Method B

12% of ? = 156.

156 ÷ .12 = 1300.

Hence, the total number of tickets sold was 1300.

Step 7. Comparison:

$$1300 \text{ is near } 1500.$$

Step 8. Check:

$$12\% \text{ of } 1300 = 156.$$

EXERCISES
---

1. James had 16 of his exercises correct. If this was 80% of his lesson, how many exercises were there in all?

2. If Rose saves 35% of her earnings, how much will she have earned when she has saved $10.50?

3. Harry sold 54 papers, which is 90% of the number he had to sell. How many papers did Harry have to sell?

4. A coat is reduced $10.80, which is 12% of its marked price. For how much was the coat marked to sell?

5. Twenty-four pupils, which is 80% of the class, made a score of above 90. How many pupils are in the class?

6. George gets a ride of 45 blocks, which is 90% of the distance to his work. How far does he live from his work?

7. Only 840,000, or 3%, of the young people in the U. S. between the ages of 12 and 22 have traveled in an airplane. What is the total number of these young people?

8. Paul is saving money to buy a camera. He has saved $18, which is 45% of the cost. What does the camera cost?

9. Twenty per cent of the boys in a class were Boy Scouts. There were 8 Scouts in the class. How many boys were in the class?

10. Andy weighs 125 pounds, which is $62\frac{1}{2}$% of his father's weight. How much does his father weigh?

REVIEW OF CHAPTER IV

Solve:

1. Mr. Jay contributed 9% of a $180 Red Cross fund. How much did he contribute?

2. Carter solved 9 of 15 exercises in English correctly. What per cent were correctly solved?

3. There is a Federal tax of 10% on airline fares. How much is the tax on a ticket that costs $28.60?

4. An agent sold $1,420 worth of flour at $1\frac{3}{4}$% commission. How much was his commission?

5. How many pounds of butterfat are there in 1,240 lb. of milk if the milk tests 3.9% butterfat?

6. Carl sold his bicycle for $31.20, which was 80% of its cost. What was the cost?

7. Mr. Peck gets a 15% discount on items he buys from the store where he works. A suit marked $29.75 would cost him how much?

8. Between 1950 and 1960, the cities of El Paso, Texas, and San Jose, California, had doubled their population. The population in 1950 was what per cent of the population in 1960?

9. A round trip plane fare from New York to London costs $350. This is $83\frac{1}{3}$% of the cost of a trip from New York to Rome. What is the cost of the trip to Rome?

10. Mr. Smith's salary in a job was $4000. Four years later he made $7000. What was the per cent of increase in his salary?

11. If $750 is invested in stock, what profit must be made in order to earn 6%?

12. Mr. Barker sells real estate at a 6% commission. For a certain sale, his commission amounts to $392.50. For how much did he sell the property?

13. Joel paid $3.78 for a history book. This was 28% of the cost of all his books. How much did his books cost him?

14. In a school of 1,300 pupils, 351 pupils were on the honor roll. What per cent were on the honor roll?

15. Tom's weight of 135 lb. is 108% of what it was a year ago. How much did he weigh a year ago?

16. Jack sold his camera for $18.60. This was 120% of the cost. What was the cost of the camera?

17. Mr. Cole had his house insulated, hoping to save 15% of his annual heating bill. If the heating cost before insulating is $220, how much should Mr. Cole save?

18. A new Little League team could use only 75% of the boys who tried out. If they were allowed to have 15 boys on the team, how many had tried out?

19. Richard made the team and he made hits 27% of the time he was up at bat. If he was at bat 84 times, how many hits did he make?

20. The team won 18 out of 27 games played. What per cent of the games were won?

21. The capsule from the Discoverer XXX Satellite was recovered in mid-air. It was the eighth capsule retrieved from space out of 30 tries. What per cent of the tries were successful?

22. In three years the export value of corn went up from $209,800,000 to $278,700,000. What was the per cent of increase?

23. A new atlas has 600 pages, of which 440 are in color. What per cent of the pages are in color?

24. A special advance sale of the atlas sold for $22.50 instead of the regular price of $35.00. What per cent discount was given on the advance copy?

*25. A farm contains seven *squares* of land (one *square* is one square mile). Fifty per cent is planted in grain. Fifty per cent is left fallow. The farmer plants 27% of his land in wheat, 11% in oats, 9% in barley, and 3% in proso (a grain used for bird seed). (a) How many acres are there on this farm? (b) How many are planted in wheat? (c) How many are planted in oats? (d) How many are planted in barley? (e) How many are planted in proso? (f) If the farmer gets an average of 30 bushels of wheat per acre, and he sells it at $1.83 per bushel, what is his gross income from his wheat?

*26. 19,000 people attended a meeting of a corporation. This was $\frac{3}{4}$% of the share owners. How many share owners are there?

*27. When the school enrollment in a local district increased from 2500 to 5000 in 6 years, a speaker said that it had increased 200%. Was he right in saying the per cent of increase was 200%? If not, what is the correct per cent?

*28. In building the new lower level of the George Washington Bridge, the lower level itself cost $25,000,000, and the new approaches cost $158,000,000. What per cent of the cost of construction was spent on the approaches (nearest whole per cent)?

**29. The owner of a storeroom receives annually in rent $7\frac{1}{2}$% of his investment on the building. If the value of the building is $26,000, what is the rent per month?

**30. Mr. King sold a car for $1,260, which was a 5% gain on the cost. What was the cost? *Note:* Cost (100%) + gain (5%) = 105%, selling price.

*31. A house was sold for 15% less than it cost. The selling price was $4,250. What was the cost?

**32. Because of illness, Floyd's attendance at school this year is 154 days. This is a $12\frac{1}{2}$% decrease from his attendance of last year. Find his last year's attendance.

**33. Mr. B. is a salesman. He receives a salary of $400 per month plus a commission of 5%. In June he received $625. How much were his sales for June?

────────── *PLAYOFF FOR CHAPTER IV* ──────────

Draw the diagram.
Write the answers in the right squares.

Horizontal

1. 60% of 80 = ?
3. 90% of 260 = ?
6. 50 increased by 16% = ?
7. 200% of 295 = ?
8. Sue's grade of 75 was increased by 12%. What is her new grade?
9. 100% of 1 = ?
11. A coat reduced $16\frac{2}{3}$% from $366 is sold for how much?
13. This number decreased by $37\frac{1}{2}$% of itself equals 50.
15. $\frac{1}{2}$% of 1200 = ?
16. During a baseball tournament, Bill had 16 hits out of 30. What was his batting average to nearest whole per cent?
17. $\frac{1}{3}$% of 2100 = ?

TABLE 1

1 4	2 8		3 2	4 3	5 4
6 5	8		7 5	9	0
	8 8	4		9 1	
10 7			11 3	0	12 5
13 8	14 0		15 6		5
	16 5	3		17 7	

Vertical

1. 30 = $66\frac{2}{3}$% of ?
2. 160% of 555 = ?
3. 14 is what per cent of 56?
4. A $3,400 salary is increased by 15%. Find the new salary.
5. A bicycle cost $60. It was sold at a $33\frac{1}{3}$% loss. Find selling price.

10. Sara learned 39 out of 50 words. What % did she learn?
11. Carl sold a toy for 24 cents. This was $33\frac{1}{3}$% less than it cost. Find cost.
12. A team won 11 ball games and lost 9. What % did it win?
14. Write 5% as a decimal.

CHAPTER V

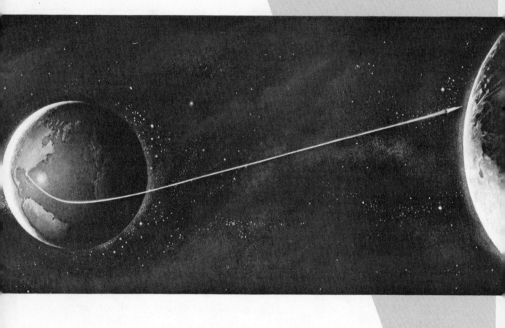

DENOMINATE NUMBERS;

RATIO AND PROPORTION

VOCABULARY

1. ratio   2. proportion   3. means   4. extremes

45. Denominate number tables. A number may or may not be used with reference to any particular thing. For instance, if the numbers 8, 3, and 5 are used without having a name attached they are called *abstract* numbers. Numbers that are designated as a specific unit of measure as 8 quarts, $5, 3 pounds, 4 feet 6 inches and so on are called *denominate* numbers since they have a specific name or denomination of measure.

Tables showing the most frequently used relationships are found in Appendix D and should be memorized. It is often necessary to change these measurements to a higher or lower unit and to add, subtract, multiply, or divide them.

(a) Reduction to lower units.

Change these measures to the specified units:

```
┌────────────── EXAMPLE ──────────────┐
│   2 yd. 2 ft. = 6 ft. + 2 ft. = 8 ft. │
└──────────────────────────────────────┘
```

Express in lower units as indicated:

1. 2 ft. = _____ in.
2. 1 ft. 4 in. = _____ in.
3. $\frac{1}{3}$ yd. = _____ in.
4. 3 mi. = _____ rd.
5. $2\frac{1}{2}$ gal. = _____ qt.

6. 5 qt. = _____ pt.
7. 2 bu. = _____ pk.
8. 4 doz. = _____ articles
9. $\frac{1}{4}$ sq. yd. = _____ sq. ft.
10. 2 hr. 40 min. = _____ min.

(b) Change to higher units.

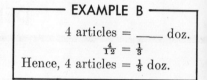

┌──────── EXAMPLE A ────────┐
40 in. = ____ ft. ____ in.
40 ÷ 12 = 3 and 4 remainder
Hence, 40 in. = 3 ft. 4 in.
└───────────────────────────┘

┌──────── EXAMPLE B ────────┐
4 articles = ____ doz.
$\frac{4}{12} = \frac{1}{3}$
Hence, 4 articles = $\frac{1}{3}$ doz.
└───────────────────────────┘

Express in higher units as indicated:

1. 20 in. = ____ ft. ____ in.
2. 4 ft. = ____ yd. ____ ft.
3. 1 ft. = ____ yd.
4. 3 in. = ____ ft.
5. 3 qt. = ____ gal.

6. 5 pt. = ____ qt. ____ pt.
7. 21 oz. = ____ lb. ____ oz.
8. 6,000 lb. = ____ tons
9. 75 min. = ____ hr. ____ min.
10. 1,280 acres = ____ sq. mi.

INVENTORY TEST 14

Relationship Between Units of Measure

Express in the specified units:

1. 18 in. = ____ ft. ____ in.
2. 2 ft. = ____ yd.
3. 1 yd. 2 ft. = ____ in.
4. 2 ft. 5 in. = ____ in.
5. $\frac{2}{3}$ yd. = ____ ft.
6. 2 bu. = ____ pk.
7. 9 pk. = ____ bu. ____ pk.
8. 4 hr. 20 min. = ____ min.
9. 2 mi. = ____ rd.
10. $1\frac{1}{2}$ gal. = ____ qt.
11. 3 qt. = ____ pt.
12. 6 pt. = ____ qt.

13. 48 oz. = ____ lb.
14. 5,000 lb. = ____ tons ____ lb.
15. $\frac{3}{4}$ ton = ____ lb.
16. $\frac{1}{2}$ yd. = ____ in.
17. 9 in. = ____ yd.
18. $\frac{1}{2}$ sq. yd. = ____ sq. ft.
19. 12 in. = ____ yd.
20. 8 in. = ____ ft.
21. 9 articles = ____ doz.
22. $\frac{1}{4}$ bu. = ____ pk.
23. 27 in. = ____ yd.
24. $\frac{3}{4}$ ft. = ____ in.

Rating	Correct	Next Step
A	23 or 24	Do Inventory Test 15.
B	21 or 22	Do Inventory Test 15, or do Practice Exercises 14a to 14c.
C	20 or less	Do Practice Exercises 14a to 14c; then do Inventory Test 14 again.

DENOMINATE NUMBERS

(c) Denominate numbers—addition.

Add these units of measure. Reduce each sum to its simplest form:

(1) 1 ft. 7 in.
     4 ft. 3 in.

(2) 5 yd. 2 ft.
     2 yd. 2 ft.

(3) 3 gal. 2 qt.
     2 gal. 3 qt.

(4) 5 hr. 30 min.
     2 hr. 45 min.

┌─── EXAMPLE ───┐
│ 8 ft. 9 in. │
│ +3 ft. 7 in. │
│ 11 ft. 16 in. = │
│ 12 ft. 4 in. │
└───────────────┘

(5) 6 lb. 9 oz.
     5 lb. 8 oz.

(6) 2 qt. 1 pt.
     3 qt. 1 pt.

(7) 45 min. 38 sec.
     30 min. 39 sec.

(8) 5 T. 1100 lb.
     2 T. 1700 lb.

INVENTORY TEST 15   Addition of Denominate Numbers

Add these units of measure. Reduce every sum to its simplest form:

1. 6 ft. 5 in.
       3 ft. 2 in.

2. 12 lb. 8 oz.
        4 lb. 9 oz.

3. 18 bu. 5 qt. 1 pt.
       13 bu. 7 qt. 1 pt.

4. 6 gal. 2 qt.
       1 gal. 3 qt.

5. 16 T. 1400 lb.
        7 T. 700 lb.

6. 7 hr. 48 min.
       9 hr. 32 min.

7. 6 yr. 9 mo.
       2 yr. 2 mo.
       3 yr. 4 mo.

8. 2 qt. 1 pt.
       3 qt. 1 pt.
       2 qt. 1 pt.

9. 6 yd. 2 ft.
       9 yd. 2 ft.
       4 yd. 1 ft.

Rating	Correct	Next Step
A	8 or 9	Do Inventory Test 16.
B	6 or 7	Do Inventory Test 16, or Practice Exercise 15a.
C	5 or less	Do Practice Exercise 15a; then do Inventory Test 15 again.

(d) Denominate numbers—multiplication.

Multiply these units of measure. Reduce each product to its simplest form:

1. 2 ft. 7 in.
   5

2. 3 qt. 1 pt.
   4

3. 2 bu. 3 pk.
   3

4. 4 hr. 30 min.
   7

5. 5 gal. 2 qt.
   3

6. 5 lb. 9 oz.
   4

INVENTORY TEST 16   Multiplication of Denominate Numbers

Multiply these units of measure and reduce each product to its simplest form:

1. 1 qt. 1 pt.
   2

2. 3 bu. 3 pk.
   4

3. 5 T. 280 lb.
   8

4. 4 ft. 3 in.
   3

5. 8 hr. 16 min.
   6

6. 2 ft. 7 in.
   10

7. 3 lb. 8 oz.
   5

8. 16 min. 50 sec.
   8

9. 12 gal. 3 qt.
   7

Rating	Correct	Next Step
A	8 or 9	Do Inventory Test 17.
B	6 or 7	Do Inventory Test 17, or do Practice Exercise 16a.
C	5 or less	Do Practice Exercise 16a; then do Inventory Test 16 again.

(e) Denominate numbers—subtraction.

Subtract these units of measure:

1. 9 ft. 7 in.
   2 ft. 9 in.

2. 11 bu. 2 pk.
   7 bu. 3 pk.

┌─────── EXAMPLE ───────┐
9 ft. 3 in. = 8 ft. 15 in.
−4 ft. 8 in. = 4 ft. 8 in.
             4 ft. 7 in.
└───────────────────────┘

3. 10 lb. 4 oz.
2 lb. 8 oz.
———

4. 8 yd. 1 ft.
2 yd. 2 ft.
———

5. 1957 yr. 6 mo. 15 da.
1776 yr. 7 mo. 4 da.
———

INVENTORY TEST 17

Subtract these units of measure:

1. 14 bu. 3 pk.
10 bu. 1 pk.
———

2. 9 hr. 30 min.
2 hr. 45 min.
———

3. 1951 yr. 11 mo. 1 da.
1776 yr. 7 mo. 4 da.
———

4. 7 yd. 2 ft.
3 yd. 1 ft.
———

5. 72 gal. 1 qt.
17 gal. 3 qt.
———

6. 14 yd. 2 ft. 8 in.
8 yd. 1 ft. 10 in.
———

7. 8 lb. 15 oz.
3 lb. 9 oz.
———

8. 27 ft. 8 in.
18 ft. 9 in.
———

9. 15 bu. 1 pk.
8 bu. 3 pk.
———

Rating	Correct	Next Step
A	8 or 9	Do Inventory Test 18.
B	6 or 7	Do Inventory Test 18, or Practice Exercise 17a.
C	5 or less	Do Practice Exercise 17a; then do Inventory Test 17 again.

(f) **Division of denominate numbers.** In the division of a denominate number, there is often a remainder. If this remainder is not already expressed in the lowest possible unit of measure, it should be (a) changed to the next lower unit, (b) added to the like unit, if any, in the dividend, and (c) divided by the given divisor.

EXAMPLE

$$4 \text{ ft. } 9\tfrac{2}{3} \text{ in.}$$
$$3)\overline{14 \text{ ft. } 5 \text{ in.}}$$

(a) 14 ft. ÷ 3 = 4 ft. and 2 ft. remainder.
(b) 2 ft. = 24 in. (changed to lower unit)
(c) 24 in. + 5 in. = 29 in. (added to like unit)
(d) 29 in. ÷ 3 = $9\tfrac{2}{3}$ in. (divided)
    Quotient is 4 ft. $9\tfrac{2}{3}$ in.

Divide:

1. 2)5 yd. 1 ft. **2.** 3)7 bu. 3 pk. **3.** 3)4 gal. 2 qt.

4. 4)3 qt. 1 pt. **5.** 6)8 hr. 15 min. **6.** 5)11 lb. 4 oz.

INVENTORY TEST 18   Division of Denominate Numbers

Divide:

1. 2)6 bu. 2 pk. **2.** 3)7 ft. 9 in. **3.** 6)8 T. 180 lb.

4. 2)4 yd. 2 ft. **5.** 4)9 ft. 5 in. **6.** 6)3 gal. 2 qt.

7. 3)2 qt. 1 pt. **8.** 3)7 hr. 14 min. **9.** 4)15 lb. 3 oz.

Rating	Correct	Next Step
A	8 or 9	You have completed all the Inventory Tests.
B	6 or 7	Do Practice Exercise 18a if you wish.
C	5 or less	Do Practice Exercise 18a; then do Inventory Test 18.

──────────────── *EXERCISES* ────────────────

1. A speed of 8 yd. 2 ft. in 1 second is what speed in 10 seconds?

2. Four peach trees yielded 1 bu. 2 pk., 2 bu. 2 pk., 3 bu. 3 pk., and 4 bu. 3 pk., respectively. What amount of peaches was produced?

3. A flagpole is 106'6" long. It stands 77'5" above the ground. How far does the pole extend into the ground?

4. Bob and Jerry shared equally the 5 bu. 3 pk. of apples that they gathered. How much did each receive?

5. A beef roast, medium done, requires 20 minutes per pound cooking time. A 5-pound roast requires how long to cook?

6. A rough piece of metal weighing 42 lb. 3 oz. is turned in a lathe. What is the loss in weight in finishing if the finished weight is 38 lb. 11 oz.?

7. A company marketed 346 tons 756 lb. of lead, 123 tons 263 lb. of copper, 21 tons 202 lb. of zinc, and 28 tons 798 lb. of nickel. Find the total weight marketed.

8. An 8'6" board is to be divided into 3 equal shelves. How long will each shelf be?

9. Mr. Mann bought four chickens at the market. Their weights were: 3 lb. 8 oz., 4 lb. 5 oz., 4 lb. 9 oz., and 5 lb. 4 oz. How many pounds of chicken did he buy?

10. John Adams was born October 19, 1735, and his son John Quincy Adams was born July 11, 1767. Find the difference in their ages?

11. If a child should drink 1 quart of milk each day, how many gallons should an institution caring for 75 children buy for the children to drink each day?

12. Clara has 2 hr. 40 min. to divide equally among three studies. How much time will she have for each study?

13. How long is it since November 11, 1918?

14. What is the distance from *A*, through *B* and *C*, and back to *A* in the diagram at the right?

15. On his way to school, Don made four consecutive stops the following distances apart: 15 rd. 9 ft., 17 rd. 6 ft., 14 rd. 8 ft., and 13 rd. 4 ft. How far does Don live from school?

16. Clara weighs 18 lb. 8 oz. Her father weighs 9 times as much. How much does Clara's father weigh?

17. How long has it been since July 4, 1776?

18. Divide 2 qt. 1 pt. of milk equally among four children.

19. Mrs. Barr gave 12 issues of a certain magazine to a school's paper drive. What did the magazines weigh, if one magazine weighed 1 lb. 7 oz.?

20. Twelve magazines of the same issue weigh 18 lb. 12 oz. What does each magazine weigh?

21. May bought three remnants of ribbon of the following lengths: 4 yd. 9 in., 2 yd. 24 in., and 3 yd. 30 in. How much ribbon did she buy?

22. The Statue of Liberty was unveiled October 28, 1886. How long ago was it unveiled?

*23. Ralph worked 5 days after school for 3 hr. 45 min. each day, and on Saturday he worked 8 hr. 30 min. How many hours did he work during the week?

*24. An airplane speed of 285 ft. per second is how many miles per hour?

*25. One bushel of potatoes weighs 60 pounds. (a) What is the weight of 2 bu. 2 pk.? (b) Of 4 bu. 3 pk.?

*26. (a) How many quart boxes will 3 gal. 3 qt. of berries fill? (b) 5 gal. 2 qt. of berries?

*27. A grocer paid $.75 a peck for pecans and sold them for 20¢ a quart. How much was his profit per peck?

*28. A grocer bought 30 pounds of carrots at 8¢ per pound. He sold them at 2 lb. for 35¢. How much was his profit?

**29. How long should curtain material be cut for a window 5'8" long, if the curtain is to hang 6 in. below the sill and is to have a 3-in. hem at the top and a $2\frac{1}{2}$-in. hem at the bottom? Allow $\frac{1}{2}$ in. for each turn-in.

**30. (optional) Measure the length and width of your teacher's desk. Calculate its perimeter.

RATIO AND PROPORTION

46. The meaning of "ratio." In a class of 20 girls and 15 boys, we may compare the number of girls and boys in the class in two ways, either by *subtraction* or by *division*. If we make the comparison by subtraction, we say, "There are 5 more girls than boys in the class." If we make the comparison by division, we say, "There are $\frac{15}{20}$ or $\frac{3}{4}$ as many boys as girls in the class," or "There are $1\frac{1}{3}$ times as many girls as boys in the class." When two quantities are compared by division, the result is called the *ratio* of one quantity to the other quantity.

Ratio means relationship. Hence, the ratio between the number of boys and the number of girls in the class is the ratio of 15 to 20; that is, the number of boys is $\frac{3}{4}$ as much as the number of girls. The ratio of the number of girls to the number of boys is $\frac{4}{3}$ or $1\frac{1}{3}$.

The ratio of one quantity to a similar quantity is their quotient, found by dividing the first quantity by the second quantity.

A ratio may be expressed as a fraction, such as $\frac{3}{4}$; as a mixed number, such as $1\frac{1}{3}$; as a per cent, such as 75% or $133\frac{1}{3}$%; or as $3 \div 4$ or $4 \div 3$ or 3:4 (read "3 to 4") or 4:3.

EXERCISES

1. What is the quotient of $5 ÷ $2? What is the ratio of $5 to $2?

2. 18 is how many times 6? What is the ratio of 18 to 6?

3. 8 = ____ times 4. What is the ratio of 8 to 4?

4. 9 = ____ times 6. What is the ratio of 9 to 6?

5. 6 = ____ times 9. What is the ratio of 6 to 9?

6. 12 = ____ times 8. What is the ratio of 12 to 8?

7. 8 = ____ times 12. What is the ratio of 8 to 12?

8. The ratio of 15 to 5 is the same as ____ to 1.

9. The ratio of 21 to 3 is the same as ____ to 1.

10. The ratio of 10 to 3 is the same as ____ to 1.

11. The ratio of 9 to 4 is the same as ____ to 1.

12. The ratio of 8 to 6 is the same as ____ to 3.

13. The ratio of 12 to 10 is the same as ____ to 5.

Both terms (numbers) of a ratio may be multiplied or divided by the same number without the value of the ratio being changed.

The ratio $\frac{8}{10}$ should be reduced to $\frac{4}{5}$, $4 \div 5$, or $4:5$. That is, 8 is to 10 is the same as 4 is to 5.

Reduce these ratios to the simplest terms:

14. $\frac{9}{15}$, $\frac{8}{12}$, $\frac{9}{6}$, $\frac{12}{15}$, $\frac{15}{20}$, $\frac{8}{4}$, $\frac{12}{3}$, $1\frac{1}{2}/3$.

15. $6 \div 2$, $12 \div 18$, $15 \div 12$, $8 \div 20$.

16. $8:6$, $4:16$, $9:12$, $25:15$.

17. $\frac{2\frac{1}{2}}{5}$, $\frac{2}{6}$, $\frac{4}{18}$, $\frac{4}{2}$, $\frac{3}{9}$, $\frac{2}{8}$, $\frac{3}{12}$.

18. 6 girls to 24 girls.

19. 8 books to 24 books.

20. Irma has 21 books and Sally has 30 books. What is the ratio of Irma's books to Sally's? Of Sally's books to Irma's?

21. Helen won 6 games of tennis and Jean won 9 games. What is the ratio of Helen's winnings to Jean's?

22. *A* and *B* formed a partnership. *A* put in $1,200 capital; *B* put in $1,800. What is the ratio of *A*'s part of the capital to *B*'s? Of *A*'s part to the total capital?

23. What is the ratio of 6 hours spent in school to a whole day?

24. The North High School has 810 boys and 1,260 girls enrolled. What is the ratio of the number of boys to the number of girls?

Of girls to boys? Of girls to the total enrollment? Of boys to the total enrollment?

25. Tony sells 36 of his 45 magazines. Find the ratio of magazines sold to the number received. Express this ratio as a per cent.

26. Schools X and Y have played 15 games of football. X has won 8 games and Y 7 games. (a) What is the ratio of X's winnings to Y's winnings? (b) Of Y's to X's?

27. A room is 12 ft. wide and 16 ft. long. (a) What is ratio of width to length? (b) Of length to width?

28. John's grades averaged 80. Jim's grades averaged 90. (a) Write the ratio of John's grades to Jim's grades. (b) Of Jim's grades to John's grades.

29. In a school 120 freshmen enrolled in science and 125 enrolled in mathematics. What is the ratio of freshmen taking mathematics to those taking science?

30. Mr. Carr drove 1640 miles on his vacation. Mr. Kem drove 1,050 miles. Write the ratio of Mr. Kem's mileage to Mr. Carr's.

31. Fred sold 148 magazines last week and 160 this week. What is the ratio of last week's sales to this week's sales? Of this week's sales to last week's?

*32. Carl earns \$4.50 per week and saves \$3. What is the ratio of money saved to money earned?

$$\frac{3}{4.50} \times \frac{100}{100} = \frac{300}{450}$$

(Get rid of the decimal in the denominator by multiplying both numerator and denominator by the same number, 100 in this case.)

*33. Find the ratio of:

(a) \$2.50 to \$4.50   (d) \$2.75 to \$22

(b) 1.5 to 6   (e) \$1.25 to \$12.50

(c) \$7 to \$7   (f) 18 in. to $4\frac{1}{2}$ in.

Numbers that are to be compared must be expressed in the same *unit*. Hence, the ratio of 40 minutes to 1 hour is not 40 to 1; it is 40 to 60 (since 1 hr. = 60 min.), or 2 to 3.

*34. Express these ratios orally in their simplest forms:

(a) The ratio of 1 lb. to 8 oz. is ____ oz. to ____ oz. or ____ : ____.

(b) The ratio of 1 gal to 2 qt. is ____ qt. to ____ qt. or ____ : ____.

(c) The ratio of 10 min. to 1 hr. is ____ min. to ____ min. or ____ : ____.

(d) The ratio of 2 bu. to 2 pk. is _____ pk. to _____ pk. or _____.

(e) The ratio of 1 gal. to 1 pt. is _____ ÷ _____ or _____ : _____.

(f) The ratio of 2 ft. to 8 in. is _____ ÷ _____ or _____ : _____.

(g) The ratio of 4 yd. to 2 ft. is _____ ÷ _____ or _____ : _____.

(h) The ratio of 9 in. to 1 yd. is _____ ÷ _____ or _____ : _____.

(i) The ratio of 50¢ to $3 is _____ ÷ _____ or _____ : _____.

(j) The ratio of $2 to 75¢ is _____ ÷ _____ or _____ : _____.

(k) The ratio of $1\frac{1}{2}$ft. to 8 in. is _____ to _____ or _____ : _____.

(l) The ratio of $1\frac{1}{4}$ hr. to 45 min. is _____ to _____ or _____ : _____.

*35. Clara bought 5 doz. cards and sold 42 cards. What is the ratio of cards purchased to cards sold? Of cards sold to cards purchased?

*36. Clark earns $6 per week and saves $2.50 of it. Find the ratio of his savings to his earnings.

*37. A cake recipe calls for $1\frac{1}{2}$ cups of flour and $\frac{3}{4}$ cups of milk. What is the ratio of flour to milk in the recipe?

*38. A recipe for ice cream calls for $\frac{3}{4}$ cup of sugar and 2 cups of cream. What is the ratio of cream to sugar in the recipe?

*39. Lt. Col. John Glenn said, in describing his three orbits of the earth in *Friendship 7*, that if the diameter of the earth were 80 inches, the flight would have been $1\frac{1}{3}$ inches from it. Considering that the diameter of the earth is actually close to 8000 miles, how high above the earth did he go?

*40. Baseball batting averages are actually ratios. They are found by taking the ratio of hits to times at bat, and expressing this ratio as a decimal rounded off to the nearest thousandth. One year Roger Maris made 159 hits out of 590 times at bat. His batting average was $\frac{159}{590}$, or .269. Find the batting averages of the following best batting records made in a recent year:

National League			American League		
Player and Team	No. times at bat	No. of hits	Player and Team	No. times at bat	No. of hits
Clemente, Pittsburgh	572	201	Cash, Detroit	535	193
Pinson, Cincinnati	607	208	Howard, New York	446	155
Boyer, St. Louis	589	194	Kaline, Detroit	586	190
Moon, Los Angeles	463	152	Piersall, Cleveland	484	156
Aaron, Milwaukee	603	197	Mantle, New York	514	163

47. Proportion. Henry earns $20 per month and saves $5. Sam earns $16 per month and saves $4. They each save $\frac{1}{4}$ of their earnings, since $\frac{5}{20} = \frac{1}{4}$ and $\frac{4}{16} = \frac{1}{4}$. This shows the two ratios to be equal. That is, $\frac{5}{20} = \frac{4}{16}$.

An expression of equality between two ratios is called a "proportion."

The above proportion may also be written

$$5:20 = 4:16$$

It is read: 5 is to 20 as 4 is to 16. The four numbers used in a proportion are the *terms* of the proportion.

In the above proportion: 5 is the first term; 20 is the second term; 4 is the third term; 16 is the fourth term.

The second and third terms are called the *means*. The first and last terms are called the *extremes*. In the proportion $5:20 = 4:16$, the 20 and the 4 are means and the 5 and the 16 are extremes.

In any proportion, the product of the means equals the product of the extremes. In the proportion $5:20 = 4:16$

$5 \times 16 = 80$, product of the extremes.

$20 \times 4 = 80$, product of the means.

If three terms of a proportion are known, the missing term can be found.

EXAMPLE

$3:4 = 6:?$

Substitute y for the missing extreme.

Then, $3:4 = 6:y$

$4 \times 6 = 24$, product of means.

$3 \times y = 24$, product of extremes.

$y = 24 \div 3$ (Product ÷ known factor = missing factor.)

$y = 8$, missing extreme.

Hence, $3:4 = 6:8$

Proof: $3 \times 8 = 6 \times 4$

$24 = 24$

EXERCISES

Find the missing term in each proportion:

1. $\dfrac{7}{8} = \dfrac{14}{x}$

2. $\dfrac{15}{24} = \dfrac{y}{8}$

3. $\dfrac{5}{9} = \dfrac{z}{27}$

4. $\dfrac{x}{7} = \dfrac{8}{28}$

5. $\dfrac{6}{w} = \dfrac{2}{24}$

6. $\dfrac{6}{14} = \dfrac{a}{21}$

7. $\dfrac{36}{90} = \dfrac{b}{75}$

8. $\dfrac{c}{15} = \dfrac{12}{18}$

9. $\dfrac{18}{s} = \dfrac{27}{30}$

10. $\dfrac{6}{10} = \dfrac{15}{d}$

11. $6:9 = 16:m$

12. $15:y = 20:24$

13. $n:12 = 12:18$

14. $25:15 = w:9$

15. $25:20 = \dfrac{5}{8}:m$

16. $\dfrac{3}{4} : \dfrac{1}{2} = \dfrac{3}{8}:y$

48. Using proportion. Certain kinds of problems can be solved if the numbers in the problems are used as terms in a proportion. In such cases, the unknown number (the answer) is one of the four terms in the proportion. If three of the terms are known, the unknown fourth term can always be found.

EXAMPLE

It has long been known that, at the same time of day, *the heights of perpendicular objects are in the same ratio as the lengths of their shadows.*

At a certain time of day, a 5-ft. fence post casts a shadow 6 ft. long. At the same time, a certain flagpole casts a shadow 60 ft. long. How high is the flagpole?

The ratio of the heights—post to pole—is $\dfrac{5 \text{ ft.}}{? \text{ ft.}}$, or $5:?$.

The ratio of the shadow lengths—post to pole—is $\dfrac{6 \text{ ft.}}{60 \text{ ft.}}$, or $6:60$.

Let h represent the height of the flagpole. Since the ratios are equal, $5:h = 6:60$. Since the product of the means = the product of the extremes,

$$5:h = 6:60$$
$$6 \times h = 5 \times 60$$
$$6 \times h = 300$$
$$h = 300 \div 6$$
$$h = 50$$

Hence, the height of the flagpole is 50 ft.

Check:

$$\tfrac{5}{50} = \tfrac{6}{60}$$
$$5 \times 60 = 6 \times 50$$
$$300 = 300$$

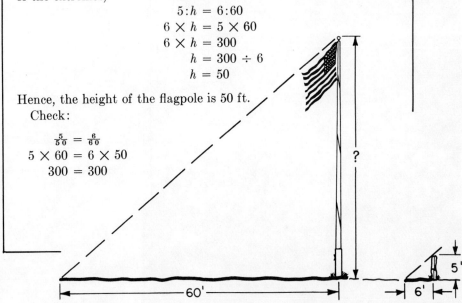

Solve by proportion:

1. A post 4 ft. high casts a shadow 6 ft. long at the same time that a pole casts a shadow 18 ft. long. Form a proportion and find the height of the pole.

2. A 5-ft. boy casts an 8-ft. shadow at the same time that a tree casts a shadow 48 ft. long. How high is the tree?

3. How long is the shadow of a 32-ft. telephone pole, when the shadow of a 6-ft. man is 9 ft. long?

4. A 100-foot tree casts a 30-ft. shadow. At the same time of day, how long a shadow will a 75-ft. tree cast?

5. How high is an electric light pole that casts a shadow 10 ft. long when a 6-ft. post casts a shadow 4 ft. long? Sketch the triangles and mark the given parts.

6. A yardstick casts a shadow 2 ft. long. At the same time a monument casts a shadow 80 ft. long. How high is the monument?

7. Jean is 5 ft. tall and at a certain time of day casts a shadow 4 ft. long. At the same time a flagpole casts a shadow 40 feet long. How high is the flagpole?

How High Is the Flagpole?

96

8. A telephone pole casts a shadow 20 ft. long when a 3-ft. stick casts a shadow 2 ft. long. What is the height of the pole?

9. If a flagstaff 60 ft. high casts a shadow of 30 ft., how long a shadow will a 40-ft. tree cast at the same time?

10. When a tower 75 ft. high casts a shadow of 60 ft., how tall is a boy who casts a shadow of 4 ft.?

11. If 2 doz. oranges cost 85¢, what will 9 doz. cost?

$$\frac{\text{A small amount}}{\text{A large amount}} = \frac{\text{cost of small amount}}{\text{cost of large amount}}$$

$$\frac{2}{9} = \frac{85¢}{?}$$

12. If 6 lb. of meat costs $8.40, what will 20 lb. cost at the same rate?

13. A grocer paid $4.60 for 12 doz. lemons. How much would 15 doz. lemons cost him?

14. If 6 gal. of gasoline cost $1.56, how many gallons at the same rate can be bought for $2.21?

15. If 840 bu. of potatoes can be raised on 6 acres, how many acres would be required to produce at the same rate 2,100 bu. of potatoes?

16. In a class, the ratio of the number of boys to girls is 6 to 8. If there are 16 girls, how many boys are in the class?

17. An ordinary tree, about the size of the tree in the picture, gives off 5 barrels of water per day (24 hours). How many barrels of water would it give off in the 7 hours that you are in school? In the 9 hours while you sleep?

18. Walter's car will run 72 mi. on 5 gal. of gasoline. How many gallons will he need to travel 180 mi.?

19. Mr. Clark divided some money between John and Mary in the ratio of 4 to 5. If John received $128, how much did Mary receive?

20. The average 7-in. lead pencil will draw a line 35 miles long. How long a line should an 8-in. pencil draw?

*21. The dimensions of a room are in the ratio of 3 to 4. The room is longer than it is wide, and its width is 12 ft. How long is the room?

*22. A carpet is 10 ft. wide. What is its length if the ratio of its width to its length is 2 to 3?

*23. A garden is 20 ft. long. Find its width if the ratio of its width to its length is 2 to 5.

*24. If a plane travels 4,500 mi. in 10 hours, how long will it take the plane to go 3,000 mi. at the same rate of speed?

*25. Two partners, X and Y, share profits in the same ratio as their investments. X invested \$2,500 and Y \$3,500. How much profit will X receive when Y receives \$210?

*26. If a \$70 commission is paid on a sale of \$2,100, what commission would be paid on a sale of \$1,500?

*27. Taxes of \$45 were paid a certain year on property assessed at \$2,000. At that rate, find the amount of taxes on property assessed at \$5,000.

*28. The ratio of Roy's winnings to Joseph's winnings in a series of games was 8:9. Roy won 32 games. How many games did Joseph win?

*29. If 6 castings cost \$14.40, what will 5 castings cost?

*30. A map that is 8 in. wide and 15 in. long is enlarged so that it is now 20 in. wide. What is the new length?

**31. If 15 boys can pick 105 qt. of berries in an hour, how many quarts can these same boys pick in $1\frac{1}{3}$ hours?

**32. A boy is paid 75¢ for 2 hours' work. How much will he be paid for 9 hours?

**33. It required 25 days to dig a trench $1\frac{1}{2}$ mi. long. At the same rate, how long would it take to dig a trench 4 mi. long?

**34. If 5 tons of coal cost \$54.50, what will $\frac{1}{2}$ ton cost?

**35. Jerry knows that he is 5' 6" tall. At the time of day that he casts a 3-ft. shadow, Larry casts a 2-ft. shadow. How tall is Larry?

**36. Bert is 5' 4" tall and at a certain time of day casts a shadow 2 ft. long. How high is a building which casts a 60-ft. shadow at the same time?

**37. At \$3.25 for 3 sq. ft., what will be the cost of a concrete walk that is $2\frac{1}{2}$ ft. wide and 60 ft. long?

**38. If 1 gal. of paint will cover 400 sq. ft., how many gallons will be needed to paint the walls of a hall that is 40 ft. long, 6 ft. wide, and 10 ft. high?

PLAYOFF FOR CHAPTER V

1. How accurately can you estimate weights that are approximately: (a) one pound? (b) five pounds? (c) ten pounds? To become efficient in estimating these weights, it is helpful to hold in mind the heaviness of an article that weighs each of the suggested weights, as 1 lb. of coffee, 5 lb. of sugar, and a 10-lb. sack of flour.

Why not work on these three weights for a week; then ask your teacher or a class committee to line up a group of articles of different weights; finally, by lifting the articles judge which articles come nearest to the 1-, 5-, and 10-lb. weights?

2. How many times have you heard it asked, "Will a five-cent stamp be enough postage on this letter?" How about practice in lifting letters weighing one ounce or less, and letters weighing more than one ounce, and then try out your judgment on a group of letters of various weights?

3.* The three jealous men and their wives. Three men, traveling with their wives, came to a river which they wished to cross. There was but one boat, and but two persons could cross at one time; and, since the husbands were jealous, no woman could be with a man unless her own husband was present. In what manner did they get across the river?

PROCEDURE FOR ACHIEVEMENT TESTS

We have now come to the first of a series of four *Achievement Tests.* The other three tests are at the close of following chapters.

After each of these Achievement Tests, record your score on one of the achievement charts found in the back of the book. Record your six separate scores as follows: (a) in the column headed "Add," place a dot on the printed line at the number which is the same as your score in addition; (b) in the same way mark your subtraction score in the column headed "Sub"; (c) likewise record your multiplication, division, percentage, and total scores; (d) with a red pencil* draw a line connecting the six dots. This line graph is a picture of your achievement in the fundamentals of arithmetic at this time.

To help you to improve your score on each of the succeeding tests, *Reviews of Fundamentals* follow the Achievement Tests.

Record the date on which each Achievement Test is taken at the extreme right of the card.

ACHIEVEMENT TEST 1

Addition

1. 8
9
6
5
4

2. 36
27
83
78

3. 585
634
127
986
469

4. 18.68
5.97
35.06
7.40

5. $\frac{1}{10}$
$\frac{4}{5}$

6. $4.51 + .182 + 2.8$
7. $\frac{1}{3} + \frac{3}{4} + \frac{1}{2}$

8. $27\frac{5}{8}$
$19\frac{2}{3}$

9. $26\frac{7}{8}$
$5\frac{3}{4}$

10. 8 ft. 9 in.
7 ft. 8 in.

Subtraction

11. 202
84

12. 5060
189

13. 814.06
312.18

14. $\$7.64 - \$.89$

15. $\$8 - 46¢$

16. $\$12\frac{1}{2} - \$1.25$
17. $\frac{9}{10} - \frac{3}{5}$

18. $48\frac{3}{4}$
$26\frac{1}{3}$

19. $76\frac{1}{4}$
$18\frac{1}{2}$

20. 42 min. 30 sec.
18 min. 45 sec.

Multiplication

21. 64
38

22. 206
307

23. 180
70

24. 12.6
.03

25. $\frac{1}{2} \times \frac{1}{3}$

27. $\frac{1}{3} \times 18\frac{3}{4}$

29. $48\frac{1}{2}$
$28\frac{3}{4}$

30. 2 gal. 2 qt.
3

26. $2\frac{1}{3} \times 63$

28. $\frac{2}{3} \times 90$

Division

31. $6\overline{)186}$

32. $.18\overline{)4.32}$

33. $28.4 \div 10$

---

* Draw the graph lines for the four Achievement Tests all on the same chart, but use a different color for each one.

34. $3.5\overline{)217}$ **35.** $4.6\overline{)83.72}$ **36.** $.46\overline{).8372}$

with 182 above 35 and 182 above 36.

37. $\frac{2}{3} \div \frac{5}{6}$ **38.** $\frac{1}{2} \div 7$ **39.** $12\frac{1}{2} \div 2\frac{1}{2}$

40. $\frac{1}{2}$ of 3 qt. 1 pt.

Per Cent

Write as common fractions:

41. 18% **42.** $33\frac{1}{3}\%$

Write as decimal fractions:

43. 83% **44.** $2\frac{1}{2}\%$

Write as per cents:

45. $\frac{7}{20}$ **46.** 3.5

Solve:

47. 80% of $72 = ?$

48. 4% of $? = 12$

49. $?\%$ of $90 = 36$

Arrange in order of size, largest first:

50. 37%, $\frac{38}{100}$, $.037$, 3.6.

Record your scores on the achievement chart.
Your graph line will show you in which of the fundamentals you need to improve.

—REVIEW OF THE FUNDAMENTALS OF ARITHMETIC—1—

Addition and Subtraction

Add and prove:

1.	2.	3.	4.	5.	6.	7.
7	69	81	585	6367	7.85	475.09
3	58	71	634	1468	19.26	18.65
5	47	45	127	5703	56.79	245.97
6	93	12	986	472	7.4	18.59
1	25	23	469			

8.
518.86
94.78
467.76
8.78

9. $68.5 + 18.097 + 65.47 + .009 + 1.07 + 74.068$

10. $5.8 + .87 + 9.583 + 48.5 + 16 + 35.629 + 79.63$

Add:

11. $\frac{3}{8} + \frac{2}{3}$

12. $\frac{5}{12} + \frac{2}{3}$

13. $\frac{7}{10}$ $\frac{3}{4}$ $\frac{2}{5}$

14. $\frac{7}{8}$ $\frac{5}{12}$ $\frac{3}{4}$

15. $162\frac{7}{12}$ $237\frac{5}{8}$

16. $16\frac{1}{2}$ $37\frac{2}{3}$ $28\frac{1}{9}$

17. $16\frac{3}{4}$ $45\frac{3}{8}$ $37\frac{3}{16}$

18. $67\frac{4}{5} + 28\frac{1}{2} + 67\frac{3}{10}$

19. $178\frac{1}{4} + 209\frac{7}{8} + 64\frac{1}{2}$

20. 8 hr. 10 min. 36 sec.
5 hr. 15 min. 24 sec.

Subtract and prove:

21. 2438
1349

22. 5479
4880

23. 1638
743

24. 40079
37939

25. 69007
50879

26. 14.7
7.3

27. 9.07
5.6

28. .07
.068

29. $46.97 - 26.08 =$

30. $8 - 5.667 =$

Subtract:

31. $\frac{2}{3} - \frac{1}{2}$ **33.** $17\frac{1}{7}$ **34.** 38   **35.** $138\frac{5}{8}$ **36.** $64\frac{1}{4}$ **37.** $48\frac{5}{8}$
32. $\frac{5}{8} - \frac{1}{2}$ 15 $27\frac{1}{4}$ $93\frac{7}{16}$ $44\frac{1}{2}$ $26\frac{3}{4}$

38. $381\frac{3}{4} - 79.125$

39. 72 gal. 1 qt.
17 gal. 3 qt.

40. 21 T. 800 lb.
16 T. 1000 lb.

— REVIEW OF THE FUNDAMENTALS OF ARITHMETIC—2 —

Multiplication and Division

Multiply and prove:

1. 485
7

2. 236
49

3. 5500
37

4. 406
504

5. 1607
49

6. .508
63

7. 5.72
.85

8. 6.67
.038

9. .0859
.206

10. 137.2
5.09

Multiply:

11. 84.65×10 **13.** 6.99×100 **15.** 6.72×1000

12. $10 \times .5675$ **14.** $100 \times .423$ **16.** 10×6.7986

17. $5 \times 1\frac{1}{2}$ **18.** $\frac{5}{8} \times \frac{4}{10} \times \frac{1}{2}$ **19.** $9\frac{1}{3} \times 9$ **20.** $2\frac{1}{4} \times 3\frac{2}{3}$

21. $42 \times 76\frac{3}{7}$ **22.** $4\frac{1}{3} \times 8\frac{2}{5}$ **23.** $44\frac{2}{5} \times 65\frac{1}{2}$ **24.** $18\frac{2}{3} \times 9\frac{1}{2}$

25. 16 yd. 2 ft. 7 in.
10

26. 12 gal. 3 qt. 1 pt.
12

Divide and prove:

27. $2736 \div 48$ **31.** $192 \div .04$ **35.** $57.68 \div 10$

28. $7283 \div 35$ **32.** $2.1432 \div .38$ **36.** $54.43 \div 100$

29. $52,272 \div 54$ **33.** $424.08 \div 9.3$ **37.** $711.27 \div 10$

30. $45,724 \div 62$ **34.** $40.608 \div 9.6$ **38.** $45 \div 1000$

Divide:

39. $\frac{1}{2} \div \frac{3}{4}$ **42.** $10 \div 3\frac{1}{3}$ **45.** $15\frac{5}{8} \div 6\frac{1}{4}$ **48.** $7\frac{1}{9} \div 26\frac{2}{3}$

40. $\frac{5}{16} \div 2$ **43.** $1\frac{1}{8} \div \frac{3}{8}$ **46.** $18\frac{2}{5} \div 3\frac{2}{5}$ **49.** $4\overline{)15 \text{ lb. 3 oz.}}$

41. $25 \div 4\frac{1}{6}$ **44.** $\frac{7}{12} \div \frac{7}{18}$ **47.** $6\frac{2}{9} \div 19\frac{1}{5}$ **50.** $3\overline{)8 \text{ ft. 7 in.}}$

— REVIEW OF THE FUNDAMENTALS OF ARITHMETIC—3 —

Percentage

Express each of the following numbers as (1) a common fraction, (2) a decimal, (3) a percentage:

1. $\frac{4}{5}$ **6.** $33\frac{1}{3}\%$ **11.** 125% **16.** $\frac{1}{400}$

2. $\frac{2}{25}$ **7.** $37\frac{1}{2}\%$ **12.** $.12$ **17.** $.136$

3. $.3$ **8.** $.25$ **13.** $166\frac{2}{3}\%$ **18.** $\frac{1}{7}$

4. $3\frac{1}{2}$ **9.** $\frac{1}{2}\%$ **14.** $.7$ **19.** $2\frac{3}{4}$

5. 75% **10.** $\frac{7}{50}$ **15.** $.12\frac{1}{2}$ **20.** 72%

Solve the following:

21. 75% of 852 **27.** $5\frac{1}{2}\%$ of 250.80 **33.** 12% of 88.50

22. $66\frac{2}{3}\%$ of $.432$ **28.** 9% of $67,475$ **34.** $16\frac{2}{3}\%$ of $4,728.6$

23. 175% of $24,600$ **29.** 14% of 555.65 **35.** $3\frac{1}{3}\%$ of $93,684$

24. $6\frac{2}{3}\%$ of 45.90 **30.** 26% of $.4205$ **36.** $\frac{1}{2}\%$ of 684

25. 38% of 756.75 **31.** 2% of $1,256.85$ **37.** $8\frac{1}{2}\%$ of 268

26. 8% of 47.50 **32.** $1\frac{3}{4}\%$ of $5,268$ **38.** $12\frac{1}{2}\%$ of $12\frac{1}{2}$

Fill in the following:

39. ?% of $75 = 9$ **43.** 3% of ? $= 78$ **47.** $2\frac{1}{2}\%$ of ? $= 75$

40. 5% of ? $= 84$ **44.** ?% of $15 = 75$ **48.** ?% of $1 = \frac{1}{2}$

41. ?% of $12 = 42$ **45.** 24% of ? $= 16$ **49.** ?% of $35 = 140$

42. 8% of ? $= 72$ **46.** 1% of ? $= 54$ **50.** 25% of ? $= 100$

Solve the following:

51. 4 is what per cent of 12?   **55.** 30 is what per cent of 80?

52. 10 is what per cent of 40?   **56.** What per cent of 25 is 7?

53. What per cent of 16 is 2?   **57.** 6 is what per cent of 9?

54. 9 is what per cent of 18?   **58.** What per cent of 10 is 8?

CHAPTER VI

DIRECT MEASUREMENT OF LINES

AND ANGLES

VOCABULARY

1. approximate	4. thickness	7. subdivision
2. gauge	5. dimension	8. measurement
3. width	6. length	9. accuracy

49. The story of our measurements. Man has always found it necessary to measure the world about him. The Egyptians undoubtedly made much use of measurement at the time of the building of the pyramids, about 3000 B.C. As early as 1400 B.C., some type of measure was used to relocate land boundaries after the annual overflow of the River Nile. The British Museum contains a work on methods of measurement that was written by an Egyptian about 1550 B.C.*

Early measurements were not made by present-day methods. Early man knew no standards of measurement. He often measured distances by comparing the distance to be measured with the length of some part of his body. Fingernails, fingers, feet, and arms all became units of length.

The first known measurement, the *cubit*, was the length of a forearm from point of elbow to end of the middle finger. As you might expect, there were various cubits differing somewhat in length, since men's forearms and middle fingers are not all the same length. An outstanding cubit was the Olympic cubit, averaging 18.24 inches. The Olympic cubit was subdivided into 2 spans (length between the tips of the thumb and the little finger of the outstretched hand—about 9 inches each), 6 palms (3 inches each), or 24 *digits* ($\frac{3}{4}$ inch each). Later, two-thirds of an Olympic cubit was called a "foot." The foot was subdivided by the Greeks

---

* The history of many of the early measurements is told in *The Story of Weights and Measures*, prepared under the auspices of the Committee on Materials of Instruction of the American Council on Education, Washington, D. C.

into 12 thumb-breadths. All measurements of the Egyptian pyramids are in multiples or fractions of cubits.

In 1324 Edward II decreed that three barleycorns taken from the center of the ear of barley, placed end to end, should equal an *inch;* a foot ranged from $9\frac{3}{4}$ inches to 19 inches in length. England's King Henry I decreed that the distance from the point of his nose to the end of his thumb on his outstretched arm was the lawful *yard.*

To standardize the yard, a bronze bar one yard in length was kept as the Standard of Reference in the King's Exchequer in England.

In 1855 two copies of the standard yard were presented to the United States. Later these copies were accepted by the Office of Weights and Measures as the standards of the United States.

In 1500 the English mile was established as 8 furlongs—a furlong being 40 rods.

The standardization of measurement aided the Industrial Revolution. Recently, new devices for accurate measurement of thickness, temperature, time, distance, weight, and even light waves have helped man to achieve finer and finer degrees of precision. Parts in planes, automobiles, refrigerators, etc. must be accurate to thousandths and millionths of an inch. If the carburator jet in a modern car is even a thousandth of an inch too big, it could cut down the mileage by a mile or more per gallon. Modern measurement provides the accuracy needed.

50. Measurement. The purpose of measurement is to determine size. The degree of accuracy required depends upon the use to which the measurement is to be applied. There are measuring tools capable of measuring to any degree of accuracy needed. They vary from the ruler to the extremely accurate gauges used to make parts for modern machines. For very precise measurements technicians now use the reflection of light rays. Since the wave length of light is always the same, this is the world's most accurate standard of measurement.*

---

* The smallest linear unit in use today is called *angstrom.* It is used in expressing the length of light waves.

  1 angstrom = 1 hundred-millionth of a centimeter, which is approximately 1 two-hundred-fifty-millionth of an inch.

The largest linear unit is called *megaparsec.* It is used in expressing interstellar space.

  1 megaparsec = 1 million parsecs.
  1 parsec = 19.2 trillion miles.

—Digit—

Equal to the breadth of a finger.
From .72 to .75 inch.

—Cubit—

About 20 inches.   Length from point of
elbow to end of the middle finger.

—Inch and Foot—

ee barley corns from the center of the ear
ced end to end equalled one inch.   (Edward II, -
324.)   A foot ranged from $9\frac{3}{4}$ to 19 inches.

—Yard—

King Henry I decreed that the distance from the
point of his nose to the end of his thumb was the
lawful yard.

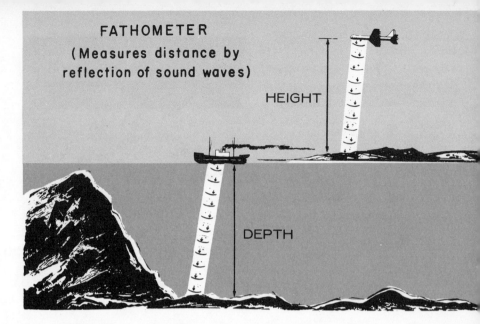

FATHOMETER
(Measures distance by
reflection of sound waves)

HEIGHT

DEPTH

Electric current and sound waves are also used in gauges to measure thickness to within ten millionths of an inch, and time to within ten microseconds (millionths of a second).

51. The ruler. The ruler is the simplest and most common measuring instrument. A steel ruler is called a *scale*. Rulers and scales make straight-line measurements and, when carefully used, will measure to within $\frac{1}{100}$ of an inch. They may be subdivided into eighths, sixteenths, thirty-seconds, and sixty-fourths of an inch; they may be divided also into tenths and hundredths, or into units of the metric system.

It is important in the use of the ruler (or scale) to follow these suggestions:

(a) Use only rulers and scales with square, clean-cut ends. A ruler or scale that is battered, rounded, or worn leads only to inaccurate measurement.

(b) When measuring rectangular pieces, make sure that the ruler or scale is placed parallel to the length being measured, not at an angle. See figures 1 and 2.

(c) Instead of laying the ruler flat upon the piece being measured, stand it on edge. The flat position leads to inaccuracy, as in this position the markings on the ruler are too far from the object being measured for the dimension to be estimated accurately. See figure 3.

(d) Curved measurements can be made with a flexible ruler.

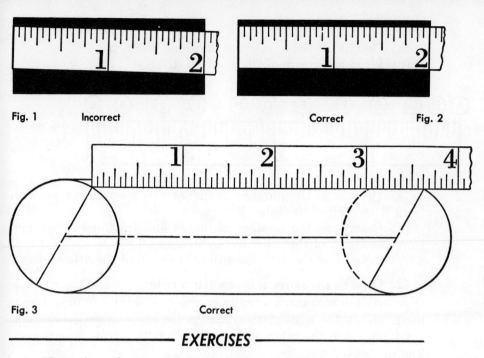

Fig. 1   Incorrect   Correct   Fig. 2

Fig. 3   Correct

EXERCISES

1. Note the ruler on which the inch is subdivided into eighths, figure 4:

- (a) How many inches long is the ruler?
- (b) Which of the subdivision marks are the longest? Which are the shortest?
- (c) Locate $1\frac{1}{2}$ in., $1\frac{1}{4}$ in., $1\frac{3}{4}$ in.
- (d) Locate $2\frac{1}{4}$ in., $2\frac{1}{8}$ in., $2\frac{3}{8}$ in.
- (e) Locate $1\frac{5}{8}$ in., $\frac{7}{8}$ in., $\frac{3}{8}$ in.
- (f) How would you locate $\frac{1}{16}$ of an inch? $\frac{3}{16}$ in.? $\frac{7}{16}$ in.? $2\frac{5}{16}$ in.? $3\frac{9}{16}$ in.? $4\frac{15}{16}$ in.?

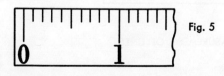

Fig. 4

2. Note the ruler, figure 5, on which the inch is subdivided into tenths.

- (a) Which of the subdivision marks are longest? Shortest?
- (b) Locate .1 in., .3 in., .5 in., .6 in., and .9 in.
- (c) Locate 1.8 in., 1.6 in., 1.1 in., and 1.5 in.

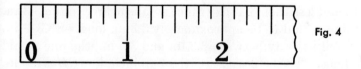

Fig. 5

109

3. On the ruler, figure 6:

(a) Determine the number of divisions per inch.
(b) What is the size of the smallest division?

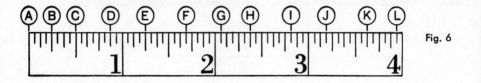

Fig. 6

(c) Determine the number of inches and fractions of an inch from *A* to each of the other letters.

(d) Determine the number of inches and fractions of an inch from *B* to each of the other letters in figure 6.

(e) Determine the distance from *C* to each of the other letters.

52. How to measure a line with a ruler.   Stand the ruler on edge with the zero mark directly on one end of the line to be measured.   Keep the edge of the ruler on the line.   Note the division mark on which the other end of the line falls.   How long is each line in figure 7 ?

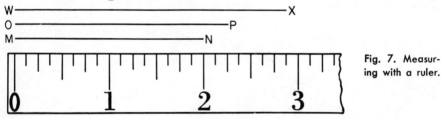

Fig. 7. Measuring with a ruler.

In figure 8, line *AB* measures 1.7 inches.   The point *D* of the line *CD* does not fall directly on one of the tenth marks.   It falls between the 3.3-in. and 3.4-in. marks, making the line *CD* greater than 3.3 in. and less than 3.4 in.   Since it falls nearer to the 3.3-in. mark, the line is said to be approximately 3.3 in. long, or 3.3+ in. long.   If *D* fell halfway between 3.3 in. and 3.4 in., the line would be 3.35 in. long.   To the nearest tenth of an inch, line *CD* is 3.3 in. long.

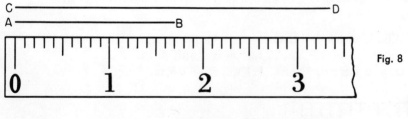

Fig. 8

1. Using a ruler marked off into eighths of an inch, measure: (a) the length of a page in your textbook, (b) the length of a printed line in your book, and (c) the length and width of the first 5 pictures in your book to the nearest eighth of an inch.

2. Using a ruler marked off into tenths of an inch, measure the length and width of the second 5 pictures in your book to the nearest tenth of an inch.

3. Draw 5 straight lines. Measure each accurately (a) to the nearest eighth of an inch; (b) to the nearest tenth of an inch.

4. Measure accurately 5 or more distances with a ruler or scale.

5. Measure the distances between points A, B, C, and D to the indicated degree of accuracy:

A •   • B

C •   • D

Distance	To Nearest	
	16th	32nd
AB		
BD		
BC		
AD		
AC		

*6. If you draw a line 96 in. long, then mark off 50% of it, then $33\frac{1}{3}\%$ of the remainder, then 25% of the remainder, then 50% of the remainder, how long is the last piece?

**7. A machinist cut a steel rod $16\frac{1}{2}$ in. long into 5 consecutive pieces by cutting off pieces $2\frac{1}{8}$ in. long, $4\frac{15}{16}$ in., $3\frac{1}{2}$ in., and $1\frac{3}{4}$ in., respectively. How long was the piece left, if $\frac{1}{16}$ in. is allowed for each cut?

53. How to draw a line with a ruler. To draw a line, place the zero mark (or the end of the ruler) at the point where you wish one end of the line to fall. Place the pencil point directly over the zero (or end) and move the pencil along the edge of the ruler to the division mark that indicates the length that the line is to be.

──────────────── *EXERCISES* ────────────────

1. Draw a line 3 in. long. Mark the inches and half-inches on the line.

2. Draw a 2-in. line. Mark off the inch, half-inch, and quarter-inch divisions.

3. Draw a line 1 in. long. Mark it off into eighths.

4. Mark off a 1-in. line into sixteenths.

5. Mark off a 1-in. line into tenths.

6. Draw lines of the following lengths: $2\frac{3}{4}$ in., $3\frac{7}{8}$ in., $4\frac{5}{8}$ in., and $3\frac{3}{8}$ in.

7. Draw the following lines: 1.4 in., 2.7 in., 3.8 in., and 4.9 in.

8. Which one of your finger joints is one inch, or approximately one inch, in length? Using this finger joint as a guide and using a straightedge that is not a ruler, draw lines which you estimate to be of the following lengths: 1 in., 2 in., 3 in., $2\frac{1}{2}$ in., and $3\frac{1}{4}$ in. Measure these lines with a ruler to the nearest eighth of an inch. How much of an error was made in each estimate? Try again if you are not satisfied with your attempt.

*9. In the same way, draw lines whose lengths you estimate to be 1.5 in., 2.7 in., 3.4 in., and 4.8 in. Measure the lines to the nearest tenth of an inch. Find the amount of error in each estimate.

**10. Draw a line $3\frac{5}{16}$ in. long.

**11. Draw a line $4\frac{15}{16}$ in. long.

54. Studying the yardstick, tapeline, and steel tape. The yardstick is more convenient than the ruler for measuring lengths of more than a foot, for the yardstick is 36 in. long. The tapeline is made in various lengths. Such lengths as 36 in., 48 in., 60 in., and 72 in. are most useful to dressmakers and tailors. Carpenters and gardeners use tapelines and steel tapes 25 ft., 50 ft., and 100 ft. long to measure the lengths of buildings and land. A tapeline has its divisions marked off on a narrow strip of cloth or steel.

──────────────── *EXERCISES* ────────────────

1. Estimate the width of the classroom to the nearest foot. Measure the width in order to verify your estimate. Estimate the length to the nearest foot and verify by measurement.

2. Let six pupils measure the length of the classroom to the nearest inch from three different points at the same time, two pupils using a ruler, two using a yardstick, and the other two using a tapeline. Note which two finish first. Compare results. Account for any difference in results.

3. Estimate and then measure to the nearest inch the lengths of such objects as the blackboard, the bulletin board, a desk, and a bookcase. Find the error in inches in each case.

*4. Estimate the height of two members of the class. Verify your estimates by measurement. How much is the error in inches? In per cent?

*5. (optional) Make accurate measurements of the school grounds so that a scale drawing may be made at a later date.

*6. (optional) Measure the schoolroom floor for linoleum. Measure the size of windows for screens or curtains.

55. The metric system of measurement. Much of the civilized world uses a simpler method of measuring than the one commonly used in England and the United States. It is the method known as the *metric system*. The basic metric units are the *meter* for length, the *liter* for capacity, and the *gram* for weight. There is a definite relationship between the meter, the liter, and the gram, as shown in figure 9. One liter of water will fill (at 20° centigrade) 1,000 cubic centimeters and weigh 1,000 grams (1 kilogram).

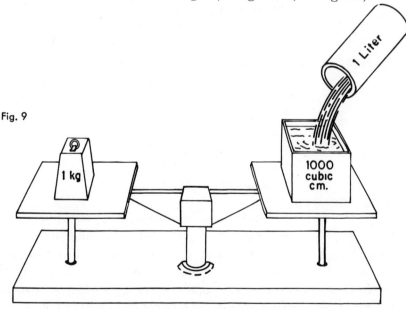

Fig. 9

The unit of length, the meter, is one ten-millionth part of the distance from the Equator to either pole. The original meter, a platinum bar made in 1799, is kept in France. Only a slight difference exists between the actual and the intended length.

The meter is divided into 10 equal parts called *decimeters*. Each decimeter is made up of 10 *centimeters;* each centimeter, of 10 *millimeters*. A centimeter, therefore, is $\frac{1}{100}$ of a meter. A millimeter is $\frac{1}{1000}$ of a meter. The meter is a little more than 39 inches long.

A small cube that measures one centimeter on a side is a measure of volume called a *cubic centimeter*. The basic unit of volume is 1000 cubic centimeters, which is called a *liter*. The liter is a little more than one liquid quart.

The gram, a unit of weight, is equal to the weight of one cubic centimeter of water (at 20° centigrade). The gram is so small the *kilogram*, or 1000 grams, is often used as a unit of weight. The kilogram weighs a little more than 2 pounds.

The meter, the liter, and the gram are subdivided decimally, the Latin prefixes *deci, centi*, and *milli* being used to indicate the order of decimal divisions of the units, while the Greek prefixes *deka, hecto*, and *kilo* are used to indicate the order of decimal multiplication of the units.

Less than one meter: More than one meter:

Latin Prefixes	*Greek Prefixes*
milli means .001	*deka* means 10
centi " .01	*hecto* means 100
deci " .1	*kilo* " 1000

The table of metric-length measurement then becomes:

1 *milli*meter =	.001 meter
1 *centi*meter =	.01 "
1 *deci*meter =	.1 "
1 meter =	1. "
1 *deka*meter =	10 meters
1 *hecto*meter =	100 "
1 *kilo*meter =	1000 "

In the same way:

1 *milli*liter =   .001 liter, and so on.

1 *milli*gram =   .001 gram, and so on.

The metric system of measurement was adopted in France in 1837 after years of struggle for and against the method. At the present time 82 per cent of the population of the world use the metric system. Only the United States and Great Britain have not adopted this simple decimal method of measurement. However, it has been legal in the United States since 1866 and is used to take and record measurements in medicine, radio, armaments, and several other fields where great accuracy of measurement is necessary.

10 millimeters (mm.) = 1 centimeter (cm.)
10 centimeters   = 1 decimeter (dm.)
10 decimeters   = 1 meter (m.) = 39.37 in.
10 meters   = 1 dekameter (dkm.)
10 dekameters   = 1 hectometer (hm.)
10 hectometers   = 1 kilometer (km.)

VOLUME

10 milliliters (ml.) = 1 centiliter (cl.)
10 centiliters   = 1 deciliter (dl.)
10 deciliters   = 1 liter (l.) = 1.0567 liquid qt.
10 liters   = 1 dekaliter (dkl.)
10 dekaliters   = 1 hectoliter (hl.)
10 hectoliters   = 1 kiloliter (kl.)

WEIGHT

10 milligrams (mg.) = 1 centigram (cg.)
10 centigrams   = 1 decigram (dg.)
10 decigrams   = 1 gram (g.)
10 grams   = 1 dekagram (dkg.)
10 dekagrams   = 1 hectogram (hg.)
10 hectograms   = 1 kilogram (kg.) = 2.2046 lb.

From the tables, you can see that the following rules may be used to change from one metric unit to another:

(1) To change a metric unit to the next larger metric unit, divide by 10.

┌─────────────── EXAMPLES ───────────────┐
│   │
│ Length: 39 millimeters = 3.9 centimeters. │
│ Weight: 39 milligrams = 3.9 centigrams. │
│ Volume: 39 milliliters = 3.9 centiliters. │
└───┘

(2) To change a metric unit to the next smaller metric unit, multiply by 10.

┌─────────────── EXAMPLES ───────────────┐
│   │
│ Length: 39 centimeters = 390 millimeters. │
│ Weight: 39 centigrams = 390 milligrams. │
│ Volume: 39 centiliters = 390 milliliters. │
└───┘

Cut a strip of heavy paper 4 centimeters wide and one meter long. Fold the strip in the center, dividing it into two ½-meter lengths. Mark each ½-meter length into five equal lengths. The *meter* is now divided into 10 equal parts each one *decimeter* long. Now divide a decimeter into 10 equal parts and you will have *centimeters*.

(a) The meter is close to the length of what English measure?

(b) The decimeter is approximately how many inches long?

(c) About how many centimeters equal one inch?

(d) If you divided a centimeter into 10 equal parts, what would each part be called?

EXERCISES

1. Estimate the height in meters of some tall person in your class. Do the same for a short person. Now measure the height of each in meters.

2. Estimate the length of the classroom in meters. Measure it in meters.

3. Estimate the length and width of your textbook in centimeters. Measure it.

4. What part of a meter is a decimeter?

5. What part of a dollar is a cent? What part of a meter is a centimeter?

6. What part of a dollar is a mill? What part of a meter is a millimeter?

7. A meter is how many times as long as (a) a decimeter? (b) a centimeter? (c) a millimeter?

8. How many meters in a (a) dekameter? (b) a hectometer? (c) a kilometer?

9. Change to lower units:

(a) 1 meter = ? decimeters.

(b) 15 meters = ? decimeters.

(c) 1 meter = ? centimeters.

(d) 20 meters = ? centimeters.

(e) 1 centimeter = ? millimeters.

(f) 12 centimeters = ? millimeters.

(g) 1 kilometer = ? hectometers.

(h) 5 kilometers = ? hectometers.

(i) 1 hectometer = ? dekameters.

(j) 6 hectometers = ? dekameters.

10. Change to higher units:

(a) 1 meter = ? dekameter.
(b) 3 meters = ? dekameter.
(c) 1 meter = ? kilometer.
(d) 50 meters = ? kilometer.
(e) 1 centimeter = ? meter.

(f) 1 centiliter = ? liter.
(g) 80 centiliters = ? liter.
(h) 1 liter = ? kiloliter.
(i) 200 liters = ? kiloliter.
(j) 30 centigrams = ? gram.

*11. Express 4 cm. as millimeters. Four millimeters are what part of a centimeter?

*12. Change 467 mm. (a) to centimeters, (b) to decimeters, (c) to fraction of a meter, (d) to fraction of a dekameter, (e) to fraction of a hectometer, (f) to fraction of a kilometer.

*13. Change 9.75 km. (a) to hectometers, (b) to dekameters, (c) to meters, (d) to decimeters, (e) to centimeters, (f) to millimeters.

**14. How many pieces 1 mm. long can be cut from a bar of metal 5 m. long?

**15. A distance of 8.5 m. is how many millimeters? What part of a kilometer?

To change millimeters to inches, multiply the number of millimeters by .03937.

To change meters to inches, multiply by 39.37.

To change meters to feet, multiply by 3.2808.

To change meters to yards, multiply by 1.0936.

```
┌──────────────── EXAMPLE ────────────────┐
│  Change 10 meters to inches:            │
│     1 meter = 39.37 inches              │
│    10 meters = 10 × 39.37 inches = 393.7 inches. │
└─────────────────────────────────────────┘
```

──────────────────────── EXERCISES ────────────────────────

1. A 35-mm. camera film is how many inches wide? (35 mm. = ? in.)

2. A 16-mm. camera film is what part of an inch wide?

3. Change 100 mm. (a) to inches; (b) to part of a foot.

4. Ten meters equal how many (a) inches? (b) feet? (c) yards?

5. A distance of 17.8 meters is (a) how many feet? (b) how many inches?

6. One-half meter is how many inches?

7. One thousand meters are how many (a) feet? (b) yards?

8. 250 millimeters are about how many (a) inches? (b) feet?

9. A 75-millimeter shell is how many inches thick?

10. Radio station wave-lengths are measured in meters. A 400-meter wave-length would be how long expressed in yards?

*11. These International Aeronautical altitude records are expressed in meters. Change the altitudes to feet:

(a) World's air record—made in 1961 by the USSR was 34,714m.

(b) Manned Space Craft — greatest altitude without earth orbit made in 1961 by the United States was 187,500m.

(c) Airplane (Class C — Propeller driven) made in 1938 by Italy was 17,083m.

(d) Gliders (Class D — Single-place) made in 1961 by the United States was 12,894m.

(e) Helicopters — made in 1958 by France was 10,984m.

To change inches to millimeters, multiply by 25.4.

To change feet to meters, multiply by .3048.

To change yards to meters, multiply by .9144.

EXERCISES
---

1. Change 15 in. (a) to millimeters, (b) to centimeters, (c) to a fraction of a meter.

2. The 100-yard dash is how many meters?

3. A building 40 ft. long and 35 ft. wide is how long and wide in meters?

4. One mile is how many meters long?

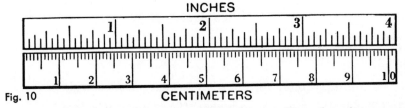

Fig. 10

5. In figure 10, note the length of 1 cm. How does it compare with the thickness of your little finger? Give an example of some article that is approximately 1 cm. in length or width. How does it compare with 1 in.?

6. Locate the 10-cm. mark. What are 10 cm. called? Name some article that is approximately 1 dm. long.

7. About how many centimeters are there in an inch? In 4 in.?

8. What is each of the 10 divisions of the centimeter called? Which of our coins has a thickness of about 1 mm.?

9. Examine a meter stick. (If none is available, draw one on the blackboard.) How many inches longer is the meter stick than the yardstick?

10. Name an object about a meter in length.

11. Change 10 in. to millimeters; 10 ft. to meters; 10 yd. to meters.

12. A 50-foot tree is how many meters high?

13. The height of the Eiffel Tower in Paris is about 300 m. How many feet high is it?

14. The earth is approximately 25,000 miles in circumference. Express this distance in kilometers.

15. If the distance from Denver to New York is 1620 miles, how many kilometers is it?

16. The Washington Monument is approximately 555 feet high. How many meters high is the monument?

17. A French boy is 1.6 m. tall. Express his height in feet.

18. A kilogram is approximately 2.2 lb. How many pounds does a bomb load of 1,250 kg. weigh? A load of 1,750 kg.?

19. The Delta Rocket used to launch the first Telstar Satellite (see page 104) weighed 112,000 pounds, and was 90 feet tall. What is this weight in kilograms? This height in meters?

*20. The diameter of the Telstar Satellite is $34\frac{1}{2}$ inches and it weighs 170 pounds. What is its diameter in centimeters and its weight in kilograms?

*21. From Paris to Calais is a distance of 295 kilometers. Express the distance in miles (1 mile = 1.6094 km.).

*22. The apogee, or greatest distance from the earth, of a Telstar Satellite is 3500 miles, and it travels at a speed of 17,000 miles per hour. What is its apogee in kilometers, and its speed in kilometers per hour?

*23. An aviator flew 160 km. per hour. How many miles is that per hour?

24. At the Olympic games in Rome in 1960, the honors of the pole vault went to the United States at a height of 4.7022 meters. How many feet and inches is this?

25. A gasoline airplane tank holds 145 gallons. This is how many liters?

26. If the fuel capacity of a large passenger liner is 3,200 gallons, what is its fuel capacity in liters?

56. Inexactness of measurement. It is interesting to note that although we can measure to extremely high degrees of precision today, no measurement is ever completely exact. It is only as exact as the units on the measuring instrument being used.

Let us say, for example, that the length of a metal machine part is actually 4.346 inches. If you were to measure this part with a ruler marked off with $\frac{1}{4}''$ markings, you would say it is $4\frac{1}{4}$ inches long, as you can see by this diagram:

If your ruler could measure to the nearest $\frac{1}{8}''$ the part would be said to be $4\frac{3}{8}''$, as you can see by this diagram:

If you had a scale that could measure to the nearest one tenth of an inch, you would say the part is 4.3 inches long.

(a) If your scale could measure to the nearest hundredth of an inch what would you say the measurement of the part is?

(b) A strip of metal is actually $2\frac{41}{64}''$ wide. What would you say its width is if your ruler were marked in $\frac{1}{8}''$ units?

57. Scale drawing. An architect draws his house plan greatly reduced in size from the house itself. He "shrinks" the size of the house to fit the size of the paper. The shrinking process is called *drawing to scale*. The plan is a *scale drawing* of the house. Each line in a scale drawing is some definite fractional part of the length of the line that it represents. Such a picture reproduces the object on a smaller *scale*. Each line in the scale drawing may be one-half of the length of the actual line, one-eighth of it, one-hundredth, one-thousandth, or some other definite ratio. All maps are scale drawings. An architect draws all his house plans to scale. He may let 1 in. represent 8 ft., 10 ft., 12 ft., or some other number of feet suitable to the dimensions which he is to represent. If a garage is to be 12 ft. by 18 ft.,1 in. might represent 12 ft., making the scale drawing 1 in. by $1\frac{1}{2}$ in. Again, $\frac{1}{3}$ in. might represent 1 ft., making the scale drawing 4 in. by 6 in.

On a scale drawing the scale should always be given. Here are some commonly used scales:

Scale	Ratio	Meaning
$6''$ to $1'$ ($6''{:}12''$)	$= \frac{6}{12} = \frac{1}{2}$	Hence, scale size $= \frac{1}{2}$ of actual size
$3''$ to $1'$ ($3''{:}12''$)	$= \frac{3}{12} = \frac{1}{4}$	Hence, scale size $= \frac{1}{4}$ of actual size
$1''$ to $1'$ ($1''{:}12''$)	$= \frac{1}{12}$	Hence, scale size $= \frac{1}{12}$ of actual size
$1\frac{1}{2}''$ to $1'$ ($1\frac{1}{2}''{:}12''$)	$= \frac{3}{24} = \frac{1}{8}$	Hence, scale size $= \frac{1}{8}$ of actual size
$\frac{3}{4}''$ to $1'$ ($\frac{3}{4}''{:}12''$)	$= \frac{3}{48} = \frac{1}{16}$	Hence, scale size $= \frac{1}{16}$ of actual size

---

EXAMPLE A

If the scale on a drawing is $1''$ to $1'$, how long would 96 in. on the object be on the scale drawing?

A scale of $1''$ to $1'$ ($1''{:}12''$) = ratio $\frac{1}{12}$.

Then $\frac{1}{12}$ of actual size $= \frac{1}{12}$ of $96'' = 8''$.

Hence, $96''$ on the object is $8''$ long on the drawing.

EXAMPLE B

If the scale of a drawing is $\frac{1}{2}$ in. to 1 ft., what is the actual size if the scale length is 3 in.?

A scale of $\frac{1}{2}$ in. to 1 ft. ($1''$ to 2 ft.) = ratio $\frac{1}{24}$.

Then scale size is $\frac{1}{24}$ of actual size and actual size is 24 times scale size.

$$24 \times \text{scale size} = 24 \times 3'' = 72''$$

Hence, a $3''$ line on a drawing is $72''$ long on the object.

A. Oral

1. Using the scale $1''$ to $1'$, find the scale lengths of the following actual lengths: $3'$, $8'$, $12'$, $9'$, $6\frac{1}{2}'$, $5\frac{3}{4}'$. (Ratio $= \frac{1}{12}$.)

2. Let $\frac{1}{4}''$ represent $1'$. Find the scale lengths when actual lengths are: $12'$, $24'$, $18'$, $30'$, $8'$, $32'$, $16'$, $10'$.

3. Let $\frac{1}{2}$ in. represent 1 ft. Find the lengths on the drawing if the measurements on the object are: 24 in., 48 in., 36 in., 5 ft., 18 ft., 15 ft.

4. If the scale on a set of drawings is 6 in. to 1 ft., what are the actual lengths when the scale lengths are 4 in., 9 in., 3 in., $2\frac{1}{2}$ in., 8 in., 10 in., $3\frac{1}{2}$ in.?

5. If a scale is $\frac{1}{2}''$ to $1'$ and a scale drawing is $4''$ long, what is the actual length of the drawing?

6. Using the scale $3''$ to $1'$, find the actual lengths of the following scale lengths: $8''$, $12''$, $15''$, $6''$, $14''$, $10''$, $9''$, $7''$.

B. Written

7. When the scale $4''$ to $1'$ is used, how long are the scale drawings for the following actual lengths: 12 in., 9 in., 15 in., 21 in., $7\frac{1}{2}$ in., $4\frac{1}{2}$ in.?

8. When the scale $2''$ to $1'$ is used, find the scale lengths when the actual lengths are: $18''$, $12''$, $24''$, $21''$, $15''$, 3 ft., $1\frac{1}{2}$ ft., $\frac{3}{4}$ ft.

9. Using the scale $\frac{1}{8}''$ to $1'$, find the scale dimensions for a house $24'$ by $32'$.

10. If $\frac{1}{16}''$ represents $1'$, what are the scale dimensions of a building $30'$ by $42'$?

11. Using the scale $\frac{1}{2}''$ to $1'$, find the actual lengths represented by these scale lengths: $2''$, $3''$, $2\frac{1}{2}''$, $3\frac{1}{4}''$, $1\frac{1}{8}''$, $2\frac{3}{4}''$, $2\frac{3}{8}''$, $1\frac{3}{4}''$.

12. Using the scale $\frac{1}{8}''$ to $1'$, find the actual lengths of the following scale lengths: $1''$, $\frac{1}{2}''$, $\frac{1}{4}''$, $2''$, $2\frac{1}{2}''$.

13. What is the actual size of a room drawn on a scale $\frac{1}{12}''$ to $1'$ if the scale size is $2''$ by $2\frac{1}{2}''$?

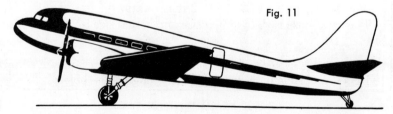

Fig. 11

14. If the airplane in figure 11 is 24' from nose to tip of tail, what is the scale of this drawing?

Using this scale find: (a) the diameter of the front wheel; (b) the diameter of the rear wheel; (c) the height of the plane from the front wheel up.

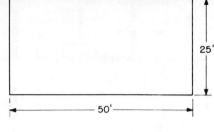

25'

50'

Fig. 12

15. Figure 12 is drawn to what scale?

16. A lot is 40 ft. by 120 ft. Draw a plan of the lot, letting 1 in. represent 20 ft.

17. Measure the length and width of your classroom to the nearest foot. Draw the floor plan to scale. You select a convenient scale to use.

18. Measure your school's swimming pool. Choose a convenient scale and draw a plan of the pool.

19. Using the measurements of your school grounds, found earlier in this chapter, draw a plan of the grounds to a convenient scale.

***20.** The first-floor plan of a Y. M. C. A. building is shown in figure 13. One inch in the scale drawing represents 20' in the building. What are the approximate dimensions of the committee room, reception hall, council room, and secretary's room? Determine by measurement.

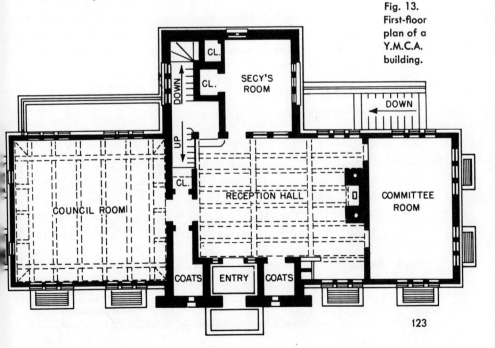

Fig. 13.
First-floor
plan of a
Y.M.C.A.
building.

123

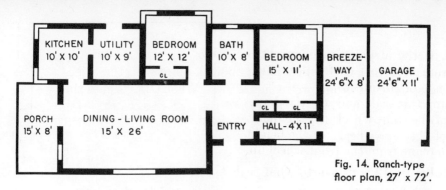

Fig. 14. Ranch-type
floor plan, 27' x 72'.

*21. Using the scale $\frac{1}{10}''$ to 1', make a drawing of a house with the following dimensions:

Width across front and back, 40'; depth front to back, 28'.
Living room (S.E. corner), 16'S. by 18'E.
Library (N.E. corner), 16'N. by 10'E.
Hall (front to back), 8' wide.
Dining room (S.W. corner), 16'S. by 16'W.
Kitchen (N.W. corner), 16'N. by 12'W.
Leave an opening for an outside door 4' wide in the front hall.
Leave openings for doors 3' wide at convenient places in the plan.

**22. Reproduce figure 14. Use the scale 1'' represents 8'.

**23. (optional) Draw to scale the floor plan of a model kitchen, including the cupboard, stove, table, and refrigerator. State the scale used and the actual length and width of the kitchen and each piece of furniture.

**24. On a picture of a Delta Rocket on its launching pad, the rocket measures 6''. The wheel of the bicycle standing nearby measures .144''. If this is a 26'' wheel, what is the height of the rocket in feet? (See picture on page 104.)

———— DIRECT MEASUREMENT OF ANGLES ————

VOCABULARY

1. angle	4. acute angle	7. protractor
2. vertex	5. obtuse angle	8. vertical angles
3. right angle	6. reflex angle	9. degree
10. ∠ symbol for "angle"		11. ⩶ symbol for "angles"

58. Angles. An angle is the opening between two lines that meet. The opening between the blades of a pair of scissors illustrates an *angle*. The wider the scissors are opened, the larger the angle becomes. Another illustration of an angle is as follows: Rotate a straight line OW in a plane about a point O in the direction indicated by the arrows in figure 15. When OW reaches the position indicated by OY, it has turned through the angle WOY.

The fixed point O is called the *vertex* of the angle; the lines OW and OY form the *sides* of the angle.

59. Lettering and reading angles. Angles are usually lettered in one of two ways. One method is to place a capital letter at the vertex and at the end of each side of the angle, as in figure 15. The point at the vertex is often labeled O and is read between the other two letters. In figure 15, the angle is read $\angle O$

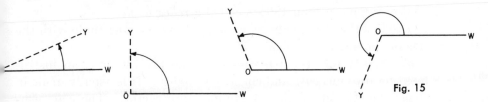

Fig. 15

(angle O), $\angle YOW$, or $\angle WOY$. The other method of lettering an angle is to place a small letter in the angle near the vertex, as in figure 18. Such angles are read $\angle a$, $\angle b$, and so forth.

60. Unit of measurement of angles. Divide the space around the center of a circle into 360 equal parts. Each of those small divisions is one *degree*. Every degree may be divided into 60 equal parts, called *minutes*. Every minute may be divided into 60 equal parts, called *seconds*. Degrees, minutes, and seconds are the units commonly used to measure angles.

$$60 \text{ seconds } ('') = 1 \text{ minute } (')$$
$$60 \text{ minutes} = 1 \text{ degree } (°)$$
$$360 \text{ degrees} = 1 \text{ circle}$$

61. Kinds of angles. The most common angle is the *right angle*. Since four right angles can be grouped around the center of a circle, each right angle contains 90°. The right angle is found in the square corners of pictures, sheets of paper, window panes, rugs, packing cases, and so forth.

An angle that is formed by one-half of a complete circle is called a *straight angle* because its sides form a straight line. It contains 180°.

Any angle that contains less than 90° is an *acute angle;* for example, an angle of 89°, 75°, 4°, 6°.

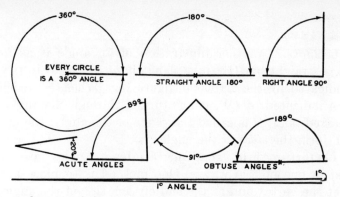

EVERY CIRCLE IS A 360° ANGLE

STRAIGHT ANGLE 180°

RIGHT ANGLE 90°

ACUTE ANGLES

OBTUSE ANGLES

1° ANGLE

Any angle containing more than 90° but less than 180° is an *obtuse angle;* for example, an angle of 91°, 100°, 165°, 179°.

An angle containing 180° is called a *straight angle.* Any angle containing more than 180° is called a *reflex angle.*

The lengths of the sides of an angle have nothing to do with the size of the angle.

62. Studying the protractor. The protractor is an instrument used to measure and construct angles. It is usually made in the shape of a semicircle. Examine a protractor. There are usually two rows of numbers on the semicircular scale, one row numbering 180° from left to right, and one row numbering 180° from right to left. This arrangement makes it easy to measure or draw angles pointed in any direction. At what number of degrees on the scale are the degrees the same? Why at this point? Find 60°, 170°, and 40°. How do you locate 65°? 45°? 42°? 38°? 134°?

Notice the triangle in the straight edge. The vertex of this triangle is on the straight line connecting the 0° and the 180° marks. It is very important in measuring or drawing angles to see that the vertex of this triangle is directly on the vertex of the angle and that the line connecting the vertex with 0° coincides with one side of the angle.

63. How to measure an angle with a protractor. To measure ∠ *ROS* in figure 16, place the protractor so that the vertex of the triangle on the protractor rests upon the vertex *O* of the angle.

Make the straight edge of the protractor coincide with the side *OR* of the angle, so that *OR* passes through the zero degrees on the protractor scale. Observe where the side *OS* of the angle intersects the curved portion of the protractor. Read the degrees. In measuring an angle, extend the sides of the angle if they are too short to be crossed by the curved edge of the protractor.

Fig. 16

126

1. Measure ∡ *AOB, MON,* and *XOY* in figure 17. How do these angles compare in size? Upon what does their size depend? Upon what does it *not* depend?

2. Measure the angles in figure 18. *Note:* You may extend the sides of the angles to reach the scale of degrees on the pro-tractor by placing a straight edge of paper along the side of the angle. Read the degrees where the straight edge of the paper crosses the scale of degrees.

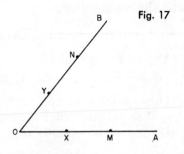

Fig. 17

3. In figure 19 measure angles *r, s, t, u,* and *v.* What is the sum of these angles?

4. In figure 20 measure angles *a, b, c,* and *d.* What do you find true about ∠ *a* and ∠ *b*? about ∠ *c* and ∠ *d*? Angles *a* and *b* are called *vertical angles* because they are on the opposite sides of two lines that cross. Angles *c* and *d* are also vertical angles. Why are none of the angles in figure 19 vertical angles?

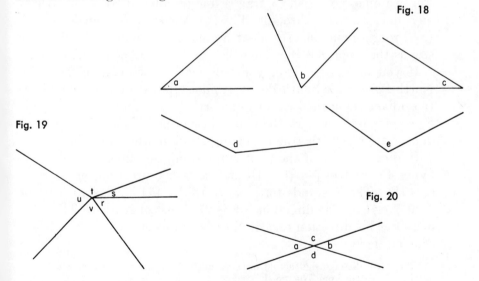

Fig. 18

Fig. 19

Fig. 20

5. Draw 10 different angles and measure each.

6. Draw 3 acute angles. Measure each angle.

7. Draw 3 obtuse angles. Measure the angles.

8. Draw 3 reflex angles. Measure the angles.

64. How to draw an angle with a protractor. To draw an angle of any size, say 40°, first draw a straight line OY to represent one side of the angle. Place the protractor so that the vertex of the triangle on the straight edge of the protractor falls upon O, the vertex of the angle, and the side OY passes through the 0° on the scale. Then find the 40° mark on the protractor scale. Now draw from this point to the vertex of the angle the line OX. $\angle XOY$ will be the required angle.

——————————————— *EXERCISES* ———————————————

1. Draw an angle of 60°; 30°; 80°; 100°; 120°; 150°.

2. Draw an angle of 45°; 125°; 65°; 75°; 38°; 187°.

3. Draw angles in this order: three acute angles, two right angles, three obtuse angles, two straight angles, and three reflex angles. Label the number of degrees in each.

65. Some uses of angles. The study of angles is important because of the use of angles in surveying, navigation, airplane piloting, gunnery, toolmaking, carpentry, metalworking, and engineering of all kinds.

Suppose that you wish to draw a line parallel to a given line. For example, you wish to draw a line parallel to VW. (a) Draw any line, as AB, through W. (b) Measure the angle AWV. (c) From a point on AB, as at X, make an angle AXY the same size as the angle AWV. Then WV and XY will be parallel, (A-1).

If you look at a map, you will see lines extending from the North Pole to the South Pole. A pilot following one of these lines (meridians) is headed either due north or due south. The needle on a compass will show the pilot whether he is flying due north or due south, or whether he is angling off in another direction.

In diagram A-2, if the pilot is following the direction OA, he is flying 45° east of North. He indicates his direction, or bearing, as 45T. The T stands for *True North.** 45T means 45° east of True North. The direction OW is 270° east of North. The pilot measures his direction east of North even when west of North is a smaller angle.

————
* The "T" distinguishes actual or True north from *magnetic north*, which is a number of degrees from True north.

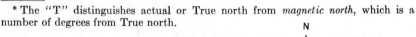

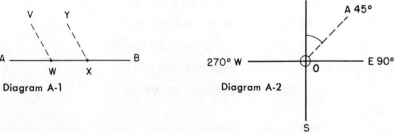

Diagram A-1   Diagram A-2

1. In diagram B, the pilot is following the direction *OR*. He is flying east of North. He indicates his direction, or bearing, as ?° east of North or ?T.

The direction *OS* is ?° east of North or ?T.

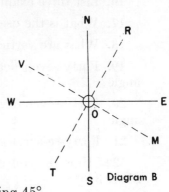

Diagram B

2. What is the bearing of a pilot who is flying in the direction: (a) Of *OE*? (b) *OM*? (c) *OS*? (d) *OT*? (e) *OW*? (f) *OV*?

3. Sketch a pup tent with its sides slanting 45°.

4. Draw a line *MN*. Draw a line parallel to *MN*.

5. Sketch N-S and E-W lines as on a compass. Draw the following bearings: 20T, 75T, 120T, 182T, 204T, and 315T.

REVIEW OF CHAPTER VI

1. Why are more accurate measurements needed at the present time than were needed by early civilization?

2. List the measuring instruments of length that you know about.

3. Give an example of where a "rough estimate" is sufficient in measurement.

4. Give an example of where a measurement must be accurate to at least one-thousandth of an inch.

5. What are the usual subdivisions on a ruler?

6. Draw by estimation a square one inch on a side.

7. Select something in the room that looks to be (a) 1 ft. long; (b) 1 yd. long.

8. What distance in the room is approximately 1 rd. long?

9. What is meant by a 75-mm. bullet?

10. Jack's father is 6 feet tall. Is he more or less than 2 meters tall?

11. Add: 39° 58′ 38″ and 46° 36′ 19″. Change to a higher denomination when possible.

12. Subtract 149° 53′ 49″ from 180° 32″.

13. Multiply 48° 37′ 41″ by 3.

14. Divide 53° 5′ 52″ by 2.

15. What is the use of a scale drawing?

16. List three examples of scale drawings that you have seen.

17. What is the use of a protractor?

18. What are vertical angles? What is true of them?

19. Forty-seven degrees plus how many degrees make a right angle?

20. Forty-seven degrees plus how many degrees make a straight angle?

21. Forty-seven degrees plus how many degrees make a circle?

*22. How do you draw, with a protractor, an angle of 189°? 240°? 325°?

**23. A railroad station has two tracks. The distance from the center of one track to the center of the other is 15 feet. The front of the station building is 33 feet north of the center of the first track, and a waiting shed across the tracks from the station is 16 feet south of the center of the second track. How far is the waiting shed from the front of the station building? Make a sketch to show how the station and the two tracks and the waiting shed are located.

─────── *PLAYOFF FOR CHAPTER VI* ───────

1. A floor plan of a house worked out on a bulletin board by using string, or paper ribbon, for the walls makes an attractive exhibit or showpiece for Visitors Day. It is an interesting problem for two pupils to work on. Two other pupils could plan location of furniture and put paper cutouts in place. See figure 21.

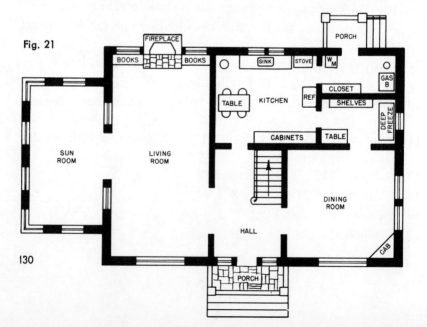

Fig. 21

2. Begin a History of Mathematics scrapbook, using such articles as:

The Story of Weights and Measures.
The Story of Time.
The Story of the Metric System.

3. By comparing actual measurements with those of a picture or scale drawing of your school, calculate the scale of the drawing.

4. Throw Contest. Contestants throw drinking straws as far as they can. Each estimates his distance, then measures it. Declare winners for closest estimate and for farthest throw.

— CHECK-UP ON THE FUNDAMENTALS OF ARITHMETIC —

Addition

1. 456
124
323
145

2. $2.16 + .234 + 1.7$

3. $\frac{1}{3} + \frac{1}{4} + \frac{5}{6}$

4. $36\frac{7}{8} + 52\frac{1}{4}$

5. 2 yd. 1 ft. 9 in.
3 yd. 2 ft. 8 in.

Subtraction

6. 5006
678

8. $\frac{4}{5}$
$\frac{3}{10}$

9. $44\frac{1}{3}$
$28\frac{1}{2}$

10. 3 gal. 2 qt. 1 pt.
1 gal. 3 qt.

7. $\$8.24 - \$.75$

Multiplication

11. 304
208

12. 14.7
.02

13. $\frac{1}{4} \times \frac{1}{4} =$

14. $2\frac{1}{2} \times 60 =$

15. 2 hr. 20 min. 30 sec.
3

Division

16. $7\overline{)175}$

17. $2.3\overline{)83.72}$

18. $\frac{4}{5} \div \frac{2}{3}$

19. $22.1 \div 10$

20. $\frac{1}{2}$ of 5 qt. 1 pt.

Per Cent

21. $37\frac{1}{2}\% =$

22. $3\frac{1}{2}\% =$

23. $\frac{4}{9} = ?\%$

24. 70% of $30 =$

25. $?\%$ of $40 = 36$

CHAPTER VII

GRAPHS

VOCABULARY

1. pictograph   2. bar graph   3. line graph   4. circle graph

66. Graphs. A *graph* is a picture of a happening. It might picture weekly grades for a period of several weeks; a graph might picture the amount of sales for each month over a period of time; it might picture the profits or losses of a business. Such pictures can be of use in planning future action.

Graph 1 pictures the standing of each team on one day in the American League while Table 1 lists them. For a record the table is more satisfactory, as it gives the standing of each team accurate to thousandths. For publicity or for casual comparison the graph shows a picture that has greater eye-appeal. The graph can be relied upon to tenths only. (Each baseball represents 10%.) The fractional part of each baseball can be estimated but cannot be

AMERICAN LEAGUE
Final Standing of Clubs

New York
Los Angeles
Minnesota
Chicago
Detroit
Baltimore
Cleveland
Boston
Kansas City
Washington

10% 20% 30% 40% 50% 60% 70%   **Graph 1.**

TABLE 1

**AMERICAN LEAGUE
AUGUST STANDING
OF CLUBS**

	Pct.
New York	.610
Los Angeles	.562
Minnesota	.554
Chicago	.516
Detroit	.496
Baltimore	.483
Cleveland	.479
Boston	.471
Kansas City	.455
Washington	.375

depended upon to be absolutely correct. However, the graph is quickly comprehended and the facts are presented in a pleasing manner, making the graph satisfactory for many purposes.

According to the table, which was the winning team? What was the standing of this team in thousandths? In per cent? How does the per cent expressed in the graph for New York compare with 60%? As each baseball represents 10%, the 6 whole baseballs represent 60%. The fraction of the baseball appears to be approximately $\frac{1}{8}$ of a baseball, or $\frac{1}{8}$ of 10%, which is 1.25%. Thus, the standing of the New York team is approximately 61.25%, (60% + 1.25%) or .6125. This is very close to the actual per cent, 61%, which is written .610.

(a) How does the graph show the standing of the Los Angeles Club to be slightly less than that of the New York Club?

(b) What per cent do you calculate for the Detroit Club, from the graph?

(c) How does the per cent compare with that of the table?

(d) How does the graph show that Chicago's standing was very close to .500?

(e) How is the standing of Baltimore's team shown to be slightly less than 50%?

(f) Boston's standing is what per cent more than Washington's standing? This made how many more whole baseballs in the graph for Boston?

(g) Why are the fractions of the baseballs of the Boston team and the Washington team so nearly the same size?

TABLE 2

NOTABLE BUILDINGS
OF
NEW YORK CITY

Empire State...... 1250 ft.
RCA............. 850 ft.
RKO............. 409 ft.

Table 2 gives the correct heights of three well-known buildings of New York City. Graph 2, by means of pictures, shows at a glance the approximate heights of the buildings and the relationship of their heights to each other.

(a) What is the approximate height shown in the table for the Empire State Building?

(b) Is the height as represented on the graph apparently the same?

(c) Do the heights of the RCA and RKO buildings as pictured on the graph appear to agree with the heights recorded in the table?

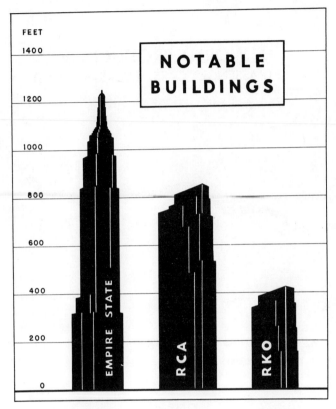

FEET

NOTABLE BUILDINGS

EMPIRE STATE

RCA

RKO

Graph 2. A Bar Graph.

Study the graph before answering the following questions. Check your answers by using the heights given in the table.

(d) How does the height of the RKO Building compare, approximately, with the height of the Empire State Building?

(e) Which building is about 100 per cent higher than the RKO Building?

(f) The Empire State Building is about one and one-half times as high as which building?

(g) Which building appears to be about twice as high as one of the other buildings?

Table 3 is a record of the world production of motor vehicles. Graph 3 gives the same record in picture form. The number of cars produced each year is rounded off to the nearest million.

Graph 3

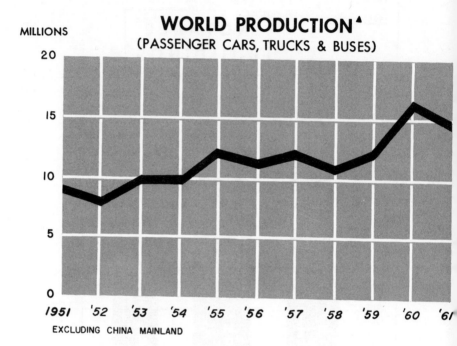

MILLIONS

WORLD PRODUCTION ▲
(PASSENGER CARS, TRUCKS & BUSES)

EXCLUDING CHINA MAINLAND

TABLE 3

Year	Million	Year	Million	Year	Million
1951	9.0	1955	12.6	1959	12.6
1952	8.0	1956	11.5	1960	16.2
1953	10.0	1957	12.5	1961	14.5
1954	10.0	1958	11.0		

1. During which year were the greatest number of cars produced? The least number?

2. What is the general trend of production for the eleven years?

3. Using the graph, estimate the number of millions of cars produced for each of the eleven years. Were your answers close to the figures shown in Table 3?

4. Total your eleven estimates.

5. Assume that the United States produced 40% of the total, how many millions of cars did the United States produce?

6. How many more cars were produced in 1955 than in 1952?

7. Which year was the production practically twice that of 1952?

Table 4 gives the reactions of the pupils of a certain school toward the sports offered. Graph 4 pictures their rating of these sports.

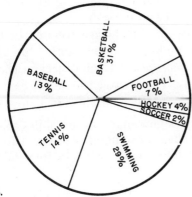

Graph 4.

TABLE 4

FAVORITE SPORTS
OF A
LARGE HIGH SCHOOL

Basketball...........	31%
Swimming...........	29%
Tennis..............	14%
Baseball............	13%
Football.............	7%
Hockey.............	4%
Soccer..............	2%

The whole circle (100 per cent) represents the whole student body. Thirty-one per cent of the students voted basketball as their favorite sport, while only 2 per cent favored soccer. At a glance the athletic director of the school can see that basketball and swimming are by far the favorite sports and that soccer and hockey are the least popular of the sports. By division he can discover that twice as many prefer tennis as football and that swimming is about four times as popular as football.

In the same way, the other sports can be compared with each other or with the total sports program.

(a) How does soccer compare with tennis as a popular sport?

(b) Football with baseball?

(c) Baseball with basketball?

(d) How do basketball and swimming together compare with the whole program of sports?

(e) If the school can have only four sports, which ones should be chosen, according to pupil preferences?

67. The use of graphs in business. Magazines, newspapers, and other printed material contain many graphs which at a glance show the trend of business in a most vivid way. The executive studies graphs representing expenditures, sales, and growth of his business. He may use the graphs to make a comparison of facts that may be presented to the public in the quickest and most appealing way. The businessman can make a fair prediction of the extent of his future business, if nothing unusual happens to upset the general trend of the past few years.

The four most commonly used graphs are *pictographs*, *bar graphs*, *line graphs*, and *circle graphs*. Each kind of graph is adaptable to a particular type of comparison.

68. Pictographs. Pictures of objects are frequently used in representing growth and in making comparisons. Such representations are often called *pictographs*. Each object in the graph represents a definite quantity. The greater the number of objects pictured, the greater the quantity represented. In figure 1,

(a) One automobile represents how many automobiles sold?
(b) In which year was passenger automobile sales greatest?
(c) In 1959 approximately how many fewer factory sales were there than in 1960?

Fig. 1. A Pictograph.

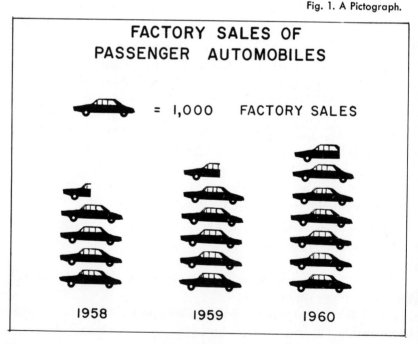

GRAPHS

(d) Approximately how many passenger cars were factory sold each year pictured?

(e) How does the graph show that in the year 1958 slightly more than 4,000 passenger cars were factory sold?

(f) Judging by the general trend of the graph, what prediction could be made for the future factory sales of passenger automobiles?

Aids in making a pictograph.

1. *Determine how large a quantity each object is to represent.* Take the largest quantity to be represented and divide it by the number of objects that will fill the longest row that you wish on your graph. If the numbers are quite large, it is usually better to round them off to a more convenient size.

In figure 1, the largest quantity to be graphed is 6,675 cars for 1960. This number can be rounded off to 7,000 cars. Using not more than 7 cars for the longest row, each car will represent 1,000 cars factory sold (7,000 ÷ 7).

2. *Determine how many objects are needed for each row*—by dividing the quantity to be represented by the quantity that each object represents.

In figure 1, the 6,675 ÷ 1,000 = 6.7 (to nearest tenth). Hence, 6.7 is the number of automobiles used for the 1960 column.

3. *Decide on the order of the rows.* The arrangement may be by consecutive periods of time, as in figure 1; by the order of size, as from the shortest to the longest row; or by some other order that will best tell the facts represented.

4. *Note how the objects should be placed.* The objects should be a uniform distance apart from each other in the rows. The space between the rows usually should be the same width as the rows.

5. *Label each graph with a self-explanatory title.*

6. *Take the utmost care to make the graph accurate and neat*—so that it will serve the purpose for which it was intended.

─────────────────── *EXERCISES* ───────────────────

1. Suggest how a pictograph might represent increased sales of airplanes if the sales doubled each year for three consecutive years.

2. Suggest how the production of wheat in the United States and the rest of the world may be pictured if for every 9 bushels produced in the United States, 6 bushels are produced in the rest of the world.

3. Suggest two pictographs to represent the number of people in the United States, compared with the number in the rest of the world, if the rest of the world has 16 times as many persons as the United States.

4. A poll of young people showed that approximately 48% of the boys and 39% of the girls in high school seldom date. Represent these figures by a pictograph.

5. Show by means of a pictograph that the United States produces approximately 5 barrels of oil to every 1 barrel produced in Europe.

6. Use sketches or pictures of ships to make a vertical bar graph of the depth of famous ship canals. Let one ship represent a ten foot depth. The depths are : Panama, 41′; Welland, 25′; St. Lawrence Seaway, 27′; Albert (Belgium), 16.5′.

7. Merchant X, believing that salespeople should be paid on the basis of what they sell, rather than for hours worked, made a pictograph of the sales made by clerks A, B, C, D, and E. Make such a picture if in a given time clerk A sold $200 worth of merchandise; clerk B, $150 worth; clerk C, $250; clerk D, $275; and clerk E, $325.

*8. By means of a pictograph represent the approximate heights of: Mt. Whitney, 14,898 (15,000) feet; Mt. McKinley, 20,464 (20,500) feet; and Pike's Peak, 14,108 (14,000) feet.

*9. Make a pictograph showing the production of television sets for the following years (Round off sets to nearest million.):

1958.	4,920,000
1959.	6,349,000
1960.	5,708,000

**10. Make a pictograph showing interesting facts from your civics or science studies, or from some magazine or newspaper.

69. Bar graphs. The bar graph is used in business to compare various quantities, such as we compared in the pictographs. A bar graph might show, for instance, the different amounts of corn produced in different states, or the amounts of business done in dollars by various concerns, or the cost of various items at a given time.

The bars may be placed in either a vertical or a horizontal position. Figure 2 is a vertical bar graph that depicts the comparative costs for an average family for gas, soft coal, oil, and hard coal in a certain locality.

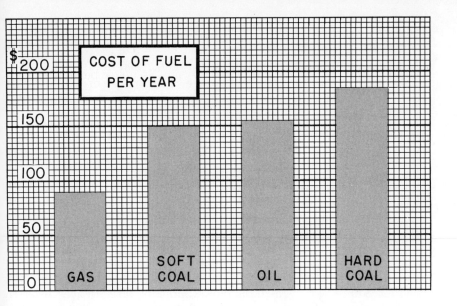

Fig. 2. A vertical bar graph.

(a) Which fuel does the graph show to be the cheapest?

(b) Which fuel is the most costly?

(c) Each large space represents how many dollars spent?

(d) Each small space represents how many dollars spent?

(e) How much is the approximate cost per year for the use of each of the different fuels?

(f) Heating by hard coal costs how much more than heating by gas? How many times as much?

(g) Compare the cost of gas and soft coal and of gas and oil in the same way.

Aids in making bar graphs:

1. *Use graph paper or draw horizontal (or vertical) lines* conveniently spaced. For the most accurate readings, divide the space between your lines into 5 or 10 equal parts by drawing *light* lines between the *heavy* ones.

2. *Arrange the numbers* to be graphed in a row or table in the order in which they are to appear on the graph.

3. Usually the *bottom line* or the *line at the left side* of the paper is used for the guide line.

4. *Choose and mark off a workable scale* on the guide line, remembering that the scale must be both small enough to represent on the paper the largest quantity in the table, and large enough for the

smallest quantity to be visible. If at any time the numbers to be represented contain a fraction whose exact length is too difficult to graph, approximate lengths should be marked off.

In figure 2 the graph paper is five large spaces deep. We must determine what amount will be represented by each large space. The tallest bar represents $185 spent for hard coal. The bar cannot be more than four large spaces high, because the top space is used for the title of the graph. Now, $185 ÷ 4 = $46¼, called the *scale*, which is the *least* number of dollars that can be allowed for each large space. It is better to use an easier number to work with than the $46¼. The number used must be *larger*—not *smaller*—and should be *close* in value to $46¼. The scale used is $50. Then $185 ÷ $50 = $3\frac{7}{10}$, which is the number of large spaces used to represent the $185.

The shortest bar represents $95, which is for the cost of gas. $95 ÷ $50 = $1\frac{9}{10}$, which is the number of large spaces used to represent the $95.

As both the longest and shortest bars can be represented on the paper, the scale 1 large space = $50 is satisfactory for all bars.

5. *To make the bars* of the graph, determine the required length of the bars and draw shaded bars of uniform width, usually leaving the space between the bars the same width as the bars.

6. *Give a title to every graph.*

--- **EXERCISES** ---

In each of the exercises 1–8, assume that you are using graph paper similar to that used in figure 2, and that you are allowing one large space for the title in each graph.

(a) Solve for the scale.

(b) If this scale is not an easy number to use, select a larger number that is close to the number found.

(c) Determine the length of the bar.

	Number of spaces	Size to be represented	Scale found	Scale to use	Length of bar
(1)	7	$50	$8⅓	$10	5 spaces
(2)	9	80 ft.	10 ft.	10 ft.	? spaces
(3)	6	24 bu.	4⅘ bu.	? bu.	? spaces
(4)	10	90 in.	? in.	? in.	? spaces
(5)	9	$49	$?	$7	7 spaces
*(6)	9	140 boys	? boys	? boys	? spaces
*(7)	8	60 girls	? girls	? girls	? spaces
*(8)	10	$1200	$?	$?	? spaces

*9. Show by a vertical bar graph that the average 14-year-old boy has gained in height over the years. Express heights in inches.

Year	Height
1877	4 ft. 9½ in.
1924	5 ft. 1 in.
1962	5 ft. 3 in.

How many inches have been gained in the 85 years?

*10. Show by a horizontal bar graph that the 14-year-old boys have gained much in weight, too. How many pounds were gained in the 85 years?

Year	Weight
1877	87 lb.
1939	107 lb.
1962	108 lb.

*11. Figure 3 is a horizontal bar graph that indicates the average number of persons included in the registration of passenger cars in various countries.

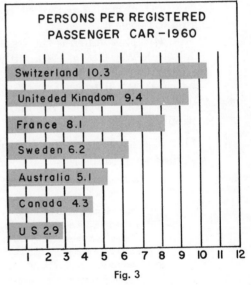

Fig. 3

(a) Which country has the smallest number of persons using the passenger car? the largest?

(b) Which country has about one-half as many as Switzerland?

(c) Which has about 50% as many as Canada and Sweden together?

(d) Which has as many as the United States and Australia together?

(e) Which two countries combined equals the United Kingdom in the use of the car?

(f) Which country has close to 100% more than Australia?

*12. It is said that by using ready-to-serve foods, the housewife of today can prepare food for one day's use for a family of four in much less time than a housewife could have prepared the food 30 years ago. Graph these facts:

Time	Hours
30 yr. ago	5½
Today	1½

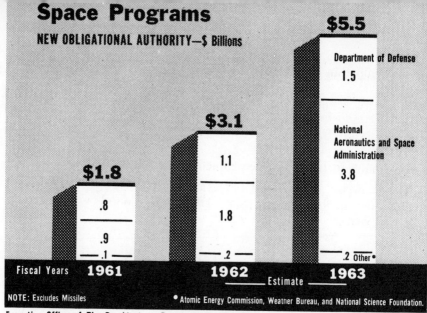

Executive Office of The President · Bureau of The Budget

Fig. 4. United States Space Programs, 1961–1963.

*13. (a) Which department of the Federal Government is estimated to be the most costly?

(b) How much is the total cost for all departments in 1961?

(c) What total estimate was made for all departments for the year 1962? For 1963?

(d) What is the trend in cost for the Department of Federal Defense? In cost for National Aeronautics and Space Administration?

*14. Make a bar graph of the following data selected from certain manufacturing industries in an "Occupational Study":

Abilities To Be Developed in School	Number of Times Named
Following directions	317
Arithmetic fundamentals	254
Mental alertness	251
Logical thinking	244
Memory	122
Physical alertness	120
Pleasant speech	78

*15. Make a bar graph showing the approximate per cent of voters who cast votes during these presidential elections:

1944	54%
1948	53%
1952	62.7%
1956	62.1%
1960	64.3%

144   GRAPHS

16. (optional) In a paragraph summarize the facts represented in a bar graph cut from a paper or magazine.

70. Line graphs. The line graph is most commonly used to picture related facts.

In figure 5 the distance traveled in a given number of hours depends upon the rate traveled per hour. The rate per hour remains constant; thus, the distance traveled will remain the same per hour. This makes a straight-line graph.

(A) The straight-line graph represents regular changes taking place over a given period of time.

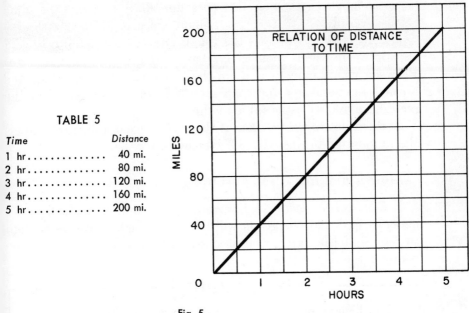

TABLE 5

Time	Distance
1 hr...............	40 mi.
2 hr...............	80 mi.
3 hr...............	120 mi.
4 hr...............	160 mi.
5 hr...............	200 mi.

Fig. 5

1. What is the scale used for one hour?
2. For the distance?
3. What number marks the starting point?
4. Reading from the graph, what is the distance traveled in two hours?
5. How do you locate this distance?
6. What is the distance traveled by the 5th hour?
7. How do you locate the distance?

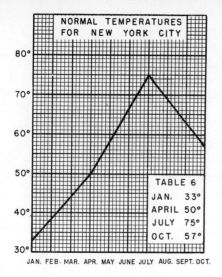

Fig. 6

NORMAL TEMPERATURES FOR NEW YORK CITY

TABLE 6

JAN.	33°
APRIL	50°
JULY	75°
OCT.	57°

(B) A broken-line graph represents changes of an irregular nature, such as variations in price of commodities in different years; profits made in a firm year by year; or variations in daily sales.

Table 6 shows the normal temperatures of New York City for every third month of the year. Figure 6 pictures these temperatures in a broken-line graph. The line is broken because the temperatures do not change the same amount for each third month.

(a) At what points does the graph line make a definite break? (b) Between which months is there the greatest change? (c) Between which months is there the least change? (d) Read the normal temperatures for each month from the graph. Do the readings agree with the table readings?

In order not to waste space at the lower edge of the graph paper, the numbering begins with 30° instead of 0°.

Aids in making a line graph:

1. *Choose two scales*—a horizontal scale and a vertical scale, being careful that the graph will be long enough and wide enough to represent the data to be used and still not be too long or too wide for the paper.

EXAMPLE

The highest point to be represented is 75°. In this exercise, numbering of degrees begins with 30° instead of 0°. This leaves only 45 of the 75 degrees to be represented on the graph. The lowest point to be represented is 33°, leaving only 3° (33° − 30°) to be represented. The vertical scale must be small enough to accommodate 75° and large enough to show the 3°. In figure 6 one small square represents how many degrees? One large square represents how many degrees? The number of degrees to the square establishes the vertical scale. The months are evenly spaced along the bottom line of the graph. This bottom line is the horizontal guide line. The horizontal scale is the number of squares apart that the months are spaced.

2. *Label the guide lines.*

3. *Make a table of data arranged by pairs.* One number of each pair is for the horizontal scale; the other number is for the vertical scale. Those numbers are used to locate points on the graph.

4. *Connect the points by a straight line.*

─────────── EXAMPLE ───────────

Where the 33° line meets the January line is the first point on the graph line to be drawn. Where the 50° line meets the April line is the second point on the graph line. Continue in this manner to locate the other two points. (Make small points at the exact point of contact.)

─────────── EXERCISES ───────────

1. The number of passenger cars in use has increased rapidly since 1910. In 1910 there was only one car for every 200 people, and by 1960 there was one car for every 2.9 people.

Figure 7 pictures this fact in an interesting way by the use of a combination of a broken-line graph and a pictograph.

In Table 7 the passenger registration figures have been rounded off to the nearest thousand cars.

TABLE 7

	Passenger Car Registrations	Population Per Car in Use
1910...............	458,000	200
1920...............	8,132,000	12.8
1930...............	22,973,000	5.3
1940...............	27,372,000	4.7
1950...............	40,185,000	3.8
1960...............	48,499,000	2.9

Fig. 7

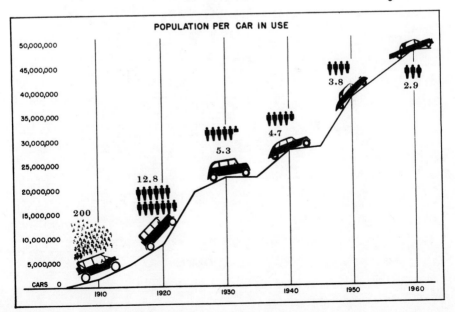

The numbers along the side represent the number of passenger cars registered. The number of cars registered for each given year is found by following the vertical year line to its point of contact with the broken line upon which the various cars rest. Following from this point a horizontal line to the scale of cars along the edge of the graph, the number of cars registered can be estimated.

For example, in 1920 the horizontal line from the point of contact to the edge of the graph falls just below 10,000,000 cars.

Where does the line representing cars for 1930 fall? The line for 1940? 1950? 1960?

Approximately how many more people for one car were there in 1910 than in 1960? In 1920 than in 1960? In 1930 than in 1960? In 1940 than in 1960? In 1950 than in 1960? From these figures, what do you predict about the number of people for one car as the years advance?

Fig. 8

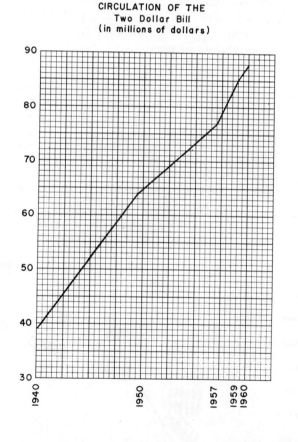

CIRCULATION OF THE
Two Dollar Bill
(in millions of dollars)

GRAPHS

2. The two dollar bill has not been a popular piece of currency compared with the popularity of the one, five, and ten dollar bills. However, Fig. 8 does show an increase in its production. The record is shown by a broken-line graph.

(a) Why is the graph line broken?

(b) Estimate to the nearest million dollars the value of the two dollar bills printed in each of the dates given.

(c) Between which two dates was the increase in value the greatest? Can you see why?

(d) Between which two dates was the increase in value the least?

(e) According to the graph, what appears to be the trend in production of the two dollar bill?

***3.** Table 8 gives the facts concerning visibility over the ocean from various heights.

Make a line graph showing these facts.

TABLE 8

Height	100′	150′	200′	250′	300′	350′
Visibility (in nautical miles, 6,080 feet each)	12	14.1	16.2	18.2	19.9	21.5

***4.** Water pressure increases 43 lb. per square inch of exposed surface for every 100 ft. of depth. (a) What was the water pressure on each square inch of the surface of the submarine *Nautilus* (see page 132) at a depth of 330 ft.?

(b) Construct a line graph illustrating this fact about water pressure.

***5.** Make a line graph of your grades for several days, or of your grades on several tests.

***6.** Make a line graph using the following data:

TABLE 10

Altitude of Plane	Ground	1,000′	2,000′	3,000′	4,000′	5,000′	6,000′	7,000′	8,000′
Temperature of Air (Fahrenheit)	81°	80°	75°	70°	60°	56°	43°	29°	6°

****7.** Make a line graph showing interesting facts from your civics or science studies, or from some magazine or newspaper.

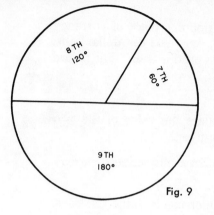

Fig. 9

71. Circle graphs. The circle graph is used to picture the *whole* or all of some one thing divided into *parts*. The *whole* might be an income which is divided into the sources from which it came or into the ways in which it will be paid out.

The circle graph is especially useful for showing the relation of one item to another and of one item to the whole number of items.

Figure 9 is a circle graph. It represents a *whole* student body divided into *three parts*: a 7th grade group, an 8th grade group, and a 9th grade group. It is easily seen that the order of size, giving the largest first, is 9th grade, 8th grade, and 7th grade.

From the graph, can you make these comparisons in size:

(a) The 9th grade is ? times as large as the 8th grade.
(b) The 9th grade is ? times the size of the 7th grade.
(c) The 8th grade is more than one-? of the whole student body.

Figure 10 is a circle graph made up of two circles. Each circle represents one dollar. One circle pictures the number of cents per dollar that are received from the several sources of income of the United States Government. The other circle shows how many cents of each dollar received by the United States Government are spent for various items.

Reading from the graphs: (a) What is the source of most of the United States Government's income? (b) What taxes do individuals pay as a direct tax to the United States Government? (c) This tax represents what per cent of the income of the United States Government? (d) What per cent of the income of the United States Government comes from income taxes paid by corporations? (e) Which two sources of income make up 81% of our nation's income? (f) Which three sources of income make up 92% of the nation's income? (g) Calculate from the graph the total in money value of the sections representing sources of income for the United States Government. (h) What item represents the largest expenditure for the Government? (i) Express the amount in (h) as a per cent of the total expenditure. (j) What is the total money value of the sections representing expenditures for the Government?

150

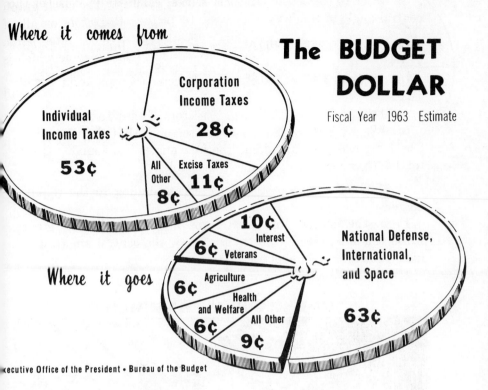

Fig. 10. The Budget Dollar As Estimated for the Fiscal Year 1963.

The portion of a circle enclosed between two radii and part of the circumference (an *arc*) is called a *sector* of a circle. Where have you seen that shape? The size of the sector is determined by the size of the angle formed by the two radii. The larger the angle, the larger the sector.

Aids in making a circle graph:

1. *Draw a circle* large enough to make a clear drawing of the facts to be pictured but not so large as to be unwieldy.

2. *Express the number facts* to be graphed as per cents. Then arrange them in a table.

In this circle, the sector between the two radii setting off "Individual Income Taxes" is marked "53¢" which is $\frac{53}{100}$ or 53 per cent of the dollar.

In order to know the size of a sector, calculate the size of the central angle in this way:

(a) 53% of 360° = 109.8°, size of sector "Individual Income Taxes."

(b) 28% of 360° = 100.8°, size of sector "Corporation Income Taxes."

(c) 11% of 360° = 39.6°, size of sector "Excise Taxes."

(d) 8% of 360° = 28.8°, size of sector "All Other Receipts." Check for accuracy by adding the four angles just found. If they total 360°, we are ready to make the table.

3. *Mark off sectors* of the circle corresponding to the required degrees.

From the center draw a straight line to the circumference. From this line, using a protractor, draw the central angles which form the sectors. Label the sectors.

4. *Give a title to the graph.*

HOW WOOD IS CONSUMED

FUEL WOOD 17 %

LUMBER 49%

PAPER AND PAPER PRODUCTS 9 %

11% LOST TO FIRE AND DISEASE

ALL OTHER 14%

Fig. 11. Various Uses of Wood.

1. Figure 11 pictures the uses of wood. (a) For which item is wood mostly used? (b) Which item pictured uses the smallest amount? (c) The 14 per cent pictures what uses? (d) What other uses are there that are not pictured in the 14 per cent? (e) What can you do to decrease the 11 per cent circle? (f) Arrange a table of the uses in the order of the per cents—largest first. (g) Prepare a circle graph of these facts.

2. Illustrate by a circle graph how you divide the 24 hours of the day. Use these activities, adding any others needed: Sleep, School, Study at Home, and Recreation.

3. Make a circle graph illustrating the facts in the following:

(a) Out of every $100 received, a certain manufacturer spends $62 for raw materials and $20 for operating expenses. The remaining $18 is his net profit.

(b) Manufacturer A finds that 60% of his selling price is spent for raw material and 24% for operating expenses. Sixteen per cent remains as net profit.

*4. A store made a survey of the ages of its employees, with the following results: 10.3% were under 40 years of age, 50.1% between 40 and 50 years, 39.6% over 50 years.

Hint: Use the nearest whole per cent, as, under 40 years = 10%.

**5. Bring a circle graph cut from a newspaper and interpret it to the class.

REVIEW OF CHAPTER VII

1. What advantages do graphs have over tables of numbers?

2. What advantages do tables of numbers have over graphs?

3. Name two purposes for which businessmen use graphs.

4. Which kind of graphs should be used: (a) to show the areas of the principal countries of the world; (b) to compare the costs of meat, vegetables, and desserts for a family for one month; (c) to compare the per cent of a monthly salary saved with the per cent spent; (d) to show the population of a city over a series of years; (e) to represent the temperature for 24 consecutive hours; (f) to illustrate the total production of different kinds of grain throughout the world; (g) to make a record of problems solved correctly for the days of one school week; (h) to show the record of accidents by grades in a high school; (i) to show the source of annual income for a business; (j) to picture enrollment in all grades in high school?

MAJOR CAUSES OF FOREST FIRES

SMOKERS 19%

ARSONISTS 30%

DEBRIS BURNERS 19%

LIGHTNING 9%

Fig. 12. Most forest fires could be prevented.

5. During a recent year, fires burned 16,556,780 acres of national and state forests. See figure 12. (a) What is the total per cent of the causes of forest fires shown in the picture? (b) What is the per cent not shown? (c) What might be some of the causes not pictured? (d) What is the total per cent caused by the carelessness of smokers and debris-burners? (e) How many acres did they cause to burn? (f) The total loss from all national and state forest fires is estimated at $32,461,804. What was the value of the forests burned by the smokers and debris-burners? (g) Of those burned by the arsonists? (h) What was the total loss caused by these three types of individuals? (i) How many $10,000 houses could have been built with the money value of the forests burned by these three causes?

REVIEW OF CHAPTER VII

Number Answers

Each expression represents an integer.   What is the integer?

1. A term used in golf.
2. How many lives is a cat said to have?
3. Freezing point on Centigrade thermometer.
4. One-half of eleven.
5. Joe is 20 years old.   Carl is the same age.   How old is Carl?
6. Sam entered a contest and did not lose or tie.
7. Also.
8. What you did three times a day yesterday and every day and what you are between the ages of 12 and 20.
9. Fourscore and a number that rhymes with "heaven."
10. Two bits.

— CHECK-UP ON THE FUNDAMENTALS OF ARITHMETIC—

Addition

1. 745
356
189

2. 6.4
$3\frac{1}{2}$
4.18

3. $\frac{2}{3} + \frac{1}{4} + \frac{5}{6} =$
4. $24\frac{7}{8} + 67\frac{1}{5} =$

5. 6 tons 1500 lb.
3 tons 1400 lb.

Subtraction

6. 3001
1608

8. $\frac{5}{8}$
$\frac{1}{3}$

9. $\frac{7}{16} - \frac{3}{8}$

10. 7 gal. 1 qt. 1 pt.
2 gal. 2 qt.

7. $2.45 − 1\frac{1}{2}$

Multiplication

11. 308
107

12. 1.6
3.9

13. $\frac{5}{12} \times 15$

14. $8\frac{1}{3} \times 3\frac{2}{5}$
15. 2 bu. 3 pk. 1 qt.
7

Division

16. 75)45150
19. .24 ÷ 1000

17. 14)179.2
20. $\frac{1}{4}$ of 3 yd. 2 ft. 8 in.

18. $\frac{5}{12} \div \frac{5}{6} =$

Per Cent

21. $16\frac{2}{3}\%$ of 85.2
24. 120% of ? = 36

22. $3\frac{1}{2}\%$ of 142
25. ?% of 50 = 6

23. 1.2% of 450

CHAPTER VIII

INSURANCE

72. Need for insurance. FIRE SWEEPS VILLAGE—DIES OF CRASH INJURIES—HAIL DESTROYS WHEAT CROP—ACRES OF FARM LAND FLOODED—RETIRED AT 65—FIFTY EMPLOYEES LOSE JOBS—AUTOMOBILE STOLEN. Such are headlines seen in the daily papers over and over again. How combat the risks of life? How replace the losses sustained?

Nothing can replace such losses as a life, a pair of eyes, or even a treasured family possession. *Insurance* is meant to replace a loss, and in a financial sense it does—in part, at least. A building can be replaced. A sum of money can be paid to the jobless, to the sick, to the retired, and to the family in the loss of a member. Insurance is not a preventive, but it is a protection in case of loss or damage.

73. Terms of insurance. The company assuming the risk is called the *insurer;* the person protected is called the *insured;* the contract between the company and the insured is called the *policy;* the amount of the *risk* is called the *face of the policy;* the person to whom the face of the policy is to be paid in case of loss or damage is called the *beneficiary;* the fixed amount of the annual cost as stated in the policy is called the *premium;* and the portion of the profits of the company allotted to the insured is called the *dividend.*

74. Kinds of insurance. Life, accident, health, hospital, fire, marine, and automobile insurance are common forms of protection. Musicians insure their hands; a merchant insures his plate-glass windows; a singer insures her voice; a contractor insures the men working for him; an automobile owner insures his car; a businessman insures his health; and a large circus insures against stormy weather.

75. Life insurance. In life insurance, the insurance company agrees to pay the beneficiary named in the policy a specified sum of money at the time of the death of the insured. In certain policies, if the insured is alive at a time named in the policy, the face of the policy may be paid to him. The insured agrees to pay the yearly premium charged by the insurance company.

The *premium* on all forms of insurance must be paid in advance by the insured to the insurer. The annual premium rate on life insurance varies with the age of the insured, the kind of insurance, the number of annual premiums, and the face of the policy. These different premium rates are listed in tables, as on page 162.

Life insurance is one of the safest financial investments anyone can make, because strict laws control insurance company operations, and the insurance departments of all the states supervise the companies.

76. Dividends. Some insurance companies divide a portion of their net earnings among their policyholders at the close of each year. If the policy states that the insured is entitled to a part of the earnings of the company, it is called a *participating policy*. The amount of the earnings that each insured receives is called his *dividend*. A policy that does not entitle the insured to share in the dividends is a *nonparticipating policy*.

The insured may use his dividend each year in one of the following ways:

(a) The dividend may be presented to the insured as a cash payment.

(b) The dividend may be applied as part payment on the premium due.

(c) The dividend may be applied to the purchase of more insurance.

(d) The dividend may be left with the company to draw interest.

The last method is a form of savings, for nearly all insurance companies pay interest compounded annually. The dividends and the interest may be withdrawn at any time.

1. A man received the following dividends on his participating policy. Give orally the total amount received for the first and second years, for the second and third years, and so on. 1st yr., $14.70; 2nd yr., $15.43; 3rd yr., $14.56; 4th yr., $15.17; 5th yr., $14.97; 6th yr., $15.49; 7th yr., $14.72; 8th yr., $14.21; 9th yr., $15.06; 10th yr., $14.53.

2. If the dividends of exercise 1 were all paid in cash to the insured, what was the total amount of cash that he received?

3. If the amount of the 5th dividend in exercise 1 is 15% of the amount of his annual premium, what does this man's insurance cost each year?

4. If, in exercise 3, the premium on the man's life insurance is $49.90 annually for each $1,000 of insurance, what is the face of his policy?

5. If the dividends on a policy are $3.38 per $1,000 of insurance for 1 yr., what would be the dividends on an $18,000 policy? On a $4,500 policy? On a $6,700 policy? On a $500 policy?

77. Kinds of life insurance. The three most common forms of life insurance are: *straight, limited payment,* and *endowment.* Each type varies slightly with different insurance companies. The insured should select the kind of life insurance that is best suited to his needs.

78. Straight life insurance. Straight, or ordinary, life insurance is used by the wage earner who wishes to provide protection for his family.

The annual premium rate for this policy is less than that for the other types of life insurance, but the premium must be paid each year during the entire life of the insured. After his death no premiums are paid; the face of the policy is paid to the beneficiary.

This type of insurance is especially desirable for a person who has dependents and only a small amount of money available to pay for insurance, for it offers the most protection at the least cost per year. If the insured lives to an old age, the policy will have a cash value which he may use as an income.

79. Limited payment life insurance. In limited payment life insurance, there is a shortening of the number of premium payments. The insured may not want to contract to pay premiums for life. In that case the insured and the company agree upon a plan of payment. The plan might be for the insured to pay over a period of 10 years, 15 years, 20 years, or some other period of years. If the insured lives beyond that period of years, no more premiums need be paid and the insurance is said to be *paid up*. If the insured dies before the policy is paid up, premium payments stop and the face of the policy is paid to the beneficiary. *Twenty-payment life* means that the premium on the insurance is to be paid each year for 20 years before the insurance is paid up. The greater the number of years before the policy is paid up, the smaller the amount of each annual premium.

This kind of insurance is desirable for a person who desires to leave some money to dependents and who wishes to pay his insurance premiums while his earning power is at its peak.

80. Endowment life insurance. Endowment insurance offers protection for others and an investment for the insured. The insured must pay the premiums on an endowment policy for a stated number of years, as in a limited payment policy. An endowment policy states that at the end of this period of years, the insured is to be paid the amount of the face of the policy; but if he should die before the end of this period, the face of the policy is to be paid to his beneficiary. No premiums are paid after the death of the insured in any form of life insurance. While endowment insurance is usually written for a period of 10, 20, or 30 years, it is sometimes written so as to be paid at a stated age; as, for example, an endowment to be paid at age 65 or age 85.

Endowment insurance has the combined advantages of life insurance and a savings account. For this reason, the annual premiums are higher than for other common types of life insurance. Endow-

Fig. 1. Annual Premium on Endowment Life Insurance at the Age of 20 Years.

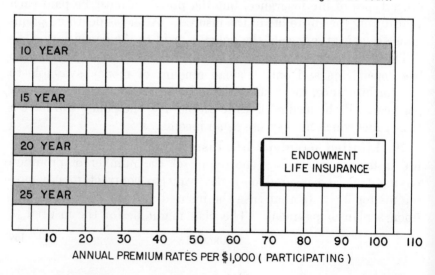

ANNUAL PREMIUM RATES PER $1,000 (PARTICIPATING)

ment insurance is desirable for a person who wishes to secure protection for his dependents and to provide savings for business deals or support in old age.

Figure 1 illustrates how the annual premiums vary in price for four endowments. The difference in rates depends largely upon the number of payments to be made to the company and upon the benefits to be paid by the company to the beneficiary.

(a) The annual premium on a 10-year endowment is approximately how many times as much as on a 25-year endowment?

(b) What is the advantage of an endowment insurance policy over a straight life policy with respect to the number of premiums to be paid and the benefits to be received?

(c) Make the same comparisons as in (b) for the 20-payment life and the straight life policies.

(d) What is the advantage of the straight life policy?

(e) The 20-payment life annual premium is approximately how many times the cost of the 25-year endowment at age 20?

81. Family income life insurance. A family income policy has been developed for the use of young parents with small children. It provides an amount of money to be paid at the death of the insured plus a regular monthly payment to the beneficiary for a certain number of years.

82. Life Annuities. The purpose of a life annuity is to provide a steady income to a person in his old age. The owner of this contract pays regular premiums until a given age, such as 65. After that, the company pays him a monthly income for as long as he lives.

83. Group insurance. Group insurance is a form of straight life insurance taken out by a group of workers in the same business organization or in similar occupations. The policy is usually issued without medical examination. The rate of premium for group insurance is less than the regular individual rate. The firm may pay all, part, or not any of each premium.

―――――――――――――― EXERCISES ――――――――――――――

A. Oral

1. Using short cuts, find the total amount of premium for 1 yr. on each of the following:

    (a) $10,000 policy @ $67.00 per $1,000
    (b)   5,000   "   "   16.00 "   1,000
    (c)   8,000   "   "   40.00 "   1,000
    (d) 12,000   "   "   25.00 "   1,000

B. Written

2. Find the annual premium on each of the following:

(a) $12,000 policy @ $56.30 per $1,000
(b) 7,500 " " 45.73 " 1,000
(c) 3,500 " " 78.07 " 1,000
(d) 3,750 " " 47.54 " 1,000
(e) 7,250 " " 76.06 " 1,000
(f) 13,750 " " 50.80 " 1,000
(g)   500 " " 48.26 " 1,000
(h) 11,000 " " 51.83 " 1,000
(i) 10,500 " " 66.78 " 1,000
(j) 25,000 " " 43.32 " 1,000

3. Complete the following:

	Face of Policy	Annual Premium	Premium Rate per $1,000 Insurance
(a)	$13,000	$_____	$42.50
(b)	5,000	105.00	_____
(c)	_____	162.00	27.00
(d)	500	_____	68.42
(e)	4,750	231.61	_____
(f)	_____	245.25	32.70

Solve the following by using the rates in Table 1:

4. Find the premiums on a $5,000 straight life policy at each of the following ages: 20, 25, 35, and 45.

5. Find the premiums on a $5,000 20-year endowment policy at each of the following ages: 20, 25, 35, and 45.

6. Find the annual premiums on a $12,000 policy, 20-payment life, at each of the following ages: 20, 25, 35, and 45.

TABLE 1

AVERAGE PREMIUM RATES PER $1000
(PARTICIPATING INSURANCE)

Age	Straight Life	20-Payment Life	20-Year Endowment
20	$17.00	$29.00	$49.00
25	20.00	32.00	50.00
35	26.00	39.00	51.00
45	37.00	48.00	56.00
55	55.00	63.00	67.00
65	88.00	91.00	92.00

For semiannual premium, multiply by .51; for quarterly premium, multiply by .2575.

INSURANCE

7. Find the premium for each plan on a $2,000 life insurance policy issued to an insured at age 35.

8. Find the premium for each plan of insurance shown in the table for an $8,000 policy issued to a person 20 years of age.

9. Why are the rates higher on the 20 year endowment policies than on the straight life policies?

10. How much more are the annual premiums on the $5,000 policies for the 20-year endowments than on the straight life policies at the ages given in exercises 4 and 5?

11. A girl takes out a $10,000 straight life policy at the age of 25. What does the insurance cost her each year? For how long must she pay the premium?

***12.** A woman 45 years old took out a 20-year endowment policy. How much would she have saved on the premium each year if she had taken out the insurance ten years earlier on $4,000? What would she have saved on premiums for the 20 years?

***13.** If you take out a 20-payment life insurance policy at the age of 25, at what age will the insurance be paid up? How much will you pay in premiums during the 20 years on $1,000?

****14.** At the age of 35, a man took out a 20-year endowment policy for $7,000. He died after he had paid 11 annual premiums. How much had he paid into the company? How much was paid to his beneficiary? How much more did his beneficiary receive than the amount that had been paid into the company?

****15.** Mr. *X* has his life insured for $15,000. He is 45 years old and has a 20-year endowment policy. What will the policy cost him for 5 years, beginning at this age? If he pays his premiums semiannually, what is the amount of each installment? If he pays the premiums quarterly, how much is each installment? (See Table 1.)

****16.** $5,000 20-year endowment policies are issued to insureds of ages 25 and 35. What is the difference in the annual premiums on the two policies? What will be the total difference for the 20 years?

84. Workmen's compensation insurance. The laws of practically every state hold an employer liable for the injury or death of an employee resulting from an accident while at work. *Workmen's compensation insurance* protects the employer from injured workmen's lawsuits for damages. The insurance company assumes this risk and pays the injured person a sum of money. The amount varies in different states and with the degree of the injury. In case of accidental death, the dependents are paid a sum of money, as in life insurance.

85. Social Security. Many of you may be among the approximately 72,000,000 Americans who possess a Social Security card.

Do you as a present, or probably a future, member of this group know what Social Security is; know who are members of the system; what the cost is to members; how the members benefit or will benefit later; and what the conditions and restrictions are upon becoming eligible for Social Security benefits?

What is Social Security? Social Security is a type of insurance which has been sponsored by the Federal Government since 1935.

Who may earn the benefits of the Social Security system? Congress has broadened the coverage of Social Security until at present it includes approximately 9 out of 10 Americans who work for a living—either as employees or as self-employed persons.

What does Social Security cost its members? A per cent of an employee's wage is deducted from his weekly or monthly pay. The amount of the per cent is matched by the employer, who sends the total amount to the Government. A self-employed person pays according to his earnings from his business or trade.

No payment is made on any earnings above $4,800. If the earnings are $5,000, the tax is paid on only $4,800.

The following table shows the tax rate over a period of years:

TABLE 2

Year	Employee	Employer	Self-employed
1961	3%	3%	$4\frac{1}{2}$%
1962	$3\frac{1}{8}$%	$3\frac{1}{8}$%	$4\frac{11}{16}$%
1963-1965	$3\frac{5}{8}$%	$3\frac{5}{8}$%	$5\frac{7}{16}$%
1966-1967	$4\frac{1}{8}$%	$4\frac{1}{8}$%	$6\frac{3}{16}$%
1968 and after	$4\frac{5}{8}$%	$4\frac{5}{8}$%	$6\frac{15}{16}$%

What are the benefits from Social Security? At retirement age, a retired employee who is not earning more than $1,200 a year is entitled, together with his family, to a certain sum of money each month. If he is still earning more than $1200 a year after he reaches retirement age, some benefits are withheld. The amount withheld increases as the amount earned increases.

There are payments to the family after the death of the insured: (a) to the widow as long as she cares for the children under 18 (or 18 or over if disabled before 18); (b) to the children under 18 (or 18 or over if disabled before 18); (c) to the widow at age 62; (d) if there are no children or widow to receive benefits, to dependent parents at age 62; (e) to the person paying insured's burial expenses; (f) to a dependent husband at age 62, if his wife dies.

What are some conditions required for Social Security protection? To become insured, a person must secure a Social Security card, to be kept and shown to every new employer of his. The number on the card is important to the insured, as it is his account number which is used by the Government to keep a record of his earnings under Social Security coverage.

To be entitled to Social Security benefits, or to make payments payable to dependents, the worker must have been in covered employment long enough to become insured. This depends on his date of birth and on the date of his retirement, disability, or death. A person is fully insured if he has a quarter* of covered employment for every year after 1950 up to, but not including the year in which he reaches age 65, dies, or becomes disabled.

Calculation of the amount of benefits is complicated. At the time due, the Government figures the amount due the insured.

To receive benefits, the insured or his beneficiary must file a claim with the local Social Security office.

At present, more than 10,000,000 persons are receiving benefits. The top benefit under the 1961 revision is $127 per month for an individual and $254 per month for a family.

──────────────────── EXERCISES ────────────────────

1. Jack, an employee who is covered by the Social Security law, earned $2,400 in 1962. What amount was deducted from his wages to cover his Social Security tax?

$$3\tfrac{1}{8}\% \text{ of } \$2,400 = ? \quad \text{Jack's tax.}$$

2. Mr. Black is employed and covered by the Social Security law. During 1963, his salary was $5,200. (a) On how much of his salary did Mr. Black pay the Social Security tax? (b) How much was held from Mr. Black's salary for his Social Security tax? (c) How much did his employer contribute toward Mr. Black's Social Security account? (d) What was the total amount added to Mr. Black's Social Security account in 1963?

---

* A "calendar quarter" is a three-month period beginning the first of January, April, July, or October.

3. Mr. Cox, an employee, has Social Security coverage. He received a salary of $5,000 in 1961. (a) How much of his salary was taxable for Social Security? (b) How much did Mr. Cox contribute to his Social Security account in 1961? (c) How much did his employer contribute? (d) Determine the total amount contributed in 1961.

4. John Marks, a student whose earnings are taxable for Social Security, earned $850 during 1962. How much was added to his Social Security account for the year 1962?

5. If Jane Jackson, an office worker, earns $3,500 in 1961 and her wages are subject to Social Security tax, how much would be added to her Social Security fund in 1961?

6. Mr. Ault is self-employed (earns no wages) and pays the Social Security tax. His net income for 1963 was $6,000. Calculate the Social Security tax paid by Mr. Ault in 1963.

7. Mr. Baker, who is self-employed (earns no wages) and is covered by the Social Security law, had a net income of $7,500 from his shoe shop in 1961. How much did he pay into his Social Security fund in 1961?

*8. Mr. Boyd has both self-employment income and a salary subject to Social Security tax. In 1961 his salary amounted to $2,000 and his net income from his self-employment was $4,000. Calculate his Social Security tax.

Explanation: No person is taxed on more than $4,800 for any year. If the salary earned for a year is $4,800 or more, the tax is all calculated on the salary and the self-employment income is not taxed. If the salary is less than $4,800, the tax on the salary is figured first; then the tax is found on that part of the self-employment income that is needed to be added to the salary to total $4,800. If both earnings do not total as much as $4,800, the tax is calculated on the full amount of both earnings.

Solution: All of Mr. Boyd's salary of $2,000 must be taxed. As Mr. Boyd has total earnings of more than $4,800, only part of his self-employment income will be taxed—the part that when added to his $2,000 salary will total $4,800.

$2,000 @ 3 % = $ _____, tax on salary.
$2,800 @ $4\frac{1}{2}$% = $ _____, tax on income.
$ _____, total tax.

*9. Mr. Long has both self-employment and wages subject to Social Security tax. If in 1963 Mr. Long's wages are $1,200 and his income from self-employment is $5,000, how much Social Security tax will Mr. Long pay?

*10. If in 1962 Carl Case receives a $3,000 salary and a net income of $2,000 from a business, and both earnings are subject to the Social Security tax, figure the amount of Social Security tax to be paid by Mr. Case.

*11. Charles starts working in 1961 for an annual salary of $5,000. His salary increases by $500 each year. How much Social Security tax will he pay in the years 1961 through 1964?

FIRE INSURANCE

86. Fire protection. Fire insurance applies only to damage or destruction of the particular property named in the policy. In case of a fire, the insurance company is not liable for the destruction of furniture, clothes, and so forth, unless they were insured with the building. Fire insurance covers destruction by the fire itself, the damage from water and chemicals, and the breakages made by the firemen while fighting the flames. Unless so stated in the policy, damage by lightning, wind, hail, tornado, earthquake, and crashes into a building by an automobile or airplane is not included in the fire insurance. These and other risks can be covered in the fire insurance policy for a small increase in the premium. A fire insurance policy should be carefully read, as there are many provisions stated in it, some of which might cause the insured to lose his protection in case he was unaware of their inclusion.

The premium on fire insurance is quoted as a certain amount for each $100 of insurance bought, as $1.20 per $100. Sometimes the rate is quoted at a certain per cent of the face of the policy, as $1\frac{1}{4}$ per cent. Fire insurance policies are usually made out for a period of 1, 3, or 5 years. The greater the number of years for which the policy is issued, the less the premium averages per year.

EXERCISES

A. Oral

1. Find the amount of insurance carried on the following buildings if each building is insured to 80 per cent of its value: (a) $5,000; (b) $2,500; (c) $10,000; (d) $1,500; (e) $1,200; (f) $50,000; (g) $20,000; (h) $9,000.

B. Written

1. Find the amount of insurance on buildings having the following values if each building is insured at 60 per cent of its value: (a) $40,000; (b) $75,000; (c) $150,000; (d) $35,000; (e) $220,000.

2. Find the amount of fire insurance on each of the following values of property if the policy in each case is insured for 80% of its value. (a) $4,550; (b) $5,250; (c) $15,000; (d) $32,500; (e) $7,500.

3. Complete the following annual fire insurance premiums:

	Amount of Insurance	Premium per $100 of Insurance	Annual Premium
(a)	$ 7,000	$ .18	_____
(b)	4,000	.23	_____
(c)	13,600	.22	_____
(d)	24,800	.34	_____
(e)	111,000	1.00	_____
(f)	54,400	1.25	_____
(g)	8,425	.22	_____
(h)	19,600	.23	_____
(i)	5,250	.22	_____
(j)	125,000	1.16	_____

4. Complete the following:

	Value of Property	Amount of Insurance	Per Cent of Insurance
(a)	$13,500	$_____	$33\frac{1}{3}$
(b)	8,000	3,000	_____
(c)	5,500	4,400	_____
(d)	4,800	_____	$62\frac{1}{2}$
(e)	_____	10,500	75
(f)	_____	7,500	50

Fire insurance is usually paid in advance for a term of years. The amount of the premium for a 3-year policy is usually $2\frac{1}{2}$ times the premium for a 1-year policy; the premium on a 5-year policy is usually 4 times the premium for a 1-year policy.

5. Find the missing premiums on this chart:

	1-Year Policy Rate	3-Year Policy Rate	5-Year Policy Rate
(a)	34¢	_____	_____
(b)	62¢	_____	_____
(c)	$1.14	_____	_____
(d)	_____	_____	$5.84

6. What is the premium for (a) a 3-year policy, (b) a 5-year policy, if the premium on a 1-year policy is $14.42? $18.68? $39.80? $126.14?

*7. A farmer had his property insured as follows:

> House insured for $4,500 at 47¢ per $100
> Barn   "   " $3,200 " 97¢ " $100

Find the total cost of the insurance for the house and barn.

*8. A merchant took out insurance on his store building, valued at $18,000, and on his stock of goods, valued at $7,450. What is the amount of insurance carried on each if both are insured for 80% of their value?

*9. If the fire insurance premium on the store in exercise 8 is 69¢ per $100, and that on the stock $1.12 per $100, what is the cost of the insurance? If a fire damages the store to the extent of $5,750, and the stock to the extent of $4,500, what settlement will be made with the merchant?

*10. What is the premium for 1 yr. on a $6,400 fire insurance policy, if the rate is $1\frac{1}{8}$ per cent of the face of the policy?

*11. Tornado insurance on a garage costs $1.65 per $100 annually. What is the amount of annual premium on such a policy for $12,500?

*12. What is the amount of the premium on a store valued at $8,500, insured for $\frac{1}{2}$ its value at 50¢ per $100?

*13. What would be the loss to the owner if a fire damaged the store in exercise 12 to the amount of $46,000?

**14. Find the premiums for insurance on each of the following buildings:

TABLE 3

Type of Building	Valuation	Annual Premium per $100 Insurance	Annual Premium	3-Year Premium	5-Year Premium
House, wood..........	$4,000	$.36	$_____	$_____	$_____
stone..........	6,000	.22	_____	_____	_____
brick..........	5,000	.23	_____	_____	_____
Store, wood..........	15,000	1.16	_____	_____	_____
stone..........	20,000	.98	_____	_____	_____
brick..........	18,000	1.05	_____	_____	_____

87. Automobile insurance. The wise automobile owner protects himself against the risk of accident and theft by purchasing automobile insurance. He may purchase the following kinds of protection:

(a) *Liability Insurance.* If his automobile kills or injures another person, the automobile owner is protected up to the amount stated in his policy. Liability insurance is written in two parts—one part tells the limit that the company will pay for damages to one person in an accident; the other part tells the limit that the company will pay for damages if more than one person is injured in one accident. Typical amounts of limits of liability are $20,000 for one person, and $40,000 for more than one person.

(b) *Property Damage Insurance.* If his automobile damages property, such as another automobile, a building, or a wall, he is protected up to the amount stated in his policy. The usual limit of liability for property damage is $10,000.

(c) *Fire Insurance.* If his automobile catches fire, he is protected for the fire loss.

(d) *Theft Insurance.* If his car is stolen, he is protected for the loss.

(e) *Collision Insurance.* If his own car is damaged in a collision, he is protected for the amount of damage to the car. Usually the insured has to pay the first $50 or $100 of collision costs. The company pays the remainder of the costs of repairs. This is called $50 or $100 deductible insurance.

The rates for the different kinds of automobile insurance vary with the size of the city, the number of past accidents in the locality, and the kind of car.

(a) Why should the various premiums on automobile insurance be higher in a city than in a small town?

(b) Why should the number of past automobile accidents in a locality affect the rates of insurance?

(c) In what way should the kind of car one has affect the rates of insurance?

(d) Which kinds of automobile insurance would have a higher rate on an old car? Why?

(e) On a new car? Why?

1. Jack Glenn insured his automobile against fire for $1,800 at the rate of 45¢ per $100 per year. How much did the insurance cost him?

2. Ben Craig took out automobile insurance against the following risks: (a) fire—$1,500, at 35¢ per $100; (b) theft—$1,500, at $1.10 per $100; (c) property damage—$10,000, at $2.25 per $1,000. Find the total premiums.

3. Harold Cooper bought a new car for $2,500. He insured it for 90 per cent of its value against fire at 40¢ per $100 and against theft at $1.20 per $100. Property damage cost him $33.75, collision insurance cost him $48, and liability insurance cost $36. Find the total of his insurance premiums.

4. Dick Wylie bought a used automobile for $1,200 and insured it for $\frac{3}{5}$ of its value. The liability insurance cost him $58, fire insurance cost $1.08 per $100, and the property damage cost him $8.64. What did his insurance cost him per year?

5. What does the insurance on Dick Wylie's car cost on the average per month?

———————————— *REVIEW OF CHAPTER VIII* ————————————

1. Why is the annual premium on a 20-payment life policy higher than on a straight life policy for the same amount?

2. Why is straight life the cheapest form of life insurance per year?

3. Why should the premium be paid annually, if possible, instead of semiannually or quarterly?

4. Compare straight life, limited payment life, and endowment policies as to annual cost per $1,000.

5. What are some outstanding advantages of group insurance?

6. What is an advantage of a monthly income settlement over a lump-sum settlement from an insurance company? What is a disadvantage?

7. Whom does workmen's compensation insurance cover?

8. Fire insurance on a garage is more expensive than fire insurance in the same amount on a house. Why?

9. Would a house with wooden shingles have a higher or lower fire insurance rate than the same house with composition shingles? Why?

10. List five conditions that cause fire insurance rates to be lower.

11. List five conditions that cause fire insurance rates to be higher.

12. Which kinds of automobile insurance protect: (a) The owner's car? (b) The other fellow's car or his other property?

PLAYOFF FOR CHAPTER VIII

Separate the class into committees, one for each type of insurance that you have studied. Make up a list of questions that you have about these kinds of insurance. Members of the committees can then visit local insurance agents and report back to the class with their findings.

ACHIEVEMENT TEST II

Addition

1. 7	**2.** 28	**3.** 247	**4.** 23.79	**5.** $\frac{3}{8}$
6	49	629	.56	$\frac{1}{3}$
8	63	324	24.38	
5	77	482	8.77	
3		138		

6. $7.5 + 2.16 + .7$ **8.** $45\frac{3}{4}$ **9.** $12\frac{1}{6}$ **10.** 4 yd. 2 ft.

7. $\frac{3}{5} + \frac{1}{10} + 2$ $\underline{18\frac{1}{2}}$ $\underline{7\frac{2}{3}}$ 5 yd. 2 ft.

Subtraction

11. 409   **12.** 6003   **13.** 722.8   **14.** $3.22 − $.76
     $\underline{36}$ $\underline{278}$ $\underline{528.2}$ **15.** $6 − 47¢

16. $72\frac{1}{4} - 18.5$ **18.** $62\frac{7}{10}$ **19.** $84\frac{1}{3}$ **20.** 8 hr. 45 min.

17. $\frac{7}{8} - \frac{1}{4}$ $\underline{50\frac{3}{5}}$ $\underline{28\frac{1}{2}}$ 2 hr. 55 min.

Multiplication

21. 72   **22.** 306   **23.** 240   **24.** 9.7
     $\underline{45}$ $\underline{408}$ $\underline{90}$ $\underline{.06}$

25. $\frac{1}{3} \times \frac{1}{3}$ **27.** $\frac{1}{5} \times 18\frac{1}{3}$ **29.** $36\frac{1}{4}$ **30.** 5 qt. 1 pt.

26. $1\frac{1}{2} \times 16$ **28.** $\frac{3}{4} \times 76$ $\underline{84\frac{2}{3}}$ $\underline{4}$

Division

31. $8\overline{)192}$ **32.** $.16\overline{)28.8}$ **33.** $7.65 \div 10$ **34.** $4.5\overline{)117}$

$$\text{35. } .38\overline{)592.8}^{156} \quad \text{36. } 38\overline{)5.928}^{156} \quad \text{37. } \tfrac{4}{5} \div \tfrac{3}{10} \quad \text{38. } 8 \div \tfrac{1}{4}$$

39. $26\tfrac{1}{4} \div 4\tfrac{1}{6}$ **40.** $3\overline{)4 \text{ gal. 1 qt.}}$

Per Cent

Write as common fractions: Solve:

41. 24%   **42.** $37\tfrac{1}{2}\%$ **47.** 30% of 84 = ?

Write as decimal fractions: **48.** 6% of ? = 18

43. 27%   **44.** $3\tfrac{1}{3}\%$ **49.** ?% of 60 = 24

Write as per cents: **45.** $\tfrac{2}{3}$ **46.** .5

Arrange in order of size—smallest first:

50. $12\tfrac{1}{2}\%$, .013, 1.2, $\tfrac{12}{100}$

Record your scores on the achievement chart.
Which of your scores show an improvement over your scores on
Achievement Test I? There will be another chance for improve-
ment of scores next quarter.

— REVIEW OF THE FUNDAMENTALS OF ARITHMETIC— 4 —

Addition and Subtraction

Add and prove:

1. 4	2. 37	3. 78	4. 326	5. 806	6. 46.17	7. 734.59
8	46	18	714	8859	5.64	17.97
6	68	32	528	9770	17.59	564.56
5	77	35	712	4997	43.58	57.48
7	29	12	501			

8. $87.96
88.09
12.86
76.57

9. 2.6 + 8.06 + 6.6 + 66.6 + .6

10. .97 + .875 + .304 + .004 + 4.44

Add:

11. $\tfrac{2}{3} + \tfrac{3}{4}$ **13.** $\tfrac{1}{2}$ **14.** $\tfrac{5}{12}$ **15.** $376\tfrac{5}{16}$ **16.** $9\tfrac{1}{2}$ **17.** $45\tfrac{5}{8}$

12. $\tfrac{1}{7} + \tfrac{2}{3}$ $\tfrac{5}{8}$ $\tfrac{1}{4}$ $478\tfrac{3}{4}$ $31\tfrac{3}{8}$ $5\tfrac{5}{24}$

     $\tfrac{3}{4}$ $\tfrac{1}{3}$ $66\tfrac{3}{4}$ $6\tfrac{2}{3}$

18. $107\frac{1}{2} + 26\frac{4}{5} + 17\frac{3}{10}$

19. $83\frac{1}{4} + 98\frac{3}{4} + 75\frac{1}{2}$

20. 18 bu. 1 pk. 2 qt.
$\underline{13 \text{ bu. } 2 \text{ pk. } 3 \text{ qt.}}$

Subtract: (Prove 21–30.)

21. 4005	**22.** 7521	**23.** 5608	**24.** 36900	**25.** 52060
$\underline{2978}$	$\underline{6850}$	$\underline{3879}$	$\underline{17099}$	$\underline{4307}$

26. 84.7
$\underline{9.3}$

27. 78.84
$\underline{55.16}$

28. 8
$\underline{4.62}$

29. $73.4 - 36.872 =$

30. $8.7 - .864 =$

31. $\frac{11}{12} - \frac{3}{4}$

32. $\frac{11}{15} - \frac{11}{30}$

33. 83
$\underline{56\frac{5}{18}}$

34. $40\frac{5}{9}$
$\underline{25\frac{1}{3}}$

35. $499\frac{3}{8}$
$\underline{307\frac{1}{2}}$

36. $38\frac{3}{20}$
$\underline{19\frac{9}{10}}$

37. $468\frac{2}{3}$
$\underline{429\frac{1}{9}}$

38. $156\frac{3}{4} - 77.5$

39. $67\frac{3}{8} - 49.125$

40. 18 hr. 10 min. 20 sec. $-$ 17 hr. 42 sec.

—REVIEW OF THE FUNDAMENTALS OF ARITHMETIC—5—

Multiplication and Division

Multiply: (Prove 1–10.)

1. 541
$\underline{7}$

2. 960
$\underline{39}$

3. 1607
$\underline{46}$

4. 709
$\underline{207}$

5. 5708
$\underline{56}$

6. 5.93
$\underline{.29}$

7. .928
$\underline{67}$

8. 4.26
$\underline{51.4}$

9. 1.006
$\underline{.209}$

10. 5.063
$\underline{.46}$

11. $100 \times .16$

12. 485×10

13. $100 \times .69842$

14. 100×43.855

15. 10×63.89

16. $1000 \times .68\frac{3}{4}$

17. $\frac{5}{9} \times \frac{3}{4} \times \frac{2}{15}$

18. $6\frac{2}{3} \times 3$

19. $\frac{9}{10} \times \frac{2}{5} \times \frac{1}{2}$

20. $7\frac{4}{11} \times 4\frac{8}{9}$

21. $27\frac{4}{5} \times 15$

22. $4\frac{3}{4} \times 24$

23. $12\frac{2}{5} \times 12\frac{1}{2}$

24. $48\frac{5}{6} \times 18\frac{2}{3}$

25. $\frac{5}{8} \times \frac{3}{4} \times \frac{8}{9} \times \frac{7}{15} \times \frac{3}{7} \times 12$

26. 5 T. 280 lb. $\times$ 8

Divide: (Prove 27–38.)

27. $7533 \div 93$

28. $26240 \div 26$

29. $7418 \div 73$

30. $28416 \div 48$ 33. $2.9088 \div 3.6$ 36. $75.6 \div 1000$

31. $4.5 \div .005$ 34. $8.055 \div 4.5$ 37. $.0468 \div 100$

32. $2.0822 \div 71$ 35. $62.85 \div 10$ 38. $6 \div 1000$

39. $\frac{3}{8} \div \frac{5}{9}$ 42. $12 \div 1\frac{1}{2}$ 45. $10\frac{1}{8} \div 6\frac{3}{4}$ 48. $45\frac{5}{6} \div 9\frac{1}{6}$

40. $\frac{2}{9} \div \frac{1}{3}$ 43. $4\frac{1}{2} \div 2\frac{1}{4}$ 46. $9\frac{3}{5} \div 8\frac{4}{7}$ 49. $5)\overline{1 \text{ qt. } 1 \text{ pt.}}$

41. $\frac{5}{6} \div \frac{5}{8}$ 44. $14 \div 3\frac{1}{2}$ 47. $13\frac{5}{7} \div 4\frac{4}{7}$ 50. $4)\overline{6 \text{ mi. } 180 \text{ rd.}}$

—REVIEW OF THE FUNDAMENTALS OF ARITHMETIC—6—

Percentage

Express each of the following numbers as (1) a common fraction, (2) a decimal, (3) a percentage:

1. 40% 6. $\frac{1}{2}$ 11. $.16$ 16. $4\frac{1}{2}\%$

2. $66\frac{2}{3}\%$ 7. $\frac{7}{10}$ 12. 38% 17. $.016$

3. 75% 8. $.09$ 13. $\frac{1}{3}$ 18. 200%

4. $\frac{3}{10}$ 9. $.4$ 14. 5% 19. $133\frac{1}{3}\%$

5. $\frac{1}{6}$ 10. 125% 15. $.125$ 20. $1\frac{1}{2}$

Solve the following:

21. 18% of 5   27. 18% of 2,074   33. $4\frac{1}{2}\%$ of 7.26

22. 60% of 30   28. 7% of 16.3   34. $3\frac{1}{3}\%$ of 9.9

23. 120% of 25   29. $\frac{1}{2}\%$ of 6,090   35. 5% of .25

24. $66\frac{2}{3}\%$ of 15   30. $12\frac{1}{2}\%$ of 608   36. 18% of 5,847

25. $1\frac{1}{2}\%$ of 16   31. 25% of 1,604   37. $\frac{3}{4}\%$ of 6,000

26. 5% of 25   32. 200% of 14.68   38. 1% of 160

Fill in the following:

39. 1% of $19 = ?$ 43. $?\%$ of $8 = 8$ 47. 12% of $? = 7.2$

40. 1% of $? = 3$ 44. 3% of $? = 15$ 48. $?\%$ of $40 = 16$

41. $?\%$ of $\$6 = \$3$ 45. $?\%$ of $12 = 24$ 49. $\frac{1}{4}\%$ of $8 = ?$

42. 3% of $12 = ?$ 46. $4\frac{1}{2}\%$ of $\$80 = ?$ 50. 8% of $? = 44.8$

Solve the following:

51. 16 is what per cent of 36?   55. 27 is what per cent of 9?

52. 7 is what per cent of 42?   56. What per cent of 24 is 2?

53. What per cent of 16 is 3?   57. 16 is what per cent of 80?

54. 21 is what per cent of 70?   58. What per cent of 25 is 9?

CHAPTER IX

BANKS, SAVINGS, AND INVESTMENTS

88. Banks. Banks were first organized to provide a safe place to keep savings. Many people, to their sorrow, have found that money is not safe hidden in the home. Most citizens have come to believe in the safety of banks. Especially has this been true since January 1, 1934, when the Federal Deposit Insurance Corporation began insuring each bank depositor against loss of deposits up to $10,000 in banks which are members of the Corporation. Modern banks are organized for the purpose of selling financial service to you and me.

You will study about two departments of banks—the commercial department and the savings department.

89. Services of the commercial department of a bank. By depositing money in the commercial department of a bank you are able to pay bills by giving a check for the amount owed. This plan does away to a large extent with the necessity of carrying sizable sums of money on your person. The commercial department of a bank is ready to serve you financially in a variety of useful ways. A few of the services are as follows:

(a) receives money for deposit which it pays back on demand,
(b) makes loans on good security,
(c) buys mortgages, notes, and other business papers,
(d) advises customers regarding investment of their money,
(e) collects money due on checks and other papers deposited for collection,
(f) rents safe-deposit boxes.

90. Opening a checking account. The steps in opening a checking account are:

(a) to get an introduction to one of the bank officials,
(b) to provide references or in some way furnish evidence of being a desirable customer,
(c) to fill out a signature card,
(d) to fill out a deposit ticket and present the ticket with the money to a teller at the bank and receive a checkbook.

91. Signature card. Each of you, early in your school life, should adopt a definite way of writing your name and thus establish a signature for yourself. Bankers advise a well-written, legible signature.

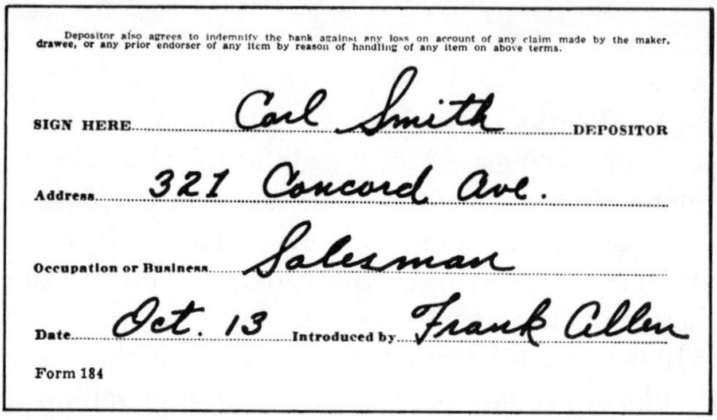

Fig. 1.
Signature card.

Depositor also agrees to indemnify the bank against any loss on account of any claim made by the maker, drawee, or any prior endorser of any item by reason of handling of any item on above terms.

SIGN HERE................*Carl Smith*................DEPOSITOR

Address................*321 Concord Ave.*................

Occupation or Business................*Salesman*

Date................*Oct. 13*................Introduced by................*Frank Allen*

Form 184

The bank, in order to know how you always sign your name, must have a copy of your signature. This is written on a *signature card*, which remains in the bank to be used in the future for comparison with the signatures on checks and other business papers handled by the bank. (See figure 1.)

92. Deposit tickets. A deposit ticket is a blank form provided by the bank to be filled out by you when making a deposit. Deposit tickets vary in details. Your name and address should be the same as on the signature card you filled out. *Currency* means paper money. *Silver* includes all metal money. The amount of each check to be deposited must be listed separately on the deposit ticket.

Banks differ as to the method of listing checks on deposit tickets. Figure 2 illustrates two methods in common use. To the left of the amount $28.40 is written *18—3*. This is the bank upon which the check is written. Such numbers are assigned to every bank by the

American Bankers' Association.   The number of the bank is found on the face of the check.   (See figure 5.)   Each number consists of two parts separated by a dash, as 18—3.   This number indicates the *third* bank in the *eighteenth* banking district.

You should learn the bank's wishes in regard to the listing of checks on the deposit ticket.

To determine the amount of the deposit, the currency, silver, and check totals are added, and the sum is then placed on the deposit ticket.

Fig. 2. Deposit tickets.

Regular account   Special account

FOR CHECKING ACCOUNTS
FORM 107-1   DEPOSITED WITH
TNB   TRADERS
NATIONAL BANK
KANSAS CITY, MISSOURI

CHECKS AS FOLLOWS: Please List separately using bank transit number. You will find this number on every check, opposite Bank Name.	DOLLARS	CENTS
18-3	2 8	40
18-9	5	80
10-4	9	36
TOTAL CHECKS	4 3	56
CURRENCY	1 0	0 0
SILVER	8	75
TOTAL DEPOSIT	6 2	31

FOR ACCOUNT OF
PLEASE PRINT YOUR NAME AND ADDRESS AS THEY ARE CARRIED ON OUR LEDGERS

NAME CARL SMITH

ADDRESS 321 CONCORD
KANSAS CITY, MO.

DATE OCT. 23 19—

ACCOUNT NUMBER → 13800

THE DEPOSITOR BY USING THIS SLIP AGREES TO THE CONDITIONS PRINTED ON THE BACK
ITEMS   FLOAT

9-3   DEPOSITED WITH
TNB   TRADERS
NATIONAL BANK
KANSAS CITY, MISSOURI

NAME Paul A. Stone
      3121 S. Elm St.

ADDRESS

	DOLLARS	CTS.	
BALANCE IN YOUR PASS BOOK			ACCOUNT NO.
AMOUNT OF THIS DEPOSIT			
BALANCE AFTER THIS DEPOSIT			DATE Nov. 16, 19—

All items credited subject to final cash payment.   Unpaid items will be charged to account. This Bank will observe due diligence in its endeavor to select responsible agents, but will not be liable in case of their failure or negligence, or for loss of items in the mail.

	DOLLARS	CENTS
CURRENCY	1 5	00
SILVER	6	55
CHECKS AS FOLLOWS: Please list separately, using bank transit number. You will find this number on every check, opposite Bank Name.		
	1 6	01
	1 3	16
	5	81
	3 4	98
TOTAL $	5 6	53

ENDORSE ACCOUNT NUMBER AND NAME ON ALL CHECKS DEPOSITED

EXERCISES

1. The following change was taken to the bank: 56 pennies, 24 nickels, 17 dimes, 11 quarters, 13 half-dollars, and 3 one-dollar bills. What was the total amount deposited?

2. Mary deposited $13.75 a week for 47 weeks. What was her total deposit during this time?

3. Find the total of the following items:

Silver........................	$65.18
Currency....................	266.00
Checks:	
12–4.....................	8.65
10–7	17.88

4. Total the following items:

Silver........................	$56.91
Currency....................	191.00
Checks:	
10–8.....................	447.62
10–12...................	9.30
10–15...................	26.71

5. Tom made the following deposits at his bank: $18.96 in coins, $37.00 in currency, and $59.37 in checks. What was his total deposit?

6. There was a balance of $437.98 in Carl's bank account before deposits of $68.45, $216.95, $75.65, and $168.87 were made. What is the new bank balance?

7. Checks for the following amounts were deposited in the bank: $216.08, $21.19, $185.37, $4.65, $81.43, $538.96, and $67.95. Find the total amount deposited.

8. To a balance of $176.56 in the bank, deposits of $264.39, $47.98, $127.49, and $63.87 are added. What is the new bank balance?

93. Checkbook. A *checkbook* is issued to you at the time that you open a checking account in the bank, and also at any later time that you need more checks. For record purposes there is either a check stub for the record of each check or there is a record sheet to be used for the record of several checks. These forms remain permanently in the checkbook.

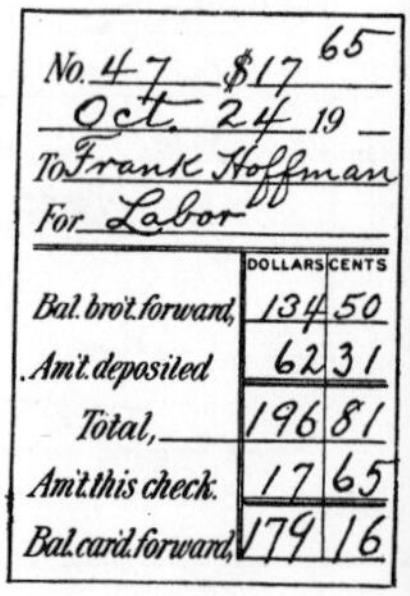

94. Checkbook stub and record sheet. The stub, or the record sheet, of checks should be filled out carefully, as they are your record of the checks, the date written, the amount to whom paid and the exact amount of money you have on deposit before and after the check is cashed. The arrangement of the items may vary. Fig. 3 shows a check stub

Fig. 3. The Stub Record of the Check.

No. _47_ $17 _65_
Oct 24 19 _
To _Frank Hoffman_
For _Labor_

	DOLLARS	CENTS
Bal. brot. forward,	134	50
Amt. deposited	62	31
Total,	196	81
Amt. this check	17	65
Bal. car'd forward	179	16

arrangement in common use. Fig. 4 shows a record sheet on which Carl Smith has recorded a $62.31 deposit on Oct. 23rd (Fig. 2) and a check written for $17.65 (Fig. 5) on Oct. 24th. What was his balance before these transactions? After the transactions? Does this balance agree with the stub balance?

You should fill out the check stub before the check is written, for then (a) you will be less likely to make a mistake when writing the check, (b) you will be less likely to write a check for a sum greater than the amount of money that you have in the bank, and (c) you are assured of a record of each check written.

Fig. 4. A Record Sheet Arrangement of the check.

DATE	CHECK NUMBER	CHECKS ISSUED TO OR DEPOSIT RECEIVED FROM	AMOUNT OF DEPOSIT	V	AMOUNT OF CHECK	BALANCE
						134 50
10/23			62 31			196 81
10/24	47	Frank Hoffman			17 65	179 16

Fig. 5. A Personal Check Written by Carl Smith and Given to Frank Hoffman, Who Took It to the Bank, Where It Was Paid and Canceled.

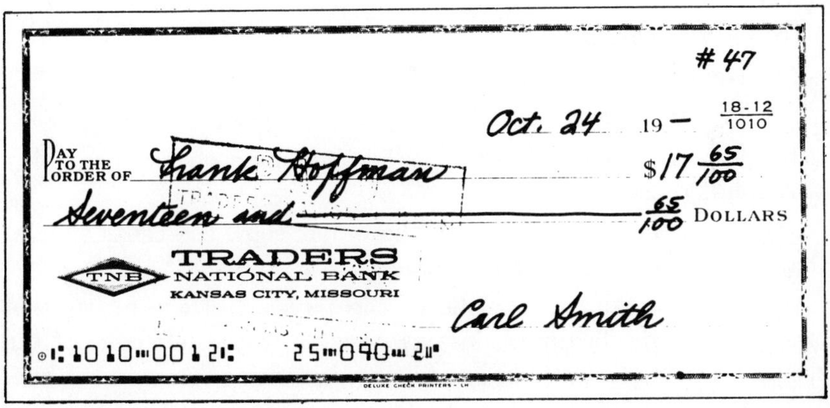
#47

Oct. 24 19— 18-12/1010

PAY TO THE ORDER OF Frank Hoffman $17 65/100

Seventeen and 65/100 DOLLARS

TRADERS NATIONAL BANK
KANSAS CITY, MISSOURI

Carl Smith

1. If the balance after the 10th check is written is $345.97, what will be the balance carried forward to the 11th stub?

2. If the balance on the stub is $345.97, and $399.89 is deposited, what is the total in the bank?

3. If the balance on the stub is $164.82, and a check is written for $73.95, what is the new balance?

*4. James Brown's checkbook showed a balance of $350.62. He deposited $46.62. He then wrote a check for $209.16. What was the new balance?

*5. If the balance on a stub is $161.96, a deposit of $74.28 is made, and then a check is written for $66.76, how much is left in the bank?

**6. The balance after the 36th check is written is $175.20. If a deposit of $37.89 is entered on the stub of the 37th check and the amount of the 37th check is $57.37, what is the balance carried forward to the 38th stub?

95. Personal check. Figure 5 illustrates a *personal check.* Carl Smith, the person whose signature appears at the bottom of the check, is the *drawer;* the Traders National Bank, the bank that is to pay the amount of the check, is the *drawee;* and Frank Hoffman, the one to whom the money is to be paid, is the *payee.*

96. Writing the check. The following cautions should be observed when writing a check:

(a) Always write a check in ink. This makes it difficult to change the amount.

(b) Write plainly.

(c) Never erase on a check. Destroy the spoiled check.

(d) Be sure that sufficient money is on deposit.

(e) Fill in the correct date. When writing a check on Sunday or a holiday, use that date.

(f) Place the figures close to the dollar sign, the cents smaller than the dollars; for example, 35\frac{45}{100}$, 35\underline{\underline{45}}$, $35/^{45}$.

(g) When writing the name of the payee and the amount of money in words, begin as close as possible to the left edge of the check. Draw in a wavy line to fill any remaining space on the line.

(h) When possible, stamp the amount on the check with one of the patented machines designed for this purpose.

(i) Write your signature exactly as written on the signature card. The bank will probably check the signature.

(j) Let the signature be the last item written on the check.

97. Indorsing the check. Figure 5 is a check which belongs to Frank Hoffman; it was made out to him by Carl Smith. Before Frank Hoffman can collect any money on the check, he must indorse it. His check then becomes the property of the person to whom he gives it. Frank Hoffman may write any one of several forms of indorsement on the check.

Three of the most common forms of indorsement are shown in figure 6: (A) a blank indorsement, (B) a full indorsement, and (C) a restrictive indorsement.

If Frank Hoffman writes only his name on the back of the check, he does not specify to whom payment is to be made. He merely releases his ownership to anyone who may have possession of the check. This is a *blank indorsement*, as illustrated in figure 6A. If Frank Hoffman lost this check with a blank indorsement on it, the finder might try to cash it, since there is no stated owner in the indorsement. In this case Frank Hoffman should immediately report the loss to the drawer of the check, who should ask the bank on which it is written to *Stop Payment.*

If Frank Hoffman writes *Pay to the order of* and then writes the name of the party to whom he is giving the check, he thereby specifies to whom payment is to be made. By placing his signature under the name of the party, he releases his ownership of the check. This is a *full indorsement*, as illustrated in figure 6B. To whom does Frank Hoffman release his ownership in this figure? A full indorsement is safer than a blank indorsement and should always be used when a check is being transferred from one person to another.

Fig. 6. Three Common Forms of Indorsement.

If Frank Hoffman wishes to deposit the check, he can protect himself by indorsing it as in figure 6C. Such an indorsement is known as a *restrictive indorsement*. If lost, the check would be of no value to the finder, since the indorsement shows that the check is to be deposited. No one can cash it.

An indorsement is placed across the back of the check near the stub end. The payee must write his name in the indorsement exactly as it was written on the face of the check by the drawer. If his name was misspelled on the check, the payee must copy the spelling and place below this name his signature correctly spelled.

98. Bank statement. The *bank statement* is issued once each month. At that time you should get your canceled checks and your bank statement from the bank. A *canceled check* is one that has been paid by the bank and has the word *Paid* and the date received pierced through the paper. A canceled check makes a good receipt, as it shows that payment has been made. Figure 7 is a bank statement. Notice the items that are listed on the bank statement.

```
                    ⌐                          ¬        OCT. 13
                        CARL SMITH                          TO
                                                        OCT. 31
                        321 CONCORD STREET               19-
                    ∟   KANSAS CITY, MO.               ⌐

                STATEMENT OF YOUR ACCOUNT FOR ABOVE DATE
```

CHECKS		DEPOSITS	DATE	BALANCE
AMOUNT BROUGHT FORWARD				
		Oct 13 150.00	Oct 13	150.00
Oct 14	5.00		Oct 14	145.00
Oct 17	10.50		Oct 17	134.50
		Oct 23 62.31	Oct 23	196.81
Oct 24	17.65		Oct 24	179.16
Oct 31	15.00 5.00		Oct 31	159.16

PLEASE EXAMINE THIS STATEMENT AND REPORT ANY EXCEPTIONS PROMPTLY.
IF YOUR NAME OR ADDRESS IS INCORRECT, PLEASE NOTIFY US.
ALL ITEMS ARE CREDITED SUBJECT TO FINAL PAYMENT.

THE LAST AMOUNT
IN THIS COLUMN
IS YOUR BALANCE

Fig. 7. Bank Statement of Carl Smith's Account.

99. Reconciliation. The stub of the checkbook, if properly kept, shows the correct balance of money in the bank. The bank statement also shows the correct balance in the bank. However, many times these two balances do not agree. The question then is, which one is correct? Both may be right or both may be wrong. The process by which the stub balance and the bank statement balance are checked against one another is called *reconciliation.*

To ascertain the correct balance, proceed as follows:

(a) See that the stubs contain every deposit listed on the bank statement. *Add any deposits not already added on stubs.*

(b) Look for penalties, such as fines or fees, that may have been subtracted on the bank statement but not on the stub balance. If so, *subtract penalties from the stub balance.*

(c) Arrange the canceled checks according to the number of each check, the first number on top. Compare every check with the corresponding stub. The checks and stubs should agree; however, there may be checks for which there are no stubs. If so, *subtract checks not already subtracted from the stub balance.*

(d) List the numbers and amounts of any stubs for which there are no canceled checks. Those checks have not been turned in to the bank for payment; hence the bank has not subtracted them from the balance. If so, *subtract these outstanding checks from the bank statement.*

(e) If the two balances still do not agree, prove each addition and subtraction on the stubs.

Here is an example showing how a reconciliation is made. (The letters in parentheses refer to the preceding rules.)

SEPTEMBER 1

A. Stub balance			$417.47
(a) Deposit not added on stubs			25.00
			$442.47
(b) Fines not subtracted on stubs			1.00
			$441.47
(c) Checks not subtracted on stubs		$21.50	
		36.75	
		28.14	
		$86.39	86.39
Correct balance			$355.08
B. Bank statement balance			$531.58
(d) Checks outstanding	#18	$106.50	
	#20	70.00	
		$176.50	176.50
Correct balance			$355.08

Hence the correct balance in the bank is $355.08.

Make a reconciliation for each of the following:

*1. On January 1 Jay Ward's account stood as follows: stub balance, $316.09; bank statement balance, $755.74; deposits not recorded on stubs, $96.69 and $61.78; checks outstanding, #64 for $21.48, #68 for $67.03, #75 for $188.17, and #76 for $4.50.

*2. On February 1 John Webb's account stood as follows: bank statement balance, $2,762.36; checks outstanding, #84 for $416.25, #93 for $26.03, #94 for $289.67; fines, $1.00; stub balance, $1,963.27; deposit missing on stub, $114.89; check with no stub, $46.75.

*3. Your stub balance is $161.42; outstanding checks, #16 for $18.75 and #20 for $4.82; bank statement balance, $223.79; fine, $1.00; checks not subtracted, #12 for $6.15 and #14 for $10.80; deposit not added on stub, $56.75.

*4. On April 1 Joan Parmer's bank account was as follows: stub balance, $318.76; bank statement balance, $320.69; checks not subtracted on stubs, $12.80 and $7.25; outstanding checks, #12 for $10.40, #13 for $4.38, and #15 for $7.20.

*5. Bank statement balance, $769.77; stub balance, $739.26; checks outstanding, #20 for $15.35, #22 for $12.18, and #25 for $20.50; checks not subtracted on stubs, $5.12 and $12.40.

*6. Stub balance, $324.80; bank statement balance, $374.60; deposit not added on stub, $45.12; checks not recorded on stubs, $18.25, $3.78, and $10.24; checks outstanding, #31 for $12.40, #33 for $18.20, and #34 for $6.35.

*7. On July 1 Henry Hunter's bank account was: checks outstanding, #42 for $18.75, #43 for $12.92, and #44 for $6.90; deposits not recorded on stubs, $41.20 and $32.45; stub balance, $125.66; bank statement balance, $237.88.

*8. Bert Casper's bank account on June 1 was: stub balance, $251.18; bank statement balance, $270.84; deposit not recorded on stub, $18.30; checks not recorded on stubs, $15.80 and $9.36; outstanding checks, $10.00, $8.64, and $7.88.

*9. Outstanding checks, #49 for $17.80, #51 for $26.00, #53 for $5.00, and #54 for $7.75; fines, $1.00, 25¢, and 25¢; stub balance, $68.72; bank statement balance, $138.17; deposit not added on stub, $14.40.

*10. Bank statement balance, $73.04; check not subtracted on stub, $50.26; deposits not added, $25.20, $17.80, and $36.19; stub balance, $44.11.

100. Interest. One function of the commercial department of a bank is to lend money to people who need it for business or personal uses. When a bank makes a loan to a person, the loan is made for a certain amount of money and for a certain period of time. The sum of money borrowed is the *principal* (p); the money paid for the use of the principal is the *interest* (i); the percent of principal that is to be paid as interest is the *rate* (r); the period allowed for the repayment of the principal is the time (t); and the sum of the principal and interest is the *amount* (a).

To find the interest, use the following formula:

Interest = principal × rate × time (in years).

The formula is written: $i = p \times r \times t$.

A. An easy method of finding interest for any number of days, months, or years is the cancellation method.

To use cancellation, express the rate (r) as a fraction. For instance, express 6% as $\dfrac{6}{100}$, 4% as $\dfrac{4}{100}$, $2\frac{1}{2}\%$ as $\dfrac{2.5}{100}$ or $\dfrac{5}{200}$.

The time (t) is computed as 360 days to the year by banks in computing simple interest. The time should be expressed as a fractional part of one year. For instance: (a) 90 days = $\frac{90}{360}$ or $\frac{1}{4}$ year, (b) 8 months = $\frac{8}{12}$ or $\frac{2}{3}$ year, (c) 3 years = $\frac{3}{1}$, (d) 1 year 6 months = 18 mo. = $\frac{18}{12}$ or $\frac{3}{2}$ yr.

────────────── EXAMPLES ──────────────

(1) Find the interest on $840 at 6% for 120 days.

$$i = \frac{\$840}{1} \times \frac{6}{100} \times \frac{120}{360} = \$16.80$$

(2) Find the amount on $720 @ $4\frac{1}{2}\%$ for 1 yr. 8 mo.

$$i = \frac{\$720}{1} \times \frac{9}{200} \times \frac{20}{12} = \$54$$

$$a = \$720 + \$54 = \$774$$

1. Express as a common fraction: (a) 4%   (b) 5%   (c) 2%
(d) $3\frac{1}{2}$%   (e) $1\frac{1}{2}$%   (f) $2\frac{1}{4}$%   (g) $2\frac{1}{3}$%   (h) $5\frac{1}{2}$%

2. Express as a fractional part of 1 year: (a) 72 da.   (b) 60 da.
(c) 45 da.   (d) 180 da.   (e) 240 da.   (f) 15 da.   (g) 6 mo.   (h)
4 mo.   (i) 10 mo.   (j) 1 yr. 9 mo.   (k) 1 yr. 8 mo.   (l) 2 yr.
3 mo.   (m) 1 yr. 2 mo.   (n) 2 yr.

Find the interest on:

3. $630 at 4% for 60 da.

4. $960 at 5% for 90 da.

5. $1200 at 3% for 75 da.

6. $1800 at 6% for 2 mo.

7. $450 at 2% for 8 mo.

8. $540 at 3% for 96 da.

9. $1050 at 4% for 10 mo.

10. $365 at 6% for 2 yr.

Find the amount on:

11. $720 at 4% for 3 mo.

12. $840 at 5% for 48 da.

13. $1020 at 3% for 10 mo.

14. $660 at 5% for 6 mo.

Find the interest on:

*15. $1600 at 6% for 1 yr. 3 mo.

*16. $1750 at 4% for 1 yr. 4 mo.

*17. $1250 at 6% for 2 yr. 6 mo.

*18. $1500 at 5% for 1 yr. 8 mo.

**19. $3600 at $2\frac{1}{2}$% for 150 da.

**20. $2400 at $3\frac{1}{2}$% for 84 da.

**21. $420 at $1\frac{1}{4}$% for 8 mo.

**22. $870 at $4\frac{1}{2}$% for 10 mo.

Find the amount of:

**23. $920 at $3\frac{1}{4}$% for 1 yr. 6 mo.

**24. $750 at $2\frac{1}{3}$% for 1 yr. 9 mo.

**25. $720 at $5\frac{1}{2}$% for 100 da.

**26. $640 at 6% for 5 mo.

**27. $1080 at 4% for 2 yr. 4 mo.

B. A short-cut method of computing interest is the "60-day" or "6%" method. If you are told that the interest on

$100 for 60 da. at 6% is $1.00
$200 " " " " " " $2.00
$420 " " " " " " $4.20
$1,800 " " " " " " $18.00

can you discover the short cut?

Rule. *To find the interest for 60 days at 6 per cent, move the decimal point in the principal 2 places to the left.*
To find the interest for 30 days at 6 per cent, divide the interest for 60 days by 2.

Using the 6% method, write the interest on the following loans at 6%:

1. (a) $300 for 60 da.   (f) $890 for 30 da.
    (b)   460 " 30 "   (g)   480 " 15 "
    (c)   655 " 60 "   (h)   60 " 30 "
    (d)   22 " 30 "   (i)   180 " 15 "
    (e)   717 " 60 "   (j)   250 " 30 "

2. (a) $600 for 60 da.   (j) $ 120 for 60 da.
    (b)   600 " 30 "   (k)   120 " 10 "
    (c)   600 " 90 "   (l)   120 " 70 "
    (d)   300 " 60 "   (m) 1500 " 60 "
    (e)   300 " 10 "   (n) 1500 " 15 "
    (f)   300 " 70 "   (o) 1500 " 75 "
    (g)   550 " 60 "   (p) 3600 " 60 "
    (h)   550 " 15 "   (q) 3600 " 10 "
    (i)   550 " 75 "   (r) 3600 " 70 "

3. (a) $ 480 for 60 da.   (g) $ 360 for 10 da.
    (b)   480 " 10 "   (h)   240 " 10 "
    (c) 7200 " 10 "   (i)   132 " 10 "
    (d) 1200 " 10 "   (j)   96 " 10 "
    (e)   660 " 10 "   (k)   108 " 10 "
    (f)   66 " 10 "   (l) 1080 " 10 "

4. (a) $ 900 for 60 da.   (h) $ 240 for 20 da.
    (b)   900 " 20 "   (i)   18 " 20 "
    (c)   33 " 20 "   (j)   144 " 20 "
    (d)   48 " 20 "   (k) 2100 " 20 "
    (e) 15,000 " 20 "   (l)   93 " 20 "
    (f)   420 " 20 "   (m)   210 " 20 "
    (g)   1800 " 20 "   (n)   390 " 20 "

*5. Find the interest for 60 days on each of the following:

(a)	$600 at 6%	(g)	$666 at 6%	(m)	$36 at 2%
(b)	600 " 3%	(h)	666 " 3%	(n)	96 " 6%
(c)	600 " 1%	(i)	666 " 1%	(o)	96 " 3%
(d)	240 " 6%	(j)	36 " 6%	(p)	96 " 1%
(e)	240 " 3%	(k)	36 " 3%	(q)	72 " 6%
(f)	240 " 1%	(l)	36 " 1%	(r)	72 " 1%

EXAMPLE

Find the interest on $840 at 6% for 88 days.

Interest for 60 da.	=	$8.40	
" " 20 da.	=	2.80	($\frac{1}{3}$ of 60-da. int.)
" " 6 da.	=	.84	($\frac{1}{10}$ of 60-da. int.)
" " 2 da.	=	.28	($\frac{1}{3}$ of 6-da. int.)
Interest for 88 da.	=	$12.32	

If the rate is not 6% but 5%, for instance, first find the interest at 6% and then take $\frac{5}{6}$ of the result.

**6. Find the interest at 6%. (See the example above.)

(a)	$960 for 80 da.	(f)	$1600 for 88 da.
(b)	720 " 75 "	(g)	420 " 36 "
(c)	425 " 72 "	(h)	487 " 120 "
(d)	848 " 96 "	(i)	3648 " 150 "
(e)	870 " 100 "	(j)	480 " 42 "

**7. Using the method illustrated above, find the interest:

(a)	$ 420 at 4% for 90 da.	(f)	$ 387 at 8% for 180 da.
(b)	450 " 4% " 72 "	(g)	456 " 3% " 240 "
(c)	1200 " 5% " 90 "	(h)	48.60 " 3% " 90 "
(d)	3600 " 8% " 88 "	(i)	672 " 8% " 190 "
(e)	720 " 7% " 6 "	(j)	1260 " 4% " 75 "

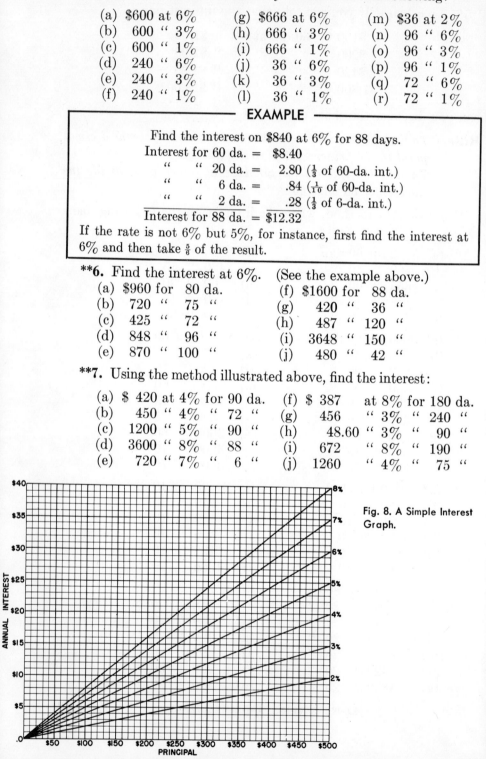

Fig. 8. A Simple Interest Graph.

101. Simple interest graph. Figure 8 is a graph by which the annual interest at various rates may be determined. Each horizontal line is divided into 50 divisions, each division representing $10 principal. Each vertical line is divided into 40 divisions, each division representing $1 interest.

To find the interest on $100 at 2%, follow the 2% rate line to the vertical line representing $100 principal. Since the intersection of these two lines is on the horizontal line representing $2 interest, the annual interest on $100 at 2% is $2. Similarly, the interest on $350 at 8% is found to be $28.

──────────────── EXERCISES ────────────────

Using the interest graph, find the annual interest on each of the following:

(a) $150 at 2%	(h) $150 at 4%	(o) $300 at 8%
(b) 350 " 4%	(i) 250 " 6%	(p) 280 " 5%
(c) 200 " 5%	(j) 300 " 7%	(q) 150 " 6%
(d) 450 " 8%	(k) 150 " 8%	(r) 260 " 5%
(e) 500 " 7%	(l) 450 " 2%	(s) 100 " 7%
(f) 300 " 3%	(m) 500 " 8%	(t) 450 " 4%
(g) 50 " 8%	(n) 300 " 4%	(u) 720 " 3%

102. Saving for a purpose. When should a person start saving? While saving a part of money received should begin at an early age, systematic saving should begin as soon as money is earned regularly.

Early savings probably will be for something especially desired in the near future, such as a baseball uniform, a radio, a used car, more schooling, or a trip to camp. Such purposeful savings later on will likely be in the nature of saving for a home, for a business, for a rainy day, or for investments.

103. Saving money in a savings bank. Just as a commercial department is a safe place to keep money which is to be checked out for current use, a savings department is a safe place to keep money which is being accumulated for a later investment.

Savings are deposited in a savings account. Interest is paid on deposits at the rate of from 1% to $4\frac{1}{2}$%. Savings banks (a) permit savings accounts to be opened with an amount as small as $1, (b) accept small deposits, (c) pay compound interest semiannually or quarterly.

To open a savings account, you fill out a signature card as for a checking account. A savings account differs from a check-

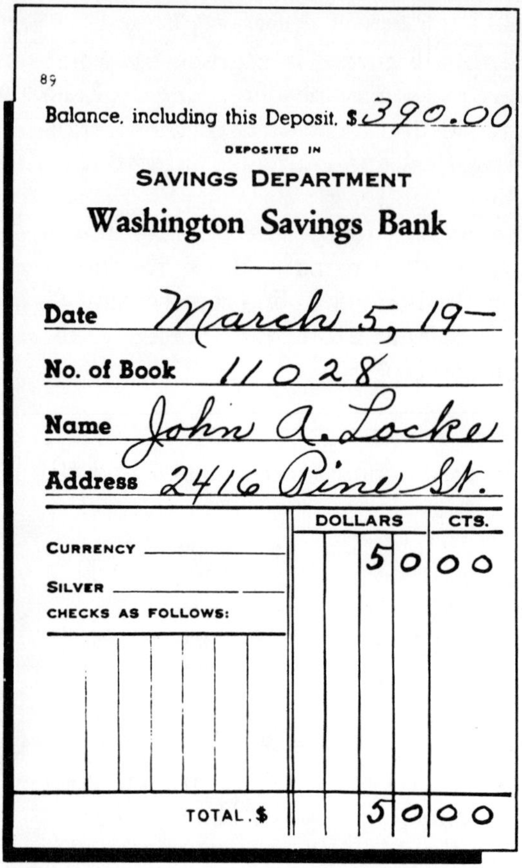

Balance, including this Deposit. $ *390.00*

DEPOSITED IN

SAVINGS DEPARTMENT

Washington Savings Bank

Date *March 5, 19—*

No. of Book *11028*

Name *John A. Locke*

Address *2416 Pine St.*

		DOLLARS		CTS.
CURRENCY		5 0	0 0	
SILVER				
CHECKS AS FOLLOWS:				
TOTAL. $		5 0	0 0	

Fig. 9. Deposit Ticket for a Savings Account.

ing account in the manner by which you deposit and withdraw your money. In filling out a deposit ticket for a savings account, two additional items are listed— the number of the passbook and the new balance after this deposit is made. (See figure 9.) The teller enters the amount of the deposit and the new balance in the passbook and returns the passbook to you. When money is to be withdrawn, you fill out a *withdrawal blank* and present it with your passbook to the teller. You receive the money from the teller, who enters the amount of withdrawal and the new balance in the book and returns the book. (See figure 10.)

104. Compound interest. Compounding of interest means that, as interest is earned, it is added to the principal, making a new principal for the next interest period. The interest-paying periods may be annual (every 12 months), semiannual (every six months), or quarterly (every three months).

When interest is compounded annually, the given rate is used and the interest is added to the principal at the close of each 12 months. This new principal (the old principal plus the interest) is used for the next year, and so it may continue for years.

When interest is compounded semiannually, one-half of the given rate is used and the interest is added to the principal at the close of each six months, making two interest periods each year.

When interest is compounded quarterly, one-fourth of the given rate is used and the interest is added to the principal at the close of each three months, making four interest periods each year.

Fig. 10. Page in Passbook for Savings Account.

Date		Deposit	Withdrawal	Interest	Balance
Jan 2	B	300. 00			300. 00
Feb 5	B	40. 00			340. 00
Mar 5	A	50. 00			390. 00
May 20	B		60. 00		330. 00
Jun 3	A	20. 00			350. 00
Jul 1				1. 47	351. 47
Jul 10	B	15. 80			367. 27

EXAMPLES

Find the compound interest on $400 at 2% for 2 years. (Compute the interest on dollars only. Disregard cents.)

Example 1

Compounded annually:

$400.00 1st Prin.
   8.00 1st Int.
$408.00 2nd Prin.
   8.16 2nd Int.
$416.16 Amt. at close of 2 yr.

Example 2

Compounded semiannually:

$400.00 1st Prin.
   4.00 1st Int.
$404.00 2nd Prin.
   4.04 2nd Int.
$408.04 3rd Prin.
   4.08 3rd Int.
$412.12 4th Prin.
   4.12 4th Int.
$416.24 Amt. at close of 2 yr.

Example 3

Compounded quarterly:

$400.00 1st Prin.
   2.00 1st Int.
$402.00 2nd Prin.
   2.01 2nd Int.
$404.01 3rd Prin.
   2.02 3rd Int.
$406.03 4th Prin.
   2.03 4th Int.
$408.06 5th Prin.
   2.04 5th Int.
$410.10 6th Prin.
   2.05 6th Int.
$412.15 7th Prin.
   2.06 7th Int.
$414.21 8th Prin.
   2.07 8th Int.
$416.28 Amt. at close of 2 yr.

Compute the amount of the following with compound interest:

*1. $500 @ 3% for 4 yr. annually.

*2. $300 @ 4% for 3 yr. annually.

*3. $300 @ 4% for 2 yr. semiannually.

*4. $240 @ 2% for 3 yr. semiannually.

*5. $600 @ 4% for 1 yr. quarterly.

*6. $1,200 @ 2% for 2 yr. quarterly.

**7. Mr. Jackson deposited $2,560 on Jan. 1 in a savings account paying $3\frac{1}{4}$% compounded semiannually. How much interest did his money earn by July 1? What was the amount?

**8. Mrs. McCall deposited $1,500 in a savings bank paying $3\frac{1}{2}$% interest compounded annually. Calculate the amount at the end of three years.

**9. John Baxter put $800 in a savings account earning 2% interest compounded quarterly. What will be the amount in $1\frac{1}{2}$ years?

105. Compound interest table. Computing compound interest can become a very slow process if the time extends through many years. Time can be saved by using a compound interest table to compute interest. See Table 1.

TABLE 1

A COMPOUND INTEREST TABLE				
Showing what $1 will amount to at compound interest				
Period	1 per cent	1½ per cent	2 per cent	3 per cent
1	1.0100 000	1.0150 000	1.0200 0000	1.0300 0000
2	1.0201 000	1.0302 250	1.0404 0000	1.0609 0000
3	1.0303 010	1.0456 784	1.0612 0800	1.0927 2700
4	1.0406 040	1.0613 636	1.0824 3216	1.1255 0881
5	1.0510 100	1.0772 840	1.1040 8080	1.1592 7407
6	1.0615 202	1.0934 433	1.1261 6242	1.1940 5230
7	1.0721 354	1.1098 450	1.1486 8507	1.2298 7387
8	1.0828 567	1.1264 926	1.1716 5928	1.2667 7008
9	1.0936 853	1.1433 900	1.1950 9257	1.3047 7318
10	1.1046 221	1.1605 408	1.2189 9442	1.3439 1638
11	1.1156 683	1.1779 489	1.2433 7431	1.3842 3387
12	1.1268 250	1.1956 182	1.2682 4179	1.4257 6089
13	1.1380 933	1.2135 524	1.2936 0603	1.4685 3371
14	1.1494 742	1.2317 557	1.3194 7876	1.5125 8972
15	1.1609 690	1.2502 321	1.3458 6834	1.5579 6742
16	1.1725 786	1.2689 855	1.3727 8570	1.6047 0644
17	1.1843 044	1.2880 203	1.4002 4142	1.6528 4763
18	1.1961 475	1.3073 406	1.4282 4625	1.7024 3306
19	1.2081 090	1.3269 507	1.4568 1117	1.7535 0605
20	1.2201 900	1.3468 550	1.4859 4740	1.8061 1123

Using the table, find the amount when the interest is compounded:
   (1) Of $300 annually for 10 years at $1\frac{1}{2}\%$:

   Rate = $1\frac{1}{2}\%$ annually.
   Periods = 10.
   Follow down $1\frac{1}{2}\%$ column to the 10th period.
   $1.1605408   Amt. of $1 for 10 yr. @ $1\frac{1}{2}\%$
   $\times$ 300
   ────────
   $348.1622400
      or
   $348.16   Amt. of $300 for 10 yr. at $1\frac{1}{2}\%$.

   (2) Of $500 semiannually for 8 years at 2%:

   Rate = 2% annually = 1% semiannually.
   Periods = $2 \times 8 = 16$.
   Follow down 1% column to the 16th period.
   $1.1725786   Amt. of $1 for 8 yr. @ 2%
   $\times$ 500
   ────────
   $586.2893000
      or
   $586.29   Amt. of $500 for 8 yr. at 2%.

EXERCISES

Using the table, find the amount when interest is compounded on the following:

*1. $600 for 5 yr. @ 3% annually.

*2. $400 for 16 yr. @ 2% annually.

*3. $800 for 20 yr. @ $1\frac{1}{2}\%$ annually.

*4. $500 for 5 yr. @ 2% semiannually.

*5. $700 for 10 yr. @ 3% semiannually.

*6. $200 for 6 yr. @ 3% semiannually.

*7. $1,000 for 20 yr. @ 1% annually.

*8. $2,000 for 10 yr. @ 2% semiannually.

*9. $300 for 7 yr. @ 3% semiannually.

*10. $800 for 4 yr. @ 2% annually.

**11. If on your 8th birthday your father had deposited $100 for you in a savings account @ 2% compounded semiannually, how much would the deposit be worth at your next birthday?

**12. If you, at age 20, deposit $500 in a savings account at 3% compounded semiannually, how much will the account amount to when you are 30 years of age?

106. Saving in a savings and loan association. A savings and loan association has two primary functions: (1) to handle savings much as a savings bank does, and (2) to loan money for use in buying homes.

Money is deposited in a savings and loan association in the same way as it is in a savings bank. Interest is compounded semiannually or quarterly. Some savings and loan associations have a systematic way of saving in which you buy shares in the association. You agree to purchase a certain number of shares in the association, for which you are to pay in monthly installments over a number of years. The payments are usually 50 cents per month for each $100 share. The association pays compound interest on the payments that are made by you. The share is paid up, or matured, when the payments made plus the interest earned equal the face value of the share being bought. It takes close to 12 years for a $100 share to mature. At maturity you may receive $100, the face value of the share, or you may leave the $100 with the association and receive dividends on it.

Savings and loan associations, which are members of the Federal Savings and Loan Insurance Corporation, are insured up to $10,000 for each account.

A savings and loan association is owned by the depositors, and they share its profits. These profits are given to the depositors as dividends, or as interest on their savings. The rate of interest depends on how much the association's money that is out on loan is earning; and may be $4\frac{1}{2}\%$ or more.

The money you place in savings and investment accounts in a savings and loan association is loaned to purchasers of real estate. The amount of loan obtainable varies from 60 to 80 per cent of the value of the property being purchased. The borrower receives the money at once, the loan of which is secured by a mortgage on the property. He is to pay back the loan in monthly installments which must also include interest on the unpaid balance.

────────────────── *EXERCISES* ──────────────────

1. Jerry has received a gift of $450. If he deposits it in a savings and loan association and interest is compounded semi-annually at 4%, what will the amount of his savings be at the end of four years?

*2. (a) Mae Martin is investing $15 per month in shares at 50 cents per month per $100 share. For how many shares has she subscribed?

(b) What will be the value of the shares when they mature?

(c) If in 11 yr. 6 mo. the shares are paid for, how much has Mae paid out in payments for them?

*3. (a) Clark Jones wishes to save $10 per month on the share buying plan. How many shares can he buy at 50¢ per month for each $100 share?

(b) What will be the value of his shares when paid up?

(c) If the shares are paid up in 11 yr. 7 mo., how much will Clark have paid for them?

*4. Jack has $486 on deposit in a savings account. What will be the amount of his savings after 6 years if interest at 4% per year is compounded quarterly?

*5. Mr. Harris wishes to buy property worth $8,000. He has $3,000 for a down payment and subscribes for enough $100 shares to cover a loan to complete the purchase price. (a) For how many shares will he have to subscribe?

(b) Find his monthly dues at 50 cents per share.

(c) What per cent of the cost did he borrow?

**6. Property worth $10,000 is bought by Mr. Senior. He pays $4,000 down and finances the remainder of the cost by subscribing for $100 shares at 50 cents per month per share. (a) For how many shares did he subscribe?

(b) Find their value at maturity.

(c) What per cent of the cost did Mr. Senior borrow?

**7. Mr. Jacobs buys real estate for $12,000. He pays $4,000 down and borrows the remainder from a building and loan association at 50 cents per month for each $100 share. (a) For how many shares must Mr. Jacobs subscribe?

(b) If the shares are paid up in 11 yr. 7 mo., how much was paid to the association in dues?

(c) What per cent of the cost was the loan?

**8. Mr. Pitt invests in property worth $9,000. He pays $3,000 down and subscribes for enough $100 shares to cover a loan to complete the cost. (a) For how many shares did he subscribe? (b) What are his monthly dues at 50¢ per share? (c) What per cent of the cost was the loan?

VOCABULARY

1. investment	4. par value	7. dividend
2. corporation	5. common stock	8. market value
3. capital stock	6. preferred stock	9. brokerage

107. Investments. By saving regularly, Mr. Hill has built up a savings account that is large enough for an investment. Realizing that he is not well informed on investments, Mr. Hill consults his banker, who advises him to consider:

(1) *Safety.* Will the money be safe? While no investment is 100 per cent safe, some investments are practically so while some others are extremely risky. Safety of the principal is of the greatest importance. No investment ranks higher in safety than United States Government bonds.

(2) *Salability.* How quickly can the investment be converted into cash if needed? Some investments have a ready market; others may take months to convert into cash. Bonds and stocks are highly salable. A business or real estate may be slow in selling.

(3) *Income.* What rate of income will the investment yield? It is usually true that a highly safe investment yields a low rate of income while a risky investment offers a high rate. For the small investor, it is wise to consider safety first. Bonds bear a low rate of interest. A business, real estate, and stocks may, or may not, earn a high rate of income for the owner.

108. Bonds. The Government and large corporations often need to borrow huge amounts of money. These loans are secured by *bonds* issued by the borrower. The bonds are a type of promissory note in that the borrower promises to pay back the loan with specified interest at a specified time. The time is usually ten or more years later.

109. Corporation bonds. The Eastern Railroad Corporation, wishing to extend its lines and improve its service, needs $5,000,000, a larger sum of money than it is able to borrow from a bank or from an individual. However, it may borrow the money from a number of different persons by issuing bonds. These bonds are usually in denominations of $1,000, or $500, payable from 5 years to 50 years after the date they are issued, and with interest at about 5%. Such a bond might be listed in the newspapers as "Eastern 5's, 2007," meaning that the Eastern Railroad bond pays 5% interest and matures in 2007. Corporation bonds are often made safe by a mortgage on the property of the corporation.

The price at which a bond can be bought is its *market value*. The value printed upon the bond is its face value, sometimes called its *par value*. If the market value is quoted at more than the face value, the bond is said to be *above par;* if at less than face value, it is said to be *below par*.

──────────── EXERCISES ────────────

1. Some $1,000 bonds are sold at the following prices. How much above or below par value is the market value of each bond?

(a) $996	(e) $1,067.46	(i) $982.25	(m) $1,169.85
(b) $1,097	(f) $992.50	(j) $1,043.80	(n) $988.24
(c) $1,016	(g) $987.70	(k) $997.75	(o) $1,014.17
(d) $989	(h) $1,145.45	(l) $1,111.11	(p) $980.28

2. The broker's fee on the purchase of $1000 bonds is as follows:

```
1 or 2 bonds.................. $5.00 each
3 bonds......................   4.00   "
4 bonds......................   3.00   "
5 or more bonds..............   2.50   "
```

What is the brokerage for buying the following number of $1,000 bonds:

(a) 2	(b) 3	(c) 4	(d) 10
(e) 12	(f) 16	(g) 24	(h) 28
(i) 9	(j) 48	(k) 19	(l) 36

3. What is the semiannual interest on a $1,000 bond at 6%? 5%? 4%?

4. If a $1,000 bond is quoted at 95, the market value is 95% of $1,000, or $950. Find the market value of the following bonds:

(a) One $1,000 Mo. Pac. $4\frac{1}{4}$'s @ $88\frac{1}{4}$.
(b) One $1,000 Tex. Corp. 3's @ $99\frac{1}{4}$.
(c) One $1,000 Firestone 3's @ $91\frac{1}{2}$.
(d) One $1,000 M.K.T. 5's @ $82\frac{5}{8}$.
(e) One $1,000 Gt. Nor. Ry. 5's @ 113.
(f) One $1,000 Lockheed $3\frac{1}{4}$'s @ 104.

*5. Find the market value and the semiannual interest on the following bonds:

(a) Twenty $1,000 Del. & Hud. 4's @ 101.
(b) Five $100 Erie 5's @ $27\frac{7}{8}$.
(c) Ten $500 Cont. Bak. $3\frac{5}{8}$'s @ $96\frac{1}{2}$.
(d) Four $500 Wabash $3\frac{1}{4}$'s @ 98.
(e) Two $1,000 M.K.T. 4's @ 65.
(f) Six $1,000 N. Y. Cen. 6's @ $104\frac{7}{8}$.
(g) Ten $500 Cities S. 3's @ $84\frac{3}{4}$.
(h) Twenty $100 Penn. R. R. $4\frac{1}{2}$'s @ $99\frac{1}{2}$.

110. United States Government bonds.

A common investment for many citizens is United States Government bonds. These bonds represent money loaned to the United States. They are safe, for they are backed by the Government's promise to pay.

Government bonds may be bought and sold on the market, their prices being quoted in per cents on the financial page of the daily newspapers.

One issue gave these quotations:

(1)	$2\frac{1}{2}$ s	'72–'67	94.26
(2)	$3\frac{1}{4}$ s	'83–'78	104.60
(3)	$2\frac{1}{4}$ s	'62–'59	96.10
(4)	$2\frac{3}{4}$ s	'65–'60	103.20
(5)	3 s	'95	98.22

The number (1) bonds pay $2\frac{1}{2}\%$ interest, some maturing in 1967 and others in 1972. They are priced at 94.26 per cent of their face value. The cost of a $100 bond would be $94.26. A $1,000 bond would cost $942.60. These bonds are priced at below their face value.

The original popular 10-year United States Savings bonds Series E have matured; yet, if not cashed, they live on, as the Treasury has extended the life of these bonds for another ten years. Series E bonds are registered bonds and at maturity are worth one-third more than their purchase price.

The Series E bonds that were issued on May 1, 1952, and thereafter are worth slightly more than the ones issued before then.

Values of government bonds fluctuate. Table 2 shows a comparison of cash values of old Series E Bonds with a recent list of cash values of a Series E Bond (bought at $75) and held for various periods of time.

TABLE 2

Cash value if bought

Years held	before May 1, 1952	on or after May 1, 1952	on or after May 1, 1952
1 yr.	$75.50	$76.20	$76.76
3 yr.	78.00	80.20	82.64
5 yr.	82.00	85.00	89.60
7 yr.	88.00	90.60	97.08
Maturity.	$100.00 (10 yr.)	$100.00 ($9\frac{2}{3}$ yr.)	$100.00 ($7\frac{3}{4}$ yr.)

TABLE 3

SERIES E BONDS

Cost Price	Maturity Value	Cost Price	Maturity Value
$18.75.	$25.00	$150.00.	$200.00
37.50.	50.00	375.00.	500.00
75.00.	100.00	750.00.	1,000.00

The Series H bonds have approximately the same yield as that of the Series E bonds. They are different in that their interest is paid semiannually and the smallest denomination is $500.

─────────────────────── EXERCISES ───────────────────────

1. How much is the interest received on a $25 Series E bond at maturity? What does the interest average per year?

2. How much interest is received on a $50 Series E bond at maturity? What is the average interest per year? How does the interest per year compare with that on the $25 Series E bond? Which is the better investment, one $50 bond or two $25 bonds?

3. Mary Hart bought a Series E bond for $150. What will be its value at maturity? How much interest will have been earned?

4. By saving $1.25 per week, how many weeks would it take to save enough to buy a $25 Series E bond?

5. Find the cost of four $100 Government bonds at 104.60.

6. Find the cost of five $100 Government bonds at 103.20.

7. Find the cost of two $1,000 Government bonds at 103.20.

8. Find the cost of ten $1,000 Government bonds at 98.22.

*9. Compute the annual interest on the bonds in exercises 5 and 6. The interest is computed on the face value of $100 each, not on the purchase price. (See page 200 for interest rates.)

*10. Compute the annual interest on the bonds in exercises 7 and 8.

**11. Mr. Reed asked his banker to invest $1,125 for him in Series E bonds. If the banker buys the largest denominations possible, how many bonds and what denominations will he buy?

111. Corporations and their stocks. At what time in life is it wise to purchase shares of stock? Surely, it is not just any time that you are approached to buy shares.

It is well to ask yourself such questions as these:

(a) Do I have the cash necessary to pay for the shares without borrowing?

(b) Do I have sufficient income to take care of my obligations if the stock should become worthless?

(c) Do I have adequate life insurance?

(d) Do I have a savings account, or other savings, large enough to carry me over a financial difficulty?

In other words, is this cash that I am about to spend for stock extra money over and above my needs in a time of financial struggle? If your answer is, "Yes," to these questions, it is likely that you should become a stockholder.

Suppose, then, as an investment you purchase shares of stock in the A. B. Corporation. This purchase of shares makes you a part owner of the corporation. As one of the owners, you will receive a portion of the earnings. When the business is prosperous, you will be likely to receive a good yield on your money. When business is slow, your yield will drop. Unless you are well informed about this corporation, you are taking a great risk in buying the shares. There is always some risk in any investment.

To reduce the risk of investments in stocks, brokers offer diversification in stock buying by the purchase of *mutual fund stocks*. In buying shares of mutual fund stocks, you are putting your money into a long list of carefully selected shares instead of putting all of your money into the shares of one corporation. One mutual fund stock certificate represents ownership in 25, 50, 100, or whatever number of corporations make up the series, or portfolio, for that fund. This protection of principal and income is available to the small investor as well as to the investor of large amounts.

The usual kinds of stock issued by corporations are *preferred stock* and *common stock*. Preferred stockholders receive a fixed rate of profits. "Five per cent preferred" stock means that the holder will receive annually five per cent of the total par value of his stock in dividends. The remaining profits, large or small, will be divided among the common stockholders in proportion to the number of shares held by each.

A *dividend* is the amount of the profits paid by a corporation to its stockholders. Dividends are always based on the par value of the stock. For instance, if you own stock with a par value of $100 per share and paying a 4% dividend, you will receive a $4 dividend (4% of $100) on each of your shares, regardless of the purchase price or the present value of the stock.

Money received from the sale of shares of stock in a corporation is called its *capital stock*. The original price stated on a share of stock is called the *par value*.

The price at which stock can be bought is its *market value*. If the market value is quoted at more than the par value, the stock is said to be *above par;* if less than par value, it is said to be *below par*.

Stock is usually sold or bought by an agent called a *stockbroker*. The fee charged for this service is called *brokerage*.

──────────────── EXERCISES ────────────────

Solve the following exercises. When the number of the exercise is in parentheses, estimate the answer and prove the result.

1. If the capital stock of a corporation is increased from $750,000 to one million dollars, what is the per cent of increase?

2. Four men own all the shares of a corporation. If Brown owns 50 shares, Smith 49 shares, Black 87 shares, and Jones 62 shares, and if the shares have a par value of $50 each, what is the total capital stock of the corporation?

3. The capital stock of a corporation is $50,000. If the par value of each share is $50, how many shares may be issued?

4. A corporation with a capital stock of $700,000 issues 20,000 shares; what is the par value of each share?

5. Mr. Allen buys 25 shares of stock at 75 ($75 per share). How much does the stock cost him without brokerage?

6. If Mr. Allen had invested the money at 6% interest, what would have been his interest the first year?

7. What is the loss on one share of stock purchased at $48\frac{1}{2}$ and sold at $39\frac{3}{4}$? On 52 shares?

8. A dividend of 4% is declared for the year. How much dividend will be paid on 25 shares of stock, par value $100 each?

9. What is the cost of each of the following shares (without brokerage):

(a)	100 shares at	38.75		(g)	48 shares at	$12\frac{1}{2}$
(b)	25	"	" 48	(h)	126	"	"	$16\frac{1}{2}$
(c)	50	"	" 37	*(i)	144	"	"	$92\frac{7}{8}$
(d)	20	"	" $84\frac{1}{4}$	*(j)	39	"	"	$89\frac{3}{4}$
(e)	10	"	" $56\frac{1}{2}$	*(k)	24	"	"	$104\frac{1}{2}$
(f)	100	"	" $126\frac{1}{4}$	*(l)	16	"	"	$116\frac{3}{8}$

10. Find the market value of the following stocks:

(a)	25 shares at	87		(f)	148 shares at	$75\frac{3}{4}$
(b)	65	"	" 38	(g)	64	"	"	$26\frac{3}{8}$
(c)	93	"	" 45	(h)	120	"	"	$218\frac{1}{2}$
(d)	137	"	" $97\frac{1}{2}$	(i)	348	"	"	$36\frac{1}{4}$
(e)	59	"	" 134	(j)	100	"	"	$94\frac{5}{8}$

* 11. A semiannual dividend of $3\frac{1}{2}\%$ is declared. What per cent is this a year? $3\frac{1}{2}\%$ quarterly is what per cent a year?

* 12. A semiannual dividend of $2\frac{3}{4}\%$ paid on stock with a par value of \$75 is how much dividend per year on 1 share of stock? On 36 shares?

* 13. How many shares of Shell Oil stock at $42\frac{3}{4}$ can be purchased for \$2,864.25?

14. Find the rate of dividend on these shares of stock:

CAPITAL STOCK	DIVIDEND	CAPITAL STOCK	DIVIDEND
(a) \$300,000........	\$15,000	*(d) \$750,000......	\$40,000
(b) \$150,000........	\$6,000	*(e) \$60,000......	\$2,400
(c) \$ 20,000........	\$1,500	*(f) \$1,800,000......	\$72,000

*15. Find the rate of income on an investment in stocks bought at the prices quoted below and paying the stated rates of dividend. Consider the par value as \$100 per share and disregard brokerage:

(a) \$50, 4%	(d) \$150, 6%	(g) \$98, 5%
(b) \$200, 4%	(e) \$125, 8%	(h) $82\frac{1}{2}$, 4%
(c) \$80, 6%	(f) \$180, 10%	(i) $96\frac{1}{4}$, 7%

**16. At what price should 5% stock (\$100 par value) be purchased to yield an investment of 6%?

**17. Make a circle graph showing that the Ace Investment Company has its customers' money invested as follows: common stock, 60%; preferred stock, 15%; commercial bonds, 10%; Government bonds, 9%; and cash, 6%.

112. Investing in life insurance. In life insurance, premiums are paid by you, the insured, in order to receive money in return from the company. The return may be to a beneficiary or it may be to you, the insured.

How does life insurance rank as an investment?

(1) *Safety.* Life insurance is safe—second to no investment unless it is Government bonds.

(2) *Income.* The rate is low, as would be expected with such a high degree of safety. The finances of life insurance companies are so skillfully managed that, if the policy is in force the expected time, the insured will receive all that he has paid for but no more.

(3) *Salability.* Life insurance policies have a cash-refund and loan value after they have been in force for two years. The value is printed on the policy. Money is sacrificed when a policy is cashed prior to its date of maturity. The nearer the policy is to maturity, the greater the cash value. Not only will the insurance company loan money on a policy, but most banks will accept a policy as security on a loan.

Endowment policies and annuities provide a satisfactory method of supplying an income from investment.

Care should be taken not to overstock on any one kind of investment or on investments as a whole. Deep study should be given before making an investment. How will it fit into your budget? Dividing the total payments for the year by 12 will tell whether your monthly budget can take care of the extra expenditure.

——————— REVIEW OF CHAPTER IX ———————

1. How has the Federal Government made bank deposits safe?
2. List the services of the commercial department of a bank.
3. What business papers are left at banks for collection?
4. What do banks consider as good security?
5. What are the steps in opening a checking account?
6. What use is made of the signature card by the bank?
7. What is "Currency"?
8. What does "Silver" include?
9. How are checks listed on the deposit ticket?
10. Give three reasons why the check stub should be filled out before the check is written.

11. What care should be taken in writing the amount of a check in figures?

12. Why is it not safe to sign a check ahead of the time that the check is to be written?

13. Distinguish between the drawer and the payee of a check.

14. What should the drawer of a check do if the check is lost?

15. Why is it not safe to put a blank indorsement on a check before taking it to the bank to be cashed?

16. Joe Pratt is the payee of a check received. He wishes to give the check to J. W. Kerns. How should he word a safe indorsement?

17. If Joe Pratt wished to deposit the check in The First National Bank, how would he word a safe indorsement?

18. What is a canceled check?

19. Why should canceled checks be saved?

20. Frank Marrs has received his bank statement. The balance does not agree with the balance on his checkbook stub. (a) What might cause this difference, as far as the bank statement is concerned? (b) As far as the stub of the checkbook is concerned?

21. What two items are to be filled out on a deposit ticket for a savings account that are not required for a checking account?

22. How is money withdrawn from a savings account?

23. What advantage does a savings account have over a checking account?

24. What advantage does a checking account have over a savings account?

25. Highly safe investments usually have a ____ rate of yield, while risky investments usually have a ____ rate of yield.

26. What is the difference between common and preferred stock?

27. What is the meaning of "par value" of stocks?

28. What is "brokerage"?

29. How do bonds differ from stock?

30. Distinguish between *market value* and *par value* of stocks.

31. At what time in life should a person start saving regularly?

***32.** How does compound interest differ from simple interest?

***33.** What is done with the money that is paid into a savings and loan association?

*34. In what way is a savings and loan association a savings institution?

*35. To what amount does the Federal Government protect deposits in a savings and loan association?

**36. What do you understand by "diversification" in buying stock?

**37. It has been recommended that a person have funds divided among cash, a fixed-income investment, and a common stock investment. In what financial institutions might a person put his money to secure this?

───────── PLAYOFF FOR CHAPTER IX ────

Cut out four pieces of paper the shape of these pieces. Place them so as to form a square.

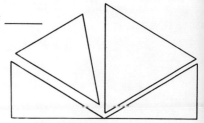

Fig. 11

— CHECK-UP ON THE FUNDAMENTALS OF ARITHMETIC —

Addition

1. 368
   127
   245

2. .75
   .16
   .34

3. $\frac{5}{6} + \frac{2}{3} + \frac{1}{2} =$

5. 4 yd. 2 ft. 10 in.
   8 yd. 1 ft. 7 in.

4. $36\frac{4}{5} + 24\frac{1}{3} =$

Subtraction

6. 1111
   546

7. $4.18 − $.75

8. $\frac{7}{9} − \frac{1}{6} =$

9. $\frac{3}{4}$
   $\frac{3}{8}$

10. 3 bu. 2 pk. 5 qt.
    1 bu. 3 pk. 7 qt.

Multiplication

11. 79
    63

12. 2.4
    3.7

13. $\frac{3}{16} \times \frac{6}{7} =$

14. $5\frac{1}{5} \times 3\frac{1}{2} =$

15. 12 Tons 800 lb.
    6

Division

16. 12)1728

17. .66 ÷ .22

18. 2.4)9126

19. $\frac{3}{16} \div \frac{3}{4}$

20. 3)16 lb. 7 oz.

Per Cent

21. .18 = ?%

22. $\frac{34}{200}$ = ?%

23. 16 = ?% of 8

24. 240% of 45 = ?

25. $16\frac{2}{3}$% of ? = 9

CHAPTER X

PROBLEMS OF THE CONSUMER

VOCABULARY

1. budget   2. income   3. expenditures

113. Planned spending. How does your allowance for the week hold out? Do you have to ask Dad for more money before the week is gone? For some of you, the answer is, "Yes," no doubt. If so, what brings on this embarrassing situation? Did you spend your money foolishly? You can do better than that, surely.

You can look ahead and foresee such expenses as tickets for the sports and plays, gifts for birthdays and Christmas, offerings to church, donations to charity, supplies for school, and numerous other things.

Only by having a plan for spending and saving can you hope to get that which you want most for your money.

When you grow older and begin to earn your own money, the responsibility of deciding how this money shall be used is mostly yours. You will want to manage your money so that it will bring you the greatest value and happiness possible. How to divide earnings so as to meet needed expenses, enjoy some of the luxuries of life, give to worthy causes, and have a fair savings account requires serious thought.

114. Budget. It takes a definite plan to apportion your money so as to spend and save wisely. It is wise to plan expenses carefully and, as far as possible, to spend according to the plan. The habit of recording and classifying expenditures is one of the best aids to wise spending and systematic saving. A statement of your probable expenditures based upon expected income is called a *budget*.

Budget of..... *Jim Hale* ... Week of.. *Oct. 20-27* ...

Expected Income			Actual Income		
Earnings.	5	00	. . . .	5	50
Allowance and Gifts	2	00	. . . .	2	00
Total.	7	00	. . . .	7	50

Items	Expected Expenses		Actual Expenses		More	Less
Lunch	1	50	1	60	10	
Carfare	1	25	1	45	20	
Savings	1	60	1	30		30
Supplies.		15		25	10	
Recreation	1	40	1	40		
Gifts		90	1	00	10	
Miscellaneous. . . .		20		50	30	
Total	7	00	7	50	80	30

Fig. 1. A Weekly Budget for a Pupil.

115. Making a weekly budget for a pupil. Suppose that each week Jim Hale, a high school freshman, earns $5.00 and receives from his father an allowance of $2.00. Jim plans how best to use his $7.00. By so doing week after week, Jim will accomplish several things: (a) He will get with his money the things that he wants most. (b) He will learn not to spend extravagantly on certain items. (c) He will learn how to handle his money so as to have some savings. (d) He will have a record showing what he did with his money. Jim makes a simple plan of expenditure as shown in figure 1.

Jim first records and totals his *Expected Income* of $5.00 and $2.00 on his budget form. He then carefully considers just how he can best use the $7.00. He decides first on the necessary items, *Lunch* and *Carfare*. He records the amounts, $1.50 and $1.25 for his lunch and carfare. Jim wishes to save $15 for his Christmas shopping, so he plans to save $1.50 each week for 10 weeks. He is also saving 10 cents per week for the Junior Red Cross Drive, which comes later. He lists the $1.60 opposite *Savings*. These first three items total $4.35, which leaves him $2.65 for his other expenses. After careful consideration of each remaining item, he sets aside 15 cents for note paper opposite

Supplies. Opposite *Recreation,* Jim records $1.40 for a school mixer (15¢), a skating party (50¢), and a football game (ticket, 75¢). Opposite *Gifts* he records 90¢ for his offering at Sunday School and a gift for his brother's birthday. The 20 cents which is unaccounted for he lists as *Miscellaneous* to take care of any expense item not listed.

Jim has now accounted for the use of the $7.00 that he expects to receive. In order to know how well he will live by his plan, he keeps a record in a notebook of all money actually received and spent during the week. (See figure 2.)

At the close of the week, Jim totals the items that are alike. By doing some extra work Jim earned $5.50 instead of the expected $5.00. His *Actual Income* totals how much? His *Actual Expenses* must also total $7.50. As would be expected, there were some items on which Jim spent more than he had planned and other items on which he had spent less. Through practice Jim will be more nearly able to make his expected and actual expenses agree.

Jim finds that he spent $1.60 for *Lunch.* This is 10 cents more than he had planned to spend. Where on the *Budget* did he put the $1.60? The 10 cents? How much did he actually spend for *Carfare?* Is this more or less than Jim's plan? By how much? Where did he put this amount? On what items did he spend more than he expected to spend? On what item less? On which item did his estimate agree with his actual expense? How much do his *Actual Expenses* total? Does this amount agree with his *Actual Income?* If so, the budget and record of expenses are correct. The difference between the total of the *More* and *Less* columns (80¢ − 30¢) must equal the difference between the *Expected Expenses* and the *Actual Expenses* ($7.50 − $7.00).

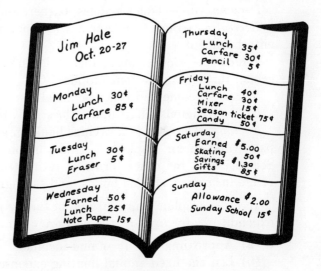

Fig. 2. The Notebook Kept by Jim Hale in Connection with his Budget.

1. Where in Jim's budget did he show evidence of good management by planning ahead?

2. Prepare a budget for yourself for one week, or more.

3. Prepare a notebook similar to figure 2 in which to record money received and paid out for one week or more.

116. Making a budget for a family. No single budget plan will meet the requirements of all families, as incomes and sizes of families vary, the cost of living in cities and villages is not the same, and the needs and wishes of individuals differ.

The expenditures may be grouped under the headings that best suit the family concerned. One method of grouping the various expenditures is as follows:

Food—All food materials.

Clothing—Ready-made and home-made.

Housing—Property taxes, repairs, property insurance, payment on mortgage, rent.

House operation—Fuel, utilities, laundry, household supplies, equipment, and maid service.

Transportation—Upkeep and insurance on automobile; streetcar, bus, and taxi service.

Health—Medical, dental, and optical care, and health insurance.

Personal care—Toilet articles, barber, and beauty shop.

Recreation—Books, magazines, music, radio, television, and entertainment.

Education—Books, magazines, television, radio, entertainment, school tuition, and school supplies.

Taxes—Income and other personal taxes.

Gifts—Religious, charitable, Christmas, birthday, and so on.

Savings—Deposits in a savings bank, in a savings and loan company, and in an employee's credit union. Payments for Social Security and for other forms of retirement benefits. Purchases of life insurance, stocks, bonds, and savings stamps.

In order to plan your personal or family program of income and expenditures for a year, it is necessary to:

(a) Approximate your annual income.

(b) List the fixed annual housing expenses.

(c) List living expenses and the cost of each, placing a fair limit on each cost in relation to other costs.

(d) List the remaining income as Savings and Life Insurance.

With some such a plan for spending, you should have less worry about meeting expenses promptly, even if you have financial emergencies.

TABLE 1

A POSSIBLE BUDGET FOR FAMILIES CONSISTING OF FATHER, MOTHER AND TWO CHILDREN WITH INCOMES OF $3,600, $5,200, AND $8,000 PER YEAR

Budget Items	$3,600 per Yr.		$5,200 per Yr.		$8,000 per Yr.	
Food	22%—	$792	21%—	$1092	20%—	$1600
Clothing	12%—	432	10%—	520	8%—	640
Housing	20%—	720	15%—	780	13%—	1040
House Operation	10%—	360	11%—	572	10%—	800
Transportation	4%—	144	6%—	312	7%—	560
Health and Personal Care....	3%—	108	3%—	156	3%—	240
Recreation and Education ...	8%—	288	9%—	468	10%—	800
Taxes	6%—	216	8%—	416	11%—	880
Gifts	5%—	180	6%—	312	6%—	480
Savings and Life Insurance ..	10%—	360	11%—	572	12%—	960
Total	100%—	$3,600	100%—	$5,200	100%—	$8,000

EXERCISES

1. Answer the following questions on the budgets of Table 1:

(a) As the family income increased, what happened to the per cents for food? To the cost of food? Account for your answer.

(b) How is it possible for a family of four to be as well fed on $66 per month as on $78 per month?

(c) What probably has caused the cost of house operation to be so much higher for the family earning $666 per month than for the family earning $300 per month?

(d) What might be the cause of transportation costing so much more for the family having the higher income?

(e) List the items in which the per cent of the income spent decreased as the income increased. How can you account for this?

(f) The greater the earnings, the ? the percentage for taxes.

2. Which items in a family budget will be likely to vary a considerable amount from summer to winter?

3. Account for the rapid increase in taxes as income increases.

4. Explain how a family can get as enjoyable and wholesome recreation by spending $2.00 as by spending $5.00 per week.

5. How would education probably be enriched by an allowance of $3.00 per week instead of $1.50 per week?

6. Which items in the budget are looking forward to the future?

***7.** Prepare a yearly budget for a family of four whose income is $6,000 per year.

****8.** Prepare an annual budget for a family. Choose the size of family and the amount of salary.

117. Cash record. After a budget has been set up for the year, it should be followed with a monthly *cash record* of all money received and paid out. This record will make it possible to know just how closely the budget has been followed. The amount of expenditures at the close of the year will not exactly equal the amount estimated at the beginning of the year. However, if certain items of the budget have not been reasonably estimated, more careful consideration should be given to these items for the following year. Keeping a cash record gives the satisfaction of knowing just how money was spent. This is valuable information for making out an income tax statement.

For most individuals and families, a simple form of cash record is better than a complicated form. A common form is illustrated in figures 3 and 4. It was compiled jointly by Mr. and Mrs. Allen

Fig. 3.

Received		Cash Record Items	Paid Out	
152	40	On hand Oct. 1		
425	00	Salary		
15	00	Dividends		
		Food	76	45
		Clothing	45	60
		Housing	65	00
		House Operation	40	00
		Transportation	30	00
		Personal Care	15	36
		Recreation	12	45
		Education	15	28
		Taxes – personal	24	00
		Gifts	22	50
		Health	7	25
		Insurance (Life)	40	00
		Savings	30	11
		On hand Oct. 31	168	40
592	40		592	40

214

and their two children Sue and Bob. The *Description* column may be omitted; however, it is worth while to keep it for future reference.

118. Making the cash record. As money is received and as it is spent, the amounts are recorded by the Allens in a notebook kept for that purpose. At the end of the month, the Allens list the items recorded in the notebook with their amounts under the various headings and total each list separately.

They are now ready to record the items and their amounts on the cash record form, recording the *Received* items first. Under *Received*, Mr. Allen lists three amounts—the $152.40 that he had *On hand* from his September earnings, his *Salary* of $425, and the $15 received as *Dividends* on investments. The Allens find that their *Food* costs them $76.45. This amount is placed in the *Paid Out* column. Clothing purchased amounts to $45.60. After recording this amount in the *Paid Out* column, the $45.60 is separated into the smaller amounts that were spent on the various members of the family. These amounts are listed in the column *Description*. How much was spent for clothes for each member of the family? What is the total cost of these clothes? What was paid for under the title *Housing*? Under *House Operation*? Under *Taxes*? Under *Gifts*?

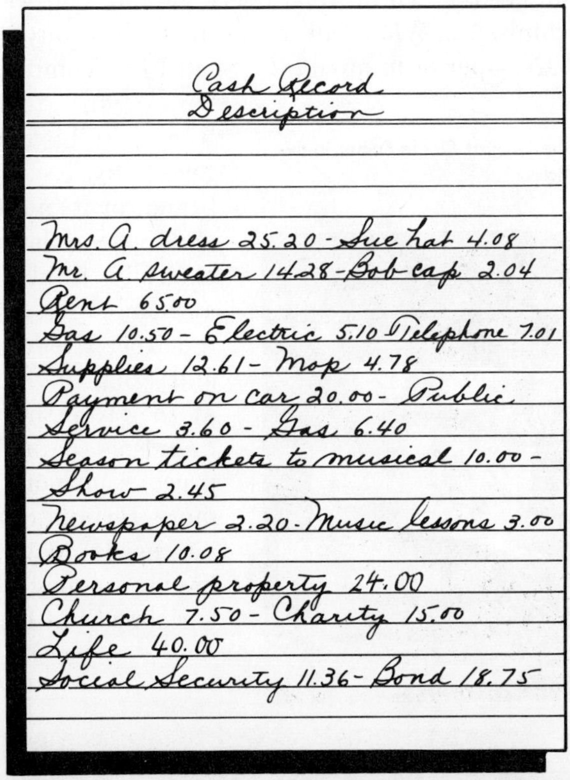

Fig. 4

Cash Record
Description

Mrs. A. dress 25.20 - Sue hat 4.08
Mr. A sweater 14.28 - Bob cap 2.04
Rent 65.00
Gas 10.50 - Electric 5.10 Telephone 7.01
Supplies 12.61 - Mop 4.78
Payment on car 20.00 - Public
Service 3.60 - Gas 6.40
Season tickets to musical 10.00 -
Show 2.45
Newspaper 2.20 - Music lessons 3.00
Books 10.08
Personal property 24.00
Church 7.50 - Charity 15.00
Life 40.00
Social Security 11.36 - Bond 18.75

215

119. Balancing the cash record. The cash record in figure 3 was balanced on October 31. To balance a cash record:

(a) Find the total of the Received column.

(b) Find the total of the Paid Out column through Savings.

(c) Find the amount of money on hand at the end of the month by subtracting the total money paid out from the total money received. This amount should equal the amount of money actually on hand.

(d) Enter the words *On hand* and the date under *Items* and the amount under *Paid Out*.

(e) The total of the *Paid Out* column should now equal the total of the *Received* column.

If the two totals agree and the cash actually on hand is the same as calculated in (c), the record is correct.

120. Deriving correct values in the home. Every person has three basic needs: he needs food, clothing, and shelter. Beyond these needs, he has desires for other things that will enrich his life. He probably wants such things as an automobile, a television set, first-class entertainment, travel, and insurance, besides other numerous items. He has just so much money with which to purchase these "wants." As he can spend each dollar of his income but once, it behooves him to buy intelligently. He must first satisfy his basic needs. To do this wisely, he must answer many questions for himself. What cut of meat shall I buy? What make of shoes are superior in quality? Shall I buy composition or wood shingles? The "best buy" is not determined by its price, its brand, or its advertising and sales claims. By carefully thinking over at home what and how much of an item is needed and then investigating at the store the various brands as to quality and price, a person can be more certain of having his needs met and of having money left for enrichment of his life.

Price Is Probably the Largest Single Factor in the Selection of an Article.

121. Thrift in buying food. In order to make the best choice of food for your money, it is far better to select your purchase in person than it is to order by telephone. Before leaving for the store, it is well to make a list of food to be bought with the prices quoted in the paper at available stores.

Stores Often Lower the Price Per Article in Order to Encourage Quantity Buying.

The price of food is controlled by such things as:

(1) *Quality.* To pay a high price does not necessarily mean a superior article, nor does a low price always indicate an inferior product.

(2) *Quantity.* To buy staples in large amounts is usually cheaper.

(3) *Season.* To buy food out of season is expensive.

─────────────── **EXERCISES** ───────────────

1. Arrange in order of price per article, the smallest first: 2 for a quarter; 3 for 50¢; 7 for $1; 13¢ each.

2. Strawberries are priced at 40¢ per quart box. A crate (16 quarts) of berries costs $5.60. (a) How much is a quart box at the crate price? (b) How much would be saved per box by buying the crate of berries if you could use the 16 quarts? (c) How much would be saved on 16 quarts?

3. At 3 for 55¢, what will a dozen cantaloupes cost?

4. At 2 for 5¢, how many pieces of candy do you receive for 15¢?

5. At 4 for 15¢, what will 2 doz. peaches cost?

*6. If the price of a head of cabbage is reduced from 10¢ to 5¢, what is the per cent reduction?

*7. Sugar purchased in a 5-lb. sack is 52¢ per sack, while a 60-lb. bale costs $6.18. What is the difference between the two costs for 60 lb.?

*8. If the price of a head of lettuce is raised from 5¢ to 10¢, what is the per cent of increase?

*9. Thirty cents per quart is what price per gallon? What price per pint?

*10. This recipe for custard ice cream serves 8 people:

1 pkg. gelatin	2 eggs
2 tablespoonfuls cold water	$\frac{1}{4}$ teaspoonful salt
$\frac{3}{4}$ cup sugar	$1\frac{1}{2}$ teaspoonfuls vanilla
1 pint milk	1 pint cream

Rewrite the recipe so as to serve (a) 4 people, (b) 16 people, (c) 12 people.

*11. If one cup of oatmeal is mixed with 3 cups of water and $\frac{1}{2}$ teaspoonful of salt, it serves 2 people. What mixture would serve 6 people? 5 people?

*12. These measures are common in the kitchen:

3 teaspoonfuls	= 1 tablespoonful	= $\frac{1}{2}$ fluid ounce	
8 tablespoonfuls	= $\frac{1}{2}$ cupful	= 4 fluid ounces	
1 cupful	= $\frac{1}{2}$ pint (2 gills)	= 8 fluid ounces	
4 cupfuls	= 1 quart		

(a) Double the measures on the left and find each equivalent measure in the other columns. (b) Take $\frac{1}{2}$ of each of the measures on the left and find their equivalents. (c) Take $\frac{1}{4}$ of each of the measures on the right and find each of the equivalents.

*13. Find the increase in cost (in per cent) of buying each of the following foods out of season:

Strawberries... (in season) 40¢ per qt.—(out of season) 78¢ per qt.
Peaches....... (in season) 10¢ per lb.—(out of season) 28¢ per lb.
Tomatoes..... (in season) 10¢ per lb.—(out of season) 59¢ per lb.
Corn.......... (in season) 30¢ per doz. ears—(out of season)
4 ears for 29¢

A GUIDE TO COMMON CAN SIZES
(See Figure 5.)

Can name	Used for	Contents
No. 1.................	Vegetables	$1\frac{1}{3}$ cups
No. 300..............	Meats, clams, beans with pork, spaghetti	$1\frac{3}{4}$ cups
No. 2.................	Vegetables, fruit, juices	$2\frac{1}{2}$ cups
No. $2\frac{1}{2}$...............	Peaches, pears, plums, tomatoes, pumpkin	$3\frac{1}{2}$ cups
No. 10..............	Fruits, vegetables (restaurant size)	13 cups

Fig. 5. Sizes of Common Cans.

Careful Planning and Thoughtful Selection Aid in Wise Spending.

EXERCISES

1. A No. 2 can contains how many times as much of vegetables as a No. 1 can?

2. A No. $2\frac{1}{2}$ can contains how many more cups of tomatoes than a No. 1 can contains?

3. A No. 10 can holds how many times as much fruit as a No. 2 can?

4. A No. 2 can contains how many more cups of food than a No. 300 can?

5. A No. 10 can holds how many servings of fruit at $\frac{1}{2}$ cup per serving?

*6. If a No. 2 can of tomatoes costs 15¢, what is the average cost per serving of the tomatoes if $\frac{1}{2}$ cup is used as a serving?

*7. How much is saved on buying one dozen No. $2\frac{1}{2}$ cans of peaches at 4 cans for $1.00 rather than paying 29¢ per can?

*8. How much cheaper is it to buy three 46-oz. cans of pineapple juice at 3 for 85¢ than to buy three at 29¢ each?

*9. Make a graph showing the number of cups of food in the contents of the five cans in figure 5.

*10. Dinner plates cost $9.60 per dozen. What will 10 plates cost?

*11. A store advertises a certain brand of tomato juice at 19¢ per can or $2.15 per case (12 cans). How much is saved on a dozen cans by buying by the case? What per cent is saved?[1]

*12. The same brand of corn is offered in one store at 3 cans for 35¢ and in a nearby store at 3 cans for 41¢. How much could be saved on a purchase of one dozen cans? What per cent could be saved?

[1] Always base the per cent saved on the higher price.

*13. A store offers the same brand of peaches as follows: A No. 2 can ($2\frac{1}{2}$ cups) for 19¢ and a No. 10 can (13 cups) for 65¢. (a) What is the price per cup (to the nearest mill) for each can? (b) How much could be saved per cup by buying the larger can? (c) What per cent could be saved per cup?

*14. Mrs. Kerr, wishing to take advantage of a food sale, bought: 6 cans of peas (15¢ value) at 3 cans for 40¢, and 12 cans of pork and beans (18¢ value) at 2 cans for 29¢. (a) How much did she save? (b) What per cent did she save?

**15. Mrs. Bly has a grocery list as follows:

> Beef roast, 4 lb. (store A, 69¢ per lb.—store B, 55¢)
> Shortening (store A, 71¢ for 3 lb.—store B, 65¢)
> 10 lb. Sugar (store A, 95¢—store B, 89¢)
> Berries (store A, 33¢—store B, 39¢)

At both stores, the beef is stamped *U.S. Good* and is the same cut of meat. The sugar and shortening are of different brands but both are acceptable. The berries are equally good.

(a) How much will Mrs. Bly save by purchasing all four items at store B instead of Store A?

(b) What per cent will she save?

**16. Potatoes are bought from a farmer at $1.90 per bushel, while the store price is 35¢ per half-peck. How much cheaper is the farmer's price per bushel?

**17. A pork shoulder roast should be baked in the oven 12 minutes at 500° Fahrenheit plus 20 minutes per pound at 300°. How long should a 5-lb. roast be baked? A $4\frac{1}{2}$-lb. roast?

**18. Mrs. Clark, in planning for a large group, needs 65 cups of canned berries. She can buy No. 2 cans ($2\frac{1}{2}$ cups) for 20¢ per can, or No. 10 cans (13 cups) for 98¢. (a) How many of the No. 2 cans would she need? (b) How many No. 10 cans would she need? (c) What would be the cost of buying the No. 2 cans? (d) The No. 10 cans? (e) Which is the cheaper buy? (f) How much cheaper?

122. Thrift in buying clothing. There are various ways to learn about the quality, value, and style of clothing.

(1) *Advertisements* usually picture the style and state the kind of fabric, the price, the color, and the size of suits, dresses, coats, shoes, and certain other clothing. While personal inspection should follow before a purchase is made, advertisements help to

start the shopping at home. Comparisons can be made and a list of "must sees" jotted down. All advertisements cannot be relied upon, but, in general, an established business cannot afford to put out false statements about its merchandise.

(2) *Salesclerks* can be of great help if they are well informed about the merchandise in their charge and if the customer knows how to tell the salesclerks what he wants.

(3) *Labels* are very important, for they present true statements. The labels "100% wool," "51 gauge," "Sanforized," and "pure silk" on clothing are an assurance of quality. However, not all clothing is labeled.

(4) *Testing agencies* put out information about the wearing quality of certain clothing, such as shoes, hose, and hats, and of fabrics. By laboratory methods, these agencies can test the wearability of merchandise. Such information is limited but quite reliable.

EXERCISES

Estimate Answers 1–4.

1. At a clearance sale, a $35 suit is offered for $25. (a) How much is the reduction? (b) What per cent?

2. Shoes which originally sold for $11.95 are on sale for $7.90. Find the per cent of reduction.

3. Coats originally selling for $79.95 are on sale for one-fourth off. What is the sale price?

4. A woman's coat is marked $160. On sale, it has a 12% discount. What is the sale price?

*5. A reduction from $8 to $7 is what per cent reduction?

*6. An increase from $7 to $8 is what per cent increase?

*7. Tablecloths damaged by water were sold at $6.25. How much was the reduction, in per cent, if the marked price had been $8.50?

*8. What are the rates of discount on a sport coat reduced from $36 to $30 and a sport coat reduced from $25 to $20?

*9. Which is the better bargain: an overcoat reduced from $40 to $35, or the same overcoat reduced 15%?

*10. Find to the nearest cent the cost of $19\frac{1}{2}$ yd. of linen at $.95 per yard.

11. A January White Sale advertised percale sheets:

Twin size, 72″ × 90″:   colored, $3.59; white, $2.79
Double size, 81″ × 108″: colored, $4.39; white, $3.69
King size, 108″ × 90″:   colored, $6.69; white, $5.49

(a) How much is saved in each size cover by purchasing the white cover instead of the colored cover? *(b) What per cent is saved in each size cover?

12. What is the reduction in the price of men's poplin jackets reduced from $12.50 to $7.50? *What is the per cent reduction?

*13. What disadvantage may there be in buying shoes at a July shoe sale?

*14. Would you expect a $3.98 pair of shoes to have the leather, workmanship, style, and comfort of a $10.95 pair? Why?

*15. A pair of shoes cost $12.90. A sales tax of 2% must be added. What is the actual cost?

*16. Mrs. Jones bought the following dress materials: $4\frac{1}{2}$ yd. gingham @ 34¢ per yard; $3\frac{1}{4}$ yd. percale @ 26¢ per yard; $1\frac{1}{2}$ yd. ribbon @ 26¢ per yard; and $2\frac{1}{3}$ doz. buttons @ 42¢ per dozen. What was the total cost of the articles?

*17. Margaret buys a fur coat for $570. She pays $90 cash and agrees to pay $30 each month until the coat is paid for. How many months are required to pay for the coat?

*18. Mary's graduation dress ready-made costs $35.00. If Mary can make the dress from 6 yards of material at $1.75 per yard, 10 covered buttons at 96¢ per dozen, collar material for $1.12, a pattern for 75¢, a zipper for 60¢, 2 spools of thread at 15¢ per spool, and 3 packages of tape at 15¢ per package, how much does she save by making the dress?

*19. At a sale white cotton shirts that regularly sell for $5.00 each are sold for $3.99 each; or a box of four for $15.75. (a) What is the saving on two shirts bought at the sale? (b) What is the saving on 4 shirts bought at the sale? (c) What per cent reduction is there on a purchase of 4 shirts?

**20. Find the cost of these furs plus a 2% sales tax and a 10% Federal Tax:

		Sale price
(a)	Beaver jacket.............	$ 295
(b)	Ranch Mink coat.........	2450
(c)	Pastel Mink cape.........	495

VOCABULARY

1. credit
2. installment
3. promissory note

4. day of maturity
5. collateral
6. bank discount
7. proceeds

8. equity
9. depreciation
10. purchase

123. Credit buying. Buying on credit is popular with the American people. Just a few years ago, the total consumer credit in the United States had risen to more than $56,000,000,000. Opening a charge account is simple. The merchant merely wants to know that the prospective purchaser will be able to pay for his purchases and that he *will* pay for them.

In a small community, a person's reputation is usually sufficient guarantee for acceptance or cause for rejection. In a city, most stores have a credit manager who interviews the applicants desiring credit. The credit manager also checks on each applicant's income and past credit record. Whether the applicant is allowed credit or not depends upon the result of the investigation. If accepted and purchases are made, a statement is rendered to the customer once a month, and payment for all purchases placed on that charge account for the month is due in full, with no extra charge, by a stated time.

Users of credit should (1) keep within a planned budget, (2) shop around, and (3) buy only as needed.

124. Consumer borrowing. George Morse, who wishes to purchase a refrigerator for his home but does not have the money available to pay cash, may buy on the installment plan. By so doing he figures that the additional cost will be equivalent to about 40% interest. To buy on a cash basis, he will need about $100 more than he has now.

Mr. Morse looks about for a reasonable rate of interest. He goes to the bank where he is known and finds that he can borrow the money at 6%.

George Morse asks the Commercial National Bank to lend him $100 for 60 days. He makes a written promise to pay back the amount of the loan. This promise (see figure 6) is called a *promissory note*, or merely a *note*. When the face of the note is paid, the banker returns the note. To make sure that George Morse will keep his promise, the bank may require him to give some form of good security, such as a mortgage on some of his property or safe stocks and bonds. Such security is called *collateral*.

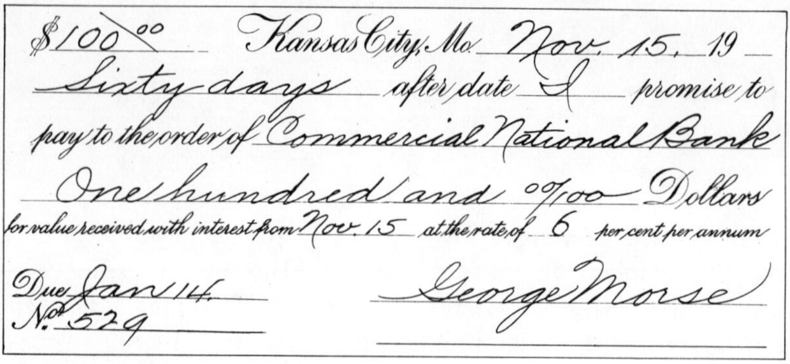

Fig. 6. Promissory Note

Instead of putting up collateral, the borrower may get one or more responsible persons to guarantee the payment of the note.

Although the amount of the George Morse loan is $100, the bank will pay Morse at the time of the loan $100 *minus* the interest from the date of the loan to the day of maturity. Interest is thus deducted in advance. Since the interest on $100 for 60 days at 6% is $1, Morse will receive $99. The collection of interest in advance is called *bank discount*, and the amount that the borrower receives is called the *proceeds*.

$$\text{Face of Note} - \text{Bank Discount} = \text{Proceeds}$$
$$\$100 \quad - \quad \$1 \quad = \quad \$99.$$

If Mr. Morse needs the money longer than the 60 days, he can have the note renewed.

EXERCISES

1. To find the interest due on his note, Mr. Morse uses the formula: $i = prt$.

$$p = \$100; r = 6\%; t = 60 \text{ da.} = \tfrac{1}{6} \text{ yr.}$$

$$i = \frac{\$100}{1} \times \frac{6}{100} \times \frac{1}{6} = \$1.00.$$

2. Find the interest on a $450 loan at 6% for 120 days.

3. What is the interest on a $720 loan at 5% for 80 days?

PROBLEMS OF THE CONSUMER

4. How much interest must be paid on a $630 loan at 8% for 90 days?

5. Find the interest on these loans:

(a)	$960 for	80 da.	@ 4%		*(f)	$1,600 for	88 da.	@ 4½%
(b)	720 "	75 "	@ 6%		*(g)	420 "	36 "	@ 3½%
(c)	425 "	72 "	@ 3%		*(h)	487 "	120 "	@ 3%
(d)	840 "	96 "	@ 5%		*(i)	3,648 "	150 "	@ 4½%
(e)	870 "	100 "	@ 6%		*(j)	480 "	42 "	@ 2½%

6. Mr. Black borrows $180 for 60 da. at 4%. How much is the bank discount? How much is paid to the borrower?

7. James Stone borrowed $1,400 for 90 da. at 6%. How much did the bank deduct as interest? How much did James Stone receive?

8. $890 is borrowed for 120 da. at 6% interest. How much is the bank discount on this note? What are the proceeds?

9. On Nov. 3, George Long borrows $860 from the Commercial National Bank for 90 da. at 6%. How much is the bank discount? How much did George Long receive? How much did he owe the bank in 90 days?

*10. Mr. Allen borrows $275 for 60 da. at 6%. How much does he pay the bank at the end of the 60 da.? What is the bank discount on his note? What are the proceeds? Who keeps the note until it is due?

*11. If $2,472 is borrowed for 30 da. at 6%, what is the bank discount? How much is paid to the borrower? Who keeps the note until it is paid?

*12. A sum of $389 is borrowed for 45 da. at 6%. What is the face of the note? How much must be paid on the note? Who has possession of the note until its payment?

**13. Mr. Carter needs $291 to pay emergency expenses. The Citizens Bank loans him the money at 6% for 180 days. How much money does Mr. Carter receive?

If Mr. Carter needs all of the $291, he must make the face of the note more than $291: that is, large enough to cover the $291 plus the discount. The discount rate is 6% per year, equivalent to 3% per ½ yr. $291 is 97% (100% − 3%) of the amount needed. Hence, the face of the note is $291 ÷ 0.97 = $300.00.

**14. Mr. Carter makes the face of the note $300. Prove that he will receive $291 from the bank.

**15. What must be the face of a 180-da. note if the discount is 4% and the proceeds desired are $490?

16. Mr. Dale must have $2,646. The discount rate is 8%. How much must he make the face of the 90-da. note? (8% for 1 yr. = ?% for ¼ yr.)

17. Determine the face of the note:

	PROCEEDS	DISCOUNT	TIME
(a)	$3,136	6%	120 da.
(b)	495	6%	60 da.
(c)	1,728	8%	180 da.
(d)	776	9%	120 da.
(e)	1,440	6%	240 da.
(f)	297	5%	72 da.
(g)	1,455	4%	270 da.
(h)	788	9%	60 da.

125. Installment buying. Installment buying is another form of credit buying. It is more often used for the purchase of expensive durable articles, such as furniture, appliances, automobiles, and television. A *down payment* is usually made at the time of the purchase. The rest of the purchase price is paid in weekly or monthly payments until the article is wholly paid for. The store usually makes a small fixed charge for this service called a *service charge* or a *carrying charge*. This charge represents interest on the unpaid balance and the cost of the bookkeeping involved.

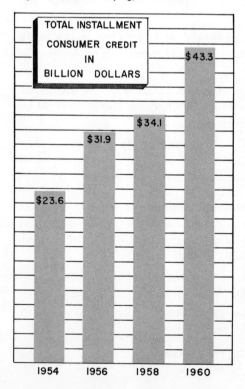

Fig. 7. Installment Buying, 1954–60

Installment buying has its dangers and its advantages. The easy-payment plan tempts some people to buy articles which they cannot afford to buy. In installment buying, if it becomes impossible for the buyer to complete the payments on an article so purchased, the seller has the right to take back the property, causing the buyer to lose the article and the payments that he has made on it. Installment buying gives the consumer the advantage of getting use of the article sooner than he would if he had to wait to save the cash before buying. Articles should be bought on time payments *only* after careful consideration of the budget.

Figure 7 shows the trend in installment credit buying in the United States over a period of seven years. (a) What was the total amount of installment buying for each of the years graphed? (b) The amount of credit in 1958 was approximately how many times as much as in 1954? (c) Approximately how many dollars more was the credit in 1960 than in 1954? (d) Which year shows the greatest increase over the preceding year? (e) Account for this rise in installment buying.

EXAMPLE

Mr. Mann buys a $50 radio on a 10-payment plan. He makes a down payment of $10. The unpaid balance bears a 6% service charge. What is the amount of each of the ten payments?

Purchase price	$50.00
Down payment	10.00
Unpaid balance	$40.00
	.06
Service charge	$2.40

$40.00 + $2.40 = $42.40

$42.40 ÷ 10 = $4.24, the amount of each payment.

EXERCISES

Copy this form. For each purchase, solve for the amount of the payment. Show your work on the back of your paper.

	Purchase Price	Down Payment	Service Charge	Number of Payments
*1.	$ 180	$ 18	6%	12
*2.	800	80	6%	12
*3.	300	None	9%	18
*4.	1,200	240	12%	24
*5.	1,800	360	12%	24
*6.	450	45	9%	18
*7.	360	36	6%	12
*8.	270	27	$15	10

*9. A piano that is priced at $750 cash can be purchased on the installment plan by the payment of $75 down and installments of $31.50 each month for 22 months. Find the difference between the cash price and the installment price.

*10. The furniture which the Jones family wants to buy will cost $1150 cash or $1280 if the Joneses pay $200 down and the rest in installments of $45 per month.

>   (a) How many payments must be made on the installment plan?
>
>   (b) What is the difference in the cost of the two plans?

*11. An electric dish washer is sold for $23 down and $9 per month for one year.

>   (a) What is the installment price?
>
>   (b) If 9% discount from the installment price is allowed for cash, what is the cash price?

*12. Mr. Jones decided to trade his old automobile for a new one. The dealer offered him $425 for his old car. The new car cost $2,412. Mr. Jones was to pay $667 cash and the balance in 12 equal monthly payments. What did he pay per month on the balance?

*13. Mr. Sams bought a gas stove for $189.50. He paid $14 down and agreed to pay $1.95 per week until the stove was paid for. For how many weeks was he paying for the stove?

*14. Mr. White bought a television set for $279.95. His down payment was $27.95. At $25.20 per month, how many months will it take him to complete his payments?

**15. A radio is priced at $22 cash or $1 down and $4 per month for six months. (a) What is the installment price of the radio? (b) How much more is the installment price than the cash price? (c) Considering this additional cost as *interest*, what rate of interest is paid for using this installment plan?

Solution

Installment price.. $4 × 6 + $1 = $25
Cash price..................... = $\underline{22}$
Interest (additional cost)........ = $ 3

To find the rate of interest, use the formula $r = \dfrac{i}{pt}$.

The principal (p) is the amount owed each month. As $4 is paid on the principal each month, the principal becomes less month by month. To arrive at a fair principal to use in computing the interest, the total owed for each of the six months is found.

Solve as follows:

$25 − $1 down   = $24 owed for 1 mo.
24 − 4 payment =   20 owed for 1 mo.
20 − 4   "   =   16 owed for 1 mo.
16 − 4   "   =   12 owed for 1 mo.
12 − 4   "   =   8 owed for 1 mo.
  8 − 4   "   =   4 owed for 1 mo.
                       $84 owed for 1 mo.

$84, the total of the monthly amounts owed, is the same as owing $84 for one month. The interest on the $84 for 1 month is $3.

The interest for 1 year is $3 × 12 or $36.

As $i = 36 for 1 yr. $r = \dfrac{36}{84 \times 1} = \dfrac{3}{7}$, or
$P = 84
$t = 1$ yr. $r = 42\frac{6}{7}\%$.

16. Mr. James can buy a suit of clothes for $40 cash or for $10 down and $6 per month for six months. What is the cost of the suit by the installment plan? How much more is this than by paying cash? What rate of interest is paid if the installment plan is used?

17. A table can be purchased for $48 cash or for a $12 down payment and $5 per month for eight months. Find the installment price. What is the rate of interest paid if the table is bought on the installment plan?

18. A rug is listed at $70 cash or $15 down plus $12 per month for five months. What is the installment price? Find the rate of interest paid if the installment plan is used.

126. Renting or owning a home. The three greatest factors entering into the question of whether to own or to rent a home are:

1. *The amount of family income.* If the annual income is $3,000 or less, the purchase of suitable shelter in most parts of the United States is out of the question.

2. *The source of the annual income.* If the income is seasonal, temporary, or uncertain, then ownership is risky.

3. *The size of the family.* The cost of home ownership is practically the same for one person as for a family of four. Hence, in a small family the cost of home ownership per person may be too high.

To own property means to have taxes to pay, insurance to buy, repairs to make, and, until the property is paid for, payments and interest on mortgage to be met.

Renting a place to live in involves paying rent regularly, running the risk of having to move at an inconvenient time, caring for the property of others, and living, to a certain extent, as others would have you live.

Home ownership promotes a feeling of security and pride. It offers a more independent and satisfactory way of living. It is much to be desired in a community.

Because home ownership is a good thing for the individual and the community, the Federal Housing Administration of the United States Government has made it easier for families to get the money to finance the purchase of a home.

The Federal Housing Administration (FHA) plan, which is for anybody interested in buying a house, is similar to the Veterans' Administration (VA) plan which is for war veterans only.

In the purchase of a house under the FHA and VA plans, and in the purchase of most houses under any plan, the buyer makes a down payment to the seller of the house at the time of purchase and makes smaller payments monthly thereafter for an agreed number of years.

Table 2 shows some of the minimum down payments and monthly payments on four different-priced houses of the FHA and VA plans. It is possible that in the future larger down payments may be asked and the loans may be closed in fewer years.

TABLE 2

Market Value of House	Minimum Down Payment			Minimum Monthly Payment excluding interest and Government fee		
	FHA House		VA House	FHA House		VA House
	New	Old	New or Old	New	Old	New or Old
$ 6,000	$ 450	$ 750	$120	$33.10	$31.31	$ 32.69
8,000	600	1,000	160	44.12	41.74	43.59
10,000	900	1,350	200	54.27	51.58	54.49
20,000	3,600	4,100	400	97.79	94.81	108.98

PROBLEMS OF THE CONSUMER

Fred Bates buys a new $20,000 FHA house. He makes the minimum down payment and the minimum monthly payments. (a) In how many months will he complete payments on the house? (b) In how many years?

$20,000 purchase price
3,600 down payment
$16,400 unpaid balance

$16,400 ÷ $97.79 = 167.7, approximately 168, months to pay.
168 ÷ 12 = 14 years to pay.

EXERCISES

1. (a) Calculate the number of months required to complete payments on a $20,000 VA house. (b) What is the number of years required to complete the payments?

2. (a) How do the number of years required to complete payments on the $20,000 VA house compare with the $20,000 FHA house in Example A? (b) Account for the difference in time.

3. In how many months will the payments on a new $10,000 FHA house be paid up, using the figures in Table 2?

4. How do the number of months needed to complete the new $10,000 and $20,000 FHA houses compare? (Use answers in Exercise 3 and Example A.)

5. Calculate the months required to complete payments on: (a) a new $8,000 FHA house; (b) an old $8,000 FHA house. Compare the answers in (a) and (b).

6. A house rents for $35 per month, and the expenses for the year were: taxes, $65; insurance, $30; water, $5; and repairs, $25. How much of the rent money was left at the end of the year? How much rent was paid the owner for the year?

7. If the expenses on a house were $154.40 for taxes, $32.80 for insurance, and $132.80 for repairs; and if the house rented for $50 per month, how much rent money did the owner have left at the end of the first year?

*8. An owner, after living 10 years in a house that cost him $9,000, sold it for $7,500. (a) How much money did he lose on the sale? (b) What was the average loss per year? (c) What was the average loss per month for the 10 years? (d) Could he have rented a house or apartment for this amount per month? (e) Did he make or lose money by owning the house for 10 years?

In buying a house outside the FHA and VA plans, it is wise to complete the payments in as few years as possible, as a long-term loan means more interest to pay. That which may seem to be easy terms because of small payments over a long period of time may prove to be a more expensive method of payment. It is to a buyer's advantage to make a study of the different plans offered and then select the best plan that it is possible for him to carry, realizing that if he does not fulfill his promise to pay, he will lose his home to the seller.

The amount of money that the buyer has paid on the principal is called his *equity*. If he has paid $2,000 on an $8,000 house, his equity is $2,000.

EXAMPLE B

Bob Jones buys a house for $15,000. He pays $3,000 down and agrees to pay $60 per month on the principal, plus interest at 6% on the unpaid balance. What are his payments?

$$\begin{array}{r} \$15,000 \text{ purchase price} \\ -3,000 \text{ down payment} \\ \hline \$12,000 \text{ unpaid balance} \end{array}$$

First Month		*Second Month*	
$12,000	unpaid balance	$11,940	unpaid balance
×.005	(6% per yr.)	×.005	(6% per yr.)
$60.00	interest for first month	$59.70	interest for second month
+60.00	payment on principal	+60.00	payment on principal
$120.00	payment for first month	$119.70	payment for second month
$12,000 − $60 = $11,940, unpaid balance		$11,940 − $60 = $11,880, unpaid balance	

For the third month, continue with $11,880 as the unpaid balance. Find the amount of interest due; add the interest and the $60 payment to find the total payment due; then subtract the $60 payment from the principal (the unpaid balance at the beginning of the month) to find the unpaid balance for the next month.

**9. Copy the table on page 233 and continue with total payments and unpaid balances for six months on the sale of the house in example B.

PROBLEMS OF THE CONSUMER

TABLE 3

Months	Principal	Payment on Principal	Interest at 6%	Total Payment	Unpaid Balance
1st	$12,000	$60.00	$60.00	$120.00	$11,940
2nd	11,940	60.00	59.70	119.70	11,880
[Etc.]					

**10. Mr. Stone bought a house and lot for $7,500 and paid $4,000 down. He paid the balance like rent. The monthly payment was $50 per month plus interest on the unpaid balance at 6%. Make a table and calculate his payments for four months.

**11. A bungalow cost $6,500. $3,000 was paid down, the interest on the unpaid balance was 6%, and the principal was reduced $40 per month. Make a table showing the total payments for the first six months.

**12. On September 4, 1963, Mr. Clark bought a farm costing $18,000. He made a down payment of $8,000. He contracted to pay the balance in $100 installments every month, beginning October 4, 1963. The unpaid balance was to bear 6% interest. Find the amounts Mr. Clark will have to pay each month up to and including June 4, 1964.

127. Making change. A clerk is expected to give change to a customer in as few coins as possible. The usual method of making change is to add coins to the cost of the purchase until the amount offered in payment is reached. If you should buy a can of soup for 8¢ and give a $1 bill in payment, the clerk would take 2¢ from the cash register, and say, "Ten cents"; then 5¢ and say, "Fifteen cents"; then 10¢ and say, "Twenty-five cents"; then 25¢ and say, "Fifty cents"; then 50¢ and say, "One dollar." He would then count to you in the same order, "8—10—15—25—50 —$1."

─────────────── *EXERCISES* ───────────────

Count the change for the following:

    1.   2¢ out of a quarter

    2.   25¢ " " " half-dollar

    3.   35¢ " " $1

4. Copy Table 4 and complete the missing data. The amount paid column shows the value in bills given by the customer. The change columns show how the change is made.

TABLE 4

Amount of Purchase	Total	Tax %	Tax $	Total with tax	Amount Paid	Change $.01	$.05	$.10	$.25	$.50	$1.00
$1.45 + $5.79 + $.62 + $.15		2			$ 10.00						
$2.18 + $.27 + $13.24 + $.50		3½			$ 20.00						
$4.32 + $3.95 + $10.75 + $15.95		2½			$ 50.00						
$4.20 + $2.98 + $6.25 + $13.84		3			$ 30.00						
$12.95 + $28.31 + $42.68		3¼			$100.00						

5. Frying chickens are advertised at 54 cents per pound. What will a 3-lb. chicken cost? How much change would be received from a $5 bill? Count the change to the customer.

6. A sale of 50 yd. of lace at 12½ cents per yard is paid for with a $10 bill. How much change is returned to the customer? Count the change.

7. Mary had $25 in currency (paper money). She bought a dozen hens at $1.80 each. Count the change back to her.

--------------------- REVIEW OF CHAPTER X ---------------------

1. What is the purpose of a budget? How does it help you to get better use from your money?

2. Expenditures for which items should be planned for first when a budget is being made? Why?

3. How can keeping a cash record help to make the next budget more nearly accurate in estimates?

4. List a few happenings that might cause the budget to be considerably out of line with actual receipts or expenditures.

5. Under what circumstances would it be wise to make changes in a budget?

6. How might budgeting your time bring better results in your school work?

7. List some things that a high school pupil probably could obtain by budgeting that otherwise might not be obtainable.

8. Why should the children in a family take an active part in planning the family budget?

9. What reasons can you suggest that would justify store A having a higher price than store B has for identical merchandise?

10. What advantage is there in purchasing a fur coat at an "August Fur Sale"?   What disadvantage?

11. Is there this same disadvantage in buying sheets at a "January White Sale"?

12. Name some ways of inspecting clothing; food; a radio; a television set; a used automobile.

13. What are two dangers of buying on credit?

14. What is the difference between buying on a charge account and buying on an installment plan?

15. (a) Give five reasons why a person would want to own his own home.   (b) Give five reasons why a person would want to rent a home.

—CHECK-UP ON THE FUNDAMENTALS OF ARITHMETIC—

Addition

1. 36
42
35
78

2. 2.1
1.75
.38
5

3. $18\frac{2}{3} + 26\frac{3}{4}$

4. 7 lb. 8 oz.
4 lb. 3 oz.
2 lb. 7 oz.

Subtraction

5. 7104
3523

6. $\frac{2}{3}$
$\frac{1}{6}$

7. $38\frac{1}{5}$
$27\frac{9}{10}$

8. 5 yd. 0 ft. 7 in.
1 yd. 2 ft. 9 in.

Multiplication

9. 84
46

10. .38
.04

11. $\frac{3}{8} \times \frac{6}{5} =$

12. $3\frac{1}{3} \times 90 =$

Division

13. $.36\overline{)8.64}$

14. $\frac{7}{15} \div \frac{3}{10} =$

15. $17.6 \div 100$

16. $\frac{1}{3}$ of 4 hr. 15 min.

Per Cent

17. $33\frac{1}{3}\%$ of 261 = ?

18. $2\frac{1}{2}\%$ of 80 = ?

19. 3% of ? = 15

20. ?% of 25 = 18

21. 12 : ? = 3 : 10

22. Find simple interest on $680 @ 4% for 270 da.

Find the annual premium on:

23. A $6,200 policy @ $32.80 per $1,000.

24. The scale is $\frac{1}{16}$ in. to 1 ft. The drawing is 2 in. by $2\frac{1}{2}$ in. What is the actual size of the object?

——————— PLAYOFF FOR CHAPTER X ———————

COUNTING BY FIVES

Man counts with tens because he has ten fingers. He could just as easily count with sevens, or twos, or fives, or any other number. Counting with numbers other than tens is very useful in working with electronic computers. Let us see how to count with fives instead of tens.

We must first review some of our old ideas about counting. When we count with tens, we use ten symbols for *digits* (0, 1, 2, 3, 4, 5, 6, 7, 8, and 9). We can count any amount of things because of the way we count "with tens". We start counting with the digit 1, then 2, etc. until we get to 9. There is no symbol for the number ten, so we use two digits, 1 and 0. We write it as 10 and we call it ten. The 1, as we just wrote it, is in what we call the *tens place*. When we write 10, we mean we have one ten and no ones.

The next number is eleven and is written as 11, or one ten and one one. The next number is twelve, written as 12, or one ten and two ones. Figure 1 shows how the place location of the digit is used in counting.

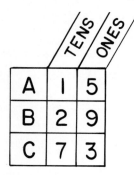

A is one ten and five ones; we call it fifteen. B is two tens and nine ones; we call it twenty-nine. C is seven tens and three ones; we call it seventy-three.

Counting by fives works the same way, except that we have only five symbols for digits (0, 1, 2, 3, and 4). To count we say one (1), two (2), three (3), four (4), and, for the next number, instead of five we say "one zero." We write 10₅ᵢᵥₑ, which now means one five and no ones. The next number is "one one" (11₅ᵢᵥₑ), or one five and one.

In order to tell our new number symbols from the base ten symbols we write a small "five" to the right of and a little below each base five number symbol. Thus 12 means twelve in base ten but 12₅ᵢᵥₑ means one five and two in base five.

Table 1 shows how the first fifteen numbers compare in the two ways of counting. Counting with tens is called counting in base ten, and counting with fives is called counting in base five.

TABLE 1

| Counting with Tens (base ten) | | Counting with Fives (base five) | |
Symbol for Number	Name of Number	Symbol for Number	Name of Number
1	one	1_{five}	one
2	two	2_{five}	two
3	three	3_{five}	three
4	four	4_{five}	four
5	five	10_{five}	one five and none
6	six	11_{five}	one five and one
7	seven	12_{five}	one five and two
8	eight	13_{five}	one five and three
9	nine	14_{five}	one five and four
10	ten (or one ten and none)	20_{five}	two fives and none
11	eleven (or one ten and one)	21_{five}	two fives and one
12	twelve (or one ten and two)	22_{five}	two fives and two
13	thirteen (or one ten and three)	23_{five}	two fives and three
14	fourteen (or one ten and four)	24_{five}	two fives and four
15	fifteen (or one ten and five)	30_{five}	three fives and none

We can continue counting as in Table 1 until we come to 24 (twenty-four), which is also 44_{five} (four fives and four). Since we have used all of our base five digits, we must start putting digits in the next place. The number 25 (twenty-five) then becomes 100_{five} which we read as one twenty-five and none. The next number is 101_{five}, or one twenty-five and one. Now see if you can read the base five numbers in Figure 2.

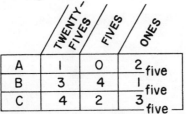

Fig. 2

A is one twenty-five and two; B is three twenty-fives, four fives and one; and C is four twenty-fives, two fives and three. Can you see that A is 27 in base ten, B is 96, and C is 113?

EXERCISES

1. Count the number of chairs, students, and books in your classroom, using base five numbers.

2. Change these base ten numbers to base five: 3, 7, 27, 38, 75, 86, 100, 120, 124.

**3. Write the number 125 in base five symbols.

**4. Write these numbers using base five symbols: 200, 250, 526.

CHAPTER XI

LOCAL, STATE, AND FEDERAL TAXES

128. Why taxes are necessary. All of us enjoy the comforts and conveniences provided by our local, state, and Federal governments. We have fire and police protection, schools, public libraries, hospitals, streets, highways, parks, mail collection and delivery, and inspected meat, milk, and drugs. We see on every hand where large sums of money have been, or are being, spent for our benefit. If your father were to try to purchase for your family all those conveniences without the aid of the government, the cost would be prohibitive. We look to the government for these services, and in return each of us must bear his share of the total cost. The share each person pays is his *tax*.

129. Kinds of taxes. Both local and state governments are supported largely by taxes on personal property and real estate. There are special taxes on estates or inheritances of over a certain sum and on the profits of a corporation. There are luxury taxes, sales taxes, amusement taxes, occupation taxes, and city, state, and federal income taxes.

The national government is supported by about 225 different forms of taxes, including income taxes, estate taxes, internal revenue taxes, and taxes on imported articles (customs duties).

——————— STATE AND LOCAL TAXES ———————

130. General property taxes. States, cities, and counties tax property—real estate and personal property. *Real estate* includes all fixed and immovable property (land, buildings, forests, mines,

quarries, and gas and oil wells). *Personal property* includes property that is easily moved from place to place, such as money, jewelry, stocks, bonds, furniture, livestock, and automobiles. Property taxes are levied in much the same way in all localities. The amount subject to tax is called the *assessed value*. Separate assessments are made for real estate and personal property.

An assessment is made, usually every year, by men called *assessors*, who place a value on every piece of real property in their districts. The assessed value is not always the *market value* of the property. In some communities, it is customary to assess property at a fractional part of its value—such as one-half or two-thirds of its market value. The sum of all the assessed values makes up the *total assessed value* of the community or state.

The estimated and approved amount of expenditures of a government for the next year is called its *budget*. The local executive body, often called the Council, approves the amount to be spent by the local community, the legislature approves for the state, and Congress for the national government.

131. Fixing the amount of property tax. After the local Council determines the amount of taxes to be collected, it figures the tax rate that will bring to the community the taxes required to meet the budget.

The amount of tax on each piece of property is found by multiplying its assessed valuation by the rate of tax. See Example.

EXAMPLE

What will be the amount of tax on real estate assessed at $4,000 with a tax rate of 1.5%?

$4,000 × .015 = $60, the amount of tax.

Some communities place a high tax rate on a low assessed valuation of property, and other communities place a low tax rate on a high assessed valuation of property.

For instance, City A and City B need to collect a tax of $150 on a $10,000 house. City A may get the $150 by assessing a $10,000 house at the low assessed valuation of $5,000 with a high 3% tax rate. (3% of $5,000 = $150.) City B may get the $150 by assessing a $10,000 house at a high assessed valuation of $9,000 with a low tax rate of $1\frac{2}{3}\%$. ($1\frac{2}{3}\%$ of $9,000 = $150.) In each case, the city gets its $150 tax on a $10,000 house.

―――――――――――――― **EXERCISES** ――――――――――――――

1. Write each of the following as a decimal: 3%, 4%, 1%, 1.2%, 2.4%, 3.25%.

2. Write each as a per cent: .06, .02, .025, .016, .108, .0125.

3. Multiply by 100: .08, .6, .023, .045, .0135, .0212.

4. Multiply by 1,000: .125, .018, .014, .0125, .021, .01.

5. Divide by 100: 25.6, 1.8, 2.1, 1.15, 1.6, 2.14.

6. Divide by 1,000: 145, 18, 17.2, 15, 20, 12.

7. Express as a decimal: 10 mills, 20 mills, 16 mills, 18 mills, 12 mills, 11 mills.

8. Find: 40% of $3,600, 60% of $2,400, 75% of $5,600, $\frac{2}{3}$ of $8,100, $\frac{3}{4}$ of $7,200.

9. Complete Table 1 by filling in the correct forms of each rate. Copy the form. Show your work on the back of the paper.

TABLE 1

Per Cent Rate	Mill Rate on the Dollar	Dollar Rate on the Hundred	Dollar Rate on the Thousand
2.5%	――――	――――	――――
――――	$.017	――――	――――
――――	――――	$2.30	――――
――――	――――	――――	$19.00

10. Jones owns property assessed at $6,500 in a city with a tax rate of 23 mills on a dollar. How much is his tax?

11. Find the tax on Mr. Adams' farm, assessed at $4,800: (a) if the tax rate is 15 mills on the dollar; (b) if the tax rate is $2.18 per hundred dollars; (c) if the tax rate is $15 per thousand dollars.

12. In the city of "X," the assessed valuation of all property is $45,850,000 and the tax rate is 17 mills. How much is due in taxes?

13. Mr. Fry pays a tax rate of 18 mills. He owns property assessed at $10,400. How much is his tax on the property?

14. Copy Table 2. Fill in the assessed valuation from each of the actual values. Show your work on the back of the paper.

TABLE 2

Part of Actual Value Assessed	$4,800	$6,500	$8,400	$12,500	$36,000
40%	_____	_____	_____	_____	_____
$\frac{2}{3}$	_____	_____	_____	_____	_____
$\frac{3}{4}$	_____	_____	_____	_____	_____
Full value	_____	_____	_____	_____	_____
50%	_____	_____	_____	_____	_____
$\frac{4}{5}$	_____	_____	_____	_____	_____

*15. Mr. Franklin owns a house and a vacant lot with market values of $8,500 and $900, respectively. Each is assessed at $\frac{2}{3}$ of the market value. What is the tax on each piece of property at the rate of 18 mills on the dollar?

*16. Mr. Allen owns a farm assessed at $10,500, 16 cows assessed at $45 each, 4 horses at $145 each, and 2 mules at $190 each. How much is his property tax, if the rate is $1.75 per hundred dollars?

*17. If a city increases the property tax rate from $1.90 to $2.50 per $100 valuation, how much will the taxes of Black & Son be increased on a valuation of $26,500?

*18. Find the amount of tax due on each of the properties in Table 3.

TABLE 3

Market Value	Per Cent Valuation	Assessed Valuation	Tax Rate	Amount of Tax
$ 18,000	40%	_____	$4.50 per $100	_____
$ 5,500	80%	_____	3.75%	_____
$ 6,200	100%	_____	24 mills	_____
$ 15,750	$66\frac{2}{3}$%	_____	$36.50 per $1,000	_____
$125,000	$87\frac{1}{2}$%	_____	$48.90 per $1,000	_____
$200,000	75%	_____	18.9 mills	_____
$250,000	50%	_____	$3.75 per $100	_____

*19. If Mr. Smith owns property which is assessed at $5,600 and is subject to the following tax rates per $100, (a) how much is each tax? (b) how much is his total tax?

State tax.........................	$ .23
County tax........................	.39
City tax...........................	1.27
School tax........................	1.05
Total tax rate....................	$2.94

20. In Merryville, the budget for school expenditures for one year is as follows:

Salaries........................	$115,400
Repairs..........................	5,725
Operating expenses..............	14,250
School bus......................	1,055
Textbooks.......................	1,290
Library.........................	4,280

What tax rate per $100 is required to meet the budget, if the total assessed value of the real and personal property is $5,680,000?

21. City X requires a tax of $90 on each $10,000 piece of real estate. What must the tax rate be to receive a tax of $90 on a $10,000 house which is assessed at $7,500?

22. City Y needs a tax of $120 on each $10,000 piece of real estate. What is the tax rate that will raise the $120 on a $10,000 house which is assessed at $6,000?

23. City E wishes to collect a 2% tax on its $10,000 houses. At what amount can a $10,000 house be assessed to produce the desired tax if the rate is 2.5%?

24. City W needs to collect a tax of $36 per $1,000 market value. What must the assessed valuation be if the tax rate is $45 per $1,000 assessed valuation?

132. State sales tax. More than half of the states have a tax, known as a *sales tax*, which is levied upon retail sales. The tax varies from 1 to $3\frac{1}{3}$ per cent of the purchase price, and, in most cases, the customer pays the per cent to the merchant, who in turn sends the tax to the state. (Cities sometimes add on a sales tax, bringing the total tax up to 4%.)

--- EXAMPLE ---

Grace bought her schoolbooks for $7.20 plus a 2% state sales tax. What is the total amount of her purchases?

$7.20	$7.20 cost of books
.02	.144 tax
$.1440 sales tax	$7.344 total cost

1. Mrs. Mills buys merchandise in the amount of $8.60 plus a state sales tax of 2 per cent. What is the total amount of her purchase? Count her change out of a $10 bill.

2. Mr. Foote purchased a $65 suit plus a 3 per cent sales tax. What was the total cost of his suit?

3. Find the total cost, including a sales tax of 3 per cent, for these rugs:

1 Rug, size 7 × 9 ft., $15.09   2 Rugs, size 2 × 5 ft., each $9.50

4. Find the total cost, including a sales tax of 2 per cent, on the following sales:

2 Wool blankets @ $10.80   2 Cotton blankets @ $2.68
3 Cotton blankets @ $2.75

5. Mrs. Casey purchased the following order, giving the clerk $20 in currency. (a) Find the total of the bill, including a 2 per cent sales tax. (b) Count Mrs. Casey's change back to her.

6 Ties @ $1.39   5 pr. Wool Hose @ $1.15   2 pr. Gloves @ $1.65

*6. Figure the following order, including a $1\frac{1}{2}$ per cent sales tax:

5 loaves Bread @ 19¢   2 lb. Coffee @ 89¢
2 lb. Butter @ 87¢   2 doz. Eggs @ 62¢
12 lb. Sugar @ 9¢   5 lb. Cheese @ 69¢

*7. A sales tax of 2 per cent is paid on merchandise purchased in certain states. How much sales tax—in cents and mills—would be paid on groceries costing $4.50? On books costing $5.20? On clothing costing $18.75?

*8. What is the cost, including a $2\frac{1}{2}$ per cent sales tax, on the following order?

3 Handkerchiefs @ 39¢   1 Pocket Comb @ 15¢
1 Belt @ 75¢   4 Spools Thread @ 9¢
1 pair Shoes @ $11.70   10 yd. Ribbon @ 12¢

*9. What is the total cost of the following order if there is a 2 per cent sales tax?

6 gross Pins @ $1.65   38 yd. Linen @ $2.18
13 yd. Tape @ 27¢   19 yd. Silk @ $4.39
27 yd. Ribbon @ 38¢   20 yd. Braid @ 17¢

133. Federal income tax. The income tax was first adopted by the Federal Government during the War between the States, but was repealed in 1870 and declared unconstitutional. The adoption of the Sixteenth Amendment in 1913 gave Congress power "to lay and collect taxes on incomes from whatever source derived." The income tax was re-adopted in 1913 and is now a source of much revenue.

During a recent year, the Bureau of Internal Revenue received about 90,000,000 tax returns and collected more than $65,000,-000,000.

In 1943 a plan was adopted by which a part of salaries and wages are withheld by the employer and applied to the payment of the income taxes of the employee. In this way, income taxes may be paid on wages and salaries as the income is earned.

Fig. 2. "Nike" on Its Supersonic Quest for a Distant High-Flying Target. The missile proper continues toward its target, guided by an electronic brain. Our Federal Government budgets a large portion of its money for the defense of our country.

The information* to be given on the Federal income tax return is divided into four groups: (a) that having to do with your salary plus any other income, (b) that which deals with your allowable deductions, (c) that which allows your exemptions, and (d) that which has to do with the computation of your tax.

Let us take a look at some of the income tax forms. Before long, these forms will be a necessary part of our lives.

---

* The rules of Federal income taxes are subject to change by Congress and may vary from year to year.

A-Z Cab Service 45-722-5282
1200 Oak Street
Joytown, Ohio 43232

Type or print EMPLOYER'S identification number, name, and address above.

WITHHOLDING TAX STATEMENT 1963
Federal taxes withheld from wages
Copy B—To be filed with employee's tax return

SOCIAL SECURITY INFORMATION		INCOME TAX INFORMATION	
$ 9.50 F.I.C.A. employee tax withheld, if any	$ Total F.I.C.A. wages paid in 1963	$ 48.00 Federal income tax withheld, if any	$ 475.00 Total wages* paid in 1963

000-xx-000

Ira N. Cast
3200 Long St.
Joytown, Ohio 43232

Type or print EMPLOYEE'S social security account no., name, and address above.

EMPLOYEE: This is not a tax return but you must file it with Form 1040A, or Form 1040. See instructions on other side and on back of copy C.
If you expect to owe more income tax for next year than will be withheld if you claim every exemption to which you are entitled, you may increase the withholding by claiming a smaller number of exemptions or you may enter into an agreement with your employer to have additional amounts withheld. See Form W-4.

FOR USE OF INTERNAL REVENUE SERVICE
Employee's copy and employer's copy compared . . . .

FORM W-2—U.S. Treasury Department, Internal Revenue Service

*Before payroll deductions or "sick pay" exclusion.

Fig. 3

Figure 3 illustrates the withholding form W-2. It shows that Ira N. Cast is employed by the A-Z Cab Service of Joytown, Ohio. The form also shows that he has earned during the year $475 working for the A-Z Cab Service. From his wages, two deductions have been made—$9.50 for his Social Security and $48.00 for his Federal Income Tax. Ira Cast owes no income tax, as his earnings all came from the Cab Service and are less than $600. Yet, he must file a return in order to receive from the government a refund of the $48.00 withheld for his income tax.

A taxpayer who earns less than $10,000 in wages that are reported on a withholding form and who has not received more than $200 from non-withheld sources, such as interest and dividends, may file his return on the card 1040A. See figure 4.

Ira Cast fills out such a card. If he had owed any tax, the Internal Revenue Service would have calculated his tax and reported the amount to him.

Fig. 4

Form 1040A **U.S. INDIVIDUAL INCOME TAX RETURN (Less than $10,000 total income)** **1963**

Please print →

1. Name (If a joint return of husband and wife, use first names and middle initials of both)
Ira N. Cast
Home address (Number and street or rural route)
3200 Long Street
City, town or post office, State and Postal ZIP code
Joytown, Ohio 43232

2. Your social security number: 0 0 0 x x 0 0 0
3. Wife's number if joint return

4. Check one:
☒ Single;
☐ Married filing joint return (even if only one had income);
☐ Married filing separately—Give name of wife or husband only if also filing separately

	5. (a) Federal Income Tax Withheld	(b) Wages and Other Income	EMPLOYER'S NAME. Where employed. Write (W) before name of each of wife's employers
If item 7(a) is $10,000 or more, or if item 6 is over $200, use Form 1040.	48 00	$ 475 00	A-Z Cab Service Joytown, Ohio
• Enter total tax withheld in item 7(a). • Enter total income in item 7(b)	6. INTEREST, DIVIDENDS, AND OTHER WAGES — Yours / Wife's		Enclose Forms W-2, Copy B. If your income was $5,000 or more, you must compute your tax. However, if your income was less than $5,000, you may have the Internal Revenue Service compute your tax by omitting items 8, 9, and 10. *If you compute your own tax, pay balance (item 9) in full with return to your District Director.*
	7(a) $ 48 00	7(b) $ 475 00	
8. Enter tax from Tax Table or from tax computation schedule →			
9. If item 8 is larger than item 7(a), enter **balance due** →			
10. If item 7(a) is larger than item 8, enter **refund** →		$ 48 00	Apply refund to: ☐ U.S. Savings Bonds, with excess refunded; or ☐ Refund only.

U.S. TREASURY DEPARTMENT • INTERNAL REVENUE SERVICE (OVER) LIST YOUR EXEMPTIONS AND SIGN ON OTHER SIDE.

A taxpayer who cannot use the card 1040A because of having more than a $200 income from non-withheld sources can in most cases make his return on page 1 of Form 1040.

A taxpayer whose sole income is from wages needs to use only pages 1 and 2 of form 1040.

Let us now consider Form 1040. The portion at the top is for information that is easily filled in by following directions carefully.

Ferd A. Somebody and his wife, Mae, who has no income, file a joint return and fill out the top portion (figure 5).

Fig. 5

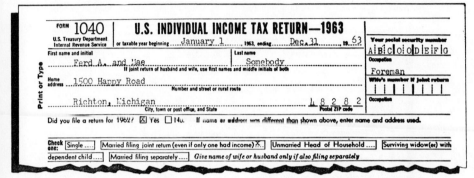

Now for their exemptions. Exemptions are amounts allowed by the government for personal expenses of the taxpayer and his dependents. At present, $600 is allowable for the taxpayer himself, his wife, unless she is earning and filing a separate return, and any dependents. Children are dependents, even though they may be earning, if the parent is paying more than half of their support for the year. Any other dependent must have a gross income of less than $600.

If the Tax Table is not used, exemptions are subtracted from the *Total Income*. The remainder is called the *Taxable Income* and is the income upon which the tax is figured.

Ferd Somebody has two dependent children, his wife, and himself as exemptions. He fills in the exemption portion of Form 1040 as shown in figure 6.

Fig. 6

FORM 1040—1963	SCHEDULE A.—EXEMPTIONS (See page 6 of instructions)					Page 2
1. Exemptions for yourself—and wife (only if all her income is included in this return, or she had no income)						

Check boxes which apply	(a) Regular $600 exemption . . . . ☒ Yourself ☒ Wife	Enter number of boxes checked	2
	(b) Additional $600 exemption if 65 or over at end of 1963 . . . . ☐ Yourself ☐ Wife		
	(c) Additional $600 exemption if blind at end of 1963 . . . . ☐ Yourself ☐ Wife →		

2. Exemptions for your children and other dependents (list below)
● If an exemption is based on a multiple-support agreement of a group of persons, attach the declarations described on page 6 of instructions.

NAME Enter figure 1 in the last column to right for each name listed (Give address if different from yours)	Relationship	ANSWER ONLY FOR DEPENDENTS OTHER THAN YOUR CHILDREN				
		Months lived in your home. If born or died during year also write "B" or "D"	Did dependent have income of $600 or more?	Amount YOU furnished for dependent's support. If 100% write "ALL"	Amount furnished by OTHERS including dependent	
Sara	daughter		$	$		1
Larry	son					1

3. Total exemptions (lines 1 and 2 above). (Enter here and on line 10 or 11c. page 1) . . . . → 4

The next section to care for is that of income.

Income varies with individuals. Some persons have only a salary to report, while others, who may or may not have a salary, may have dividends from one or more shares of stocks, interest from money, rents from property owned, or profits from business deals. With few exceptions, all sources of income must be totaled. This total is the *total income.*

Ferd Somebody's wages amounted to $4,500 of which $540 was withheld as payment on his income tax. This he recorded as seen in figure 7.

● Attach Copy B of Forms W-2 Here ●

If joint return, include all income of both husband and wife—**INCOME**—If either you or your wife worked for more than one employer, see page 4 of instructions.

1. Wages, salaries, tips, etc., and excess of allowances over business expenses: Employer's name	Where employed (city and state)	(a) Federal income tax withheld		(b) Wages, etc.	
Fast Plane Company	Richton, Michigan	$ 540	00	$ 4500	00
2. Totals →		540	00	4500	00
3. "Sick pay" if included in line 1 (attach required statement)					
4. Subtract line 3 from line 2				4500	00
5a. Dividends (Schedule B)					
b. Interest (Schedule B or list of payers and amounts)				280	00
c. Rents, royalties, pensions, etc. (Schedule B)					
6a. Business income (Schedule C)					
b. Sale or exchange of property (Schedule D)					
c. Farm income (Schedule F)					
7. Total (add lines 4 through 6c)				4780	00
8. Payments by self-employed persons to retirement plans, etc. (attach Form 2950 SE)					
9. Total income (subtract line 8 from line 7)				4780	00

Fig. 7

Mr. Somebody had received $280 interest from savings bank deposits, which he listed in a special space on page 3 as shown in figure 8. This interest, with any other non-withheld income, is totaled and recorded on page 1, line 10. This brings the Total Income to $4,780.

Part II.—INTEREST INCOME (This includes interest credited to your account) Note: A separate attachment may be used if interest is the only income to be reported on this schedule.	Amount	
1. Name of payer (more than one entry may be made on a line)		
Richton Bank	$ 100	00
State Bank	180	00
2. Total—Enter here and on line 5b, page 1, Form 1040	$ 280	00

Fig. 8. Interest Received—Form 1040

Mr. Somebody, like other folks, is interested in just how much he can subtract from his income to reduce his tax. This brings us to another section of Form 1040.

Deductions. The purpose of deductions is to prevent the taxpayer from being taxed unfairly. People who have given money to religious, scientific, educational, or charitable institutions, or who have suffered losses from calamities for which they received no insurance, or from debts that are not collectible, are allowed to subtract a figured amount from their income. The deductions are subtracted from the Total Income.

Instead of listing deductions, many taxpayers take 10% of the Total Income, which is allowable for deductions.

Not having any unusually large deductions to list, Ferd Somebody decided to take the 10% of his Total Income? His taxable income being less than $5,000 Mr. Somebody can use the Tax Table 4. To do so, he first locates the column which is set up for four exemptions. Then he locates his taxable income of $4,780, which is between incomes $4,750 and $4,800. He follows that line across the table until he reaches the column indicated by four exemptions. He reads that his tax for 1963 is $380.

TABLE 4

A Small Portion of the Tax Table—Form 1040

TAX TABLE FOR CALENDAR YEAR 1963
INCOMES UNDER $5,000

		And the number of exemptions claimed on line 4, page 1, is –						
At least	But less than	1	2	3	– – – – – –	4	5	– – – –
		Your tax is—						
$0	$675	$0	$0	$0	– – – – – –	$0	$0	– – –
675	700	4	0	0		0	0	
4,600	4,650	744	728	612		353	233	
4,650	4,700	754	738	622		362	242	
4,700	4,750	764	747	632		371	251	
4,750	4,800	773	756	641	– – – – –	380	260	– – – –
4,800	4,850	783	766	651		389	269	
4,850	4,900	793	775	661		398	278	
4,900	4,950	803	785	671		407	287	
4,950	5,000	813	794	681		416	296	

10. Tax Table *(FIGURE YOUR TAX BY USING EITHER 10 OR 11)* **11.** Tax Rate Schedule	
If line 9 is less than $5,000 and you do not itemize deductions; Complete page 2 exemption schedule.	**a.** If you itemize deductions, enter total from page 2 . . . . If line 9 is $5,000 or more and you do not itemize, enter 10% of line 9 but not more than $1,000 *($500 if married and filing separate return).*
Copy total exemptions here ..4.... Find your tax in table on page 10 of instructions. Do not use lines 11a, b, c, or d. Enter tax on line 12.	**b.** Subtract line 11a from line 9. . . . .
	c. Copy total exemptions from page 2 here ......, multiply by $600 . . .
	d. Subtract line 11c from line 11b. (Figure your tax on this amount by using tax rate schedule on page 9 of instructions and enter tax on line 12.) . •

TAX—CREDITS—PAYMENTS

12. Tax (from either tax table or tax rate schedule) . . . . •	380 | 00
13a. Dividends received credit.	
b. Retirement income credit	
c. Investment credit (Form 3468) . . . . •	
d. Other credits (Specify—see page 5 of instructions) . . . . •	
e. Total (add lines 13a, b, c, and d) . . . . •	
14. Balance (subtract line 13e from line 12) . . . . •	380 | 00
15. Tax from recomputing prior year investment credit (attach statement) . . . . •	
16. Total (add lines 14 and 15) . . . . •	380 | 00
17. Self-employment tax (Schedule C-3 or F-1) . . . . •	
18. Total tax (add lines 16 and 17) . . . . •	380 | 00
19a. Tax withheld (line 2, column (a) above) 540.00	
b. 1963 Estimated tax payments and credits------------------------•	
c. Total (add lines 19a and b) . . . . **(Office where paid)**	540 | 00

TAX DUE OR REFUND

20. If payments (line 19c) are less than tax (line 18), enter Balance Due. **Pay in full with this return.** ——▶	
21. If payments (line 19c) are larger than tax (line 18), enter Overpayment . . . .——▶	160 | 00
22. Amount of line 21 you wish credited to 1964 Estimated Tax	
23. Subtract line 22 from 21. Apply to: ☐ U.S. Savings Bonds, with excess refunded; or ☒ Refund only .	160 | 00

★ LIST YOUR EXEMPTIONS AND SIGN ON OTHER SIDE

Fig. 9

Turning back to page 1, he follows these directions carefully:

1. He enters his tax of $380 on line 12.

2. He enters the $540 tax withheld on line 19 twice.

3. He enters the difference between $540 and $380 on line 21, as the tax withheld is larger than his tax.

4. He checks the squares which follow the questions about the Return. Then he and his wife each sign the blank and fill in the date. The return is now ready to be given to the office of the Internal Revenue Service.

An income tax return requires careful preparation and a knowledge of income and expenditures. A great help in computing income taxes is an accurately kept record of income and expenditures.

————————————— *EXERCISES* —————————————

1. Mr. Blair's income consists of a salary of $6,000, interest of $80 and $175, and rents of $480. Find his Total Income.

2. Mr. Blair's deductions are: contributions, $125; taxes, $85; and bad debts, $280. Find his total deductions.

3. Subtract Mr. Blair's total deductions and one exemption from his Total Income to find his Taxable Income.

4. Mr. Black's income consists of a salary of $12,000; income from rents amounting to $40, $65, and $15; interest from various sources, $25, $38, and $76; and a gain of $780 from the sale of property. What is his Total Income?

5. Mr. Black had these deductions: contributions to church, $250; to charity, $180; to scientific research, $25; to an educational fund, $16; to the American Red Cross, $8; and to the Boy Scouts of America, $6. He also deducted: taxes, $140 and $28; bad debts, $72; other deductions, $87. Find the total amount of his deductions.

6. From Mr. Black's Total Income subtract his deductions and two exemptions. What is his Taxable Income?

*7. Miss Case's gross income is $2,500, and she has paid a doctor's bill for $80, a hospital bill for $100, a dentist's bill for $60, and $30 for health insurance. Being past 65 years of age, she may deduct these sums from her Total Income. Find the amount of the deductions.

*8. If Carl Cross has a Total Income of $2,760.30 and a personal exemption of $600, and he takes the 10 per cent deduction from his Total Income, find his balance subject to tax.

*9. Mr. Carl Jackson has a salary of $7,200 per year. He has interest on Government bonds of $20, interest on his savings account of $17.50, and rent from his garage of $60. He has paid $82.50 to church and charity. His taxes, not including Federal taxes, amount to $125.18. He has a bad debt of $300 owed him.

Mr. Jackson's wife is not employed. They have two dependent children. On what amount of income will Mr. Jackson pay a Federal income tax?

*10. If Mr. Singer has a Total Income of $8,500.00 and a personal deduction of $600, credit for two bad debts of $500 each, and a 10 per cent Total Income deduction, what is his balance subject to tax?

*11. Obtain a Tax Rate Schedule and calculate the income tax of Mr. Jackson (exercise 9) and Mr. Singer (exercise 10).

———————— REVIEW OF CHAPTER XI ————————

1. What is a tax?

2. What is the difference between assessed value and market value? When are they the same?

3. List five improvements in your community made possible by taxes. Justify taxation for these improvements.

4. How many of the following does your community provide for you?

(a) firemen	(e) boulevards	(i) schools
(b) parks	(f) street lights	(j) courts
(c) libraries	(g) playgrounds	(k) sidewalks
(d) highways	(h) water works	(l) sewers

5. List as real or personal property: (a) farm, (b) radio, (c) garage, (d) motorboat, (e) rock quarry, (f) jewelry, (g) bonds, (h) automobile, (i) cows, (j) coal mine, (k) money, (l) gas well.

6. How is the amount of taxation for personal property determined?

7. Explain a tax rate of 18 mills.

8. What is a sales tax?

9. Explain the sales tax in your state.

10. What is the value of the government budget?

11. Name five sources of income that are taxed.

12. Name five deductions allowed in computing the Federal income tax.

13. Explain the difference between exemptions and deductions as used in connection with the income tax.

14. Mr. Colt owns a house with an assessed value of $4,500. The tax rate is 16 mills. How much tax is paid on the house?

15. Mr. Risk owns a farm which is assessed at $5,200. The tax rate is $1.52 per $100. Find the tax on the farm.

16. Mrs. Cook owns property assessed at $12,800. The tax rate on her property is $14 per $1,000. Calculate her tax.

17. Jim bought a bicycle for $42.50 plus a sales tax of 2%. What was the total cost of the bicycle?

*18. Mrs. Patt purchased 8 yards of cloth at 60¢ per yard and 20 yards of braid at 15¢ per yard. What is the total cost of the purchases, if there is a $2\frac{1}{2}\%$ sales tax on the purchases?

*19. Find the amount of tax due on property that has a market value of $15,000, if the assessed value is $66\frac{2}{3}\%$ of the market value and the tax rate is 18.2 mills.

*20. Find the tax on property with a market value of $124,800 which is assessed at $87\frac{1}{2}\%$ of its market value. The tax rate is $36.25 per $1,000.

**21. What is the total cost of a $249.50 television set where there is a $2\frac{1}{2}\%$ state sales tax and a 1% city sales tax?

**22. In a recent year, the percentages of national income taken by taxes were:

United States.............. 26%
Britain................... 32.5%
Canada................. 30.1%

Show these percentages by means of a graph.

**23. Copy and explain the Sixteenth Amendment to the Constitution.

**24. Why are schools, hospitals, charitable institutions, and churches not taxed?

**25. Paying taxes is a co-operative matter.   Explain.

——————— PLAYOFF FOR CHAPTER XI ———————

1. On an income tax form, prepare a simple tax that you have thought out.

2. *Given, the following sum in addition:

$$111$$
$$777$$
$$\underline{999}$$

Required, to strike out six of these numbers, so that the total of the remaining numbers shall be 20 only.

ACHIEVEMENT TEST III
Addition

1. 5	2. 45	3. 128	4. 31.65	5. $3.4 + 21.8 + 6$
7	38	277	4.87	6. $\frac{1}{3} + \frac{5}{6}$
8	26	455	23.69	
4	57	688	.47	7. $\frac{2}{3} + \frac{1}{5} + \frac{3}{5}$
6		329		

8. $36\frac{5}{7}$ **9.** $14\frac{3}{4}$ **10.** 18 lb. 8 oz.
   $27\frac{1}{2}$ $8\frac{5}{8}$ 6 lb. 9 oz.

Subtraction

11. 305	12. 3030	13. 63.14	14. $1.67 − $1.39
28	286	17.29	15. $5 − 67¢

* Courtesy of Burroughs Corp.

16. $78\frac{2}{3}$ — **17.** 8   **18.** $55\frac{2}{3}$ **19.** $60\frac{1}{5}$ **20.** 5 ft. 7 in.

17. $\frac{5}{6} - \frac{2}{3}$ $24\frac{8}{9}$ $20\frac{2}{3}$ 2 ft. 9 in.

Multiplication

21. 87   **22.** 109   **23.** 170   **24.** 8.4

      49   509   70   .07

25. $\frac{1}{4} \times \frac{1}{4}$ **26.** $1\frac{3}{4} \times 8$ **27.** $\frac{1}{6} \times 11\frac{1}{3}$ **28.** $\frac{5}{8} \times 160$

29. $57\frac{1}{2}$ **30.** 6 bu. 2 pk.

      $28\frac{2}{3}$.   3

Division

31. $9\overline{)216}$ **32.** $.17\overline{).442}$ **33.** $45.2 \div 100$

                              178   178

34. $2.8\overline{).420}$ **35.** $2.4\overline{)427.2}$ **36.** $.24\overline{)4.272}$

37. $\frac{3}{4} \div \frac{3}{5}$ **38.** $\frac{1}{3} \div \frac{1}{3}$ **39.** $19\frac{1}{2} \div 3\frac{1}{4}$ **40.** $2\overline{)7 \text{ ft. 5 in.}}$

Per Cent

Write as common fractions: **47.** 20% of 158 = ?

41. 5%   **42.** $62\frac{1}{2}\%$ **48.** 12% of ? = 60

Write as decimal fractions: **49.** ?% of 40 = 18

43. 8%   **44.** 150%   Arrange in order of size—smallest first:

Write as per cents:

45. $\frac{7}{20}$ **46.** 1.6   **50.** $.087\frac{1}{2}$, $87\frac{1}{2}\%$, $8.7\frac{1}{2}$, $\frac{88}{100}$

Record your scores on the Achievement Chart.

Which of your scores are moving upward? Just one more Achievement Test. Make it a topper.

—REVIEW OF THE FUNDAMENTALS OF ARITHMETIC—7—

Addition and Subtraction

Add and prove:

1. 5	**2.** 74	**3.** 89	**4.** 256	**5.** 3284	**6.** 57.00	**7.** $9167.82
8	88	76	342	7158	19.06	8605.75
2	64	35	979	2101	4.09	1084.25
1	39	47	508	3764	47.52	5837.75
9	52	58	634			

8. 12.1645
9.875
.6667
5.4167

9. 3.8 + 4.05 + 6.032 + 3.4 + 26.8 + .3

10. .36 + .275 + .308 + .001 + 2.38

Add:

11. $\frac{4}{9} + \frac{2}{3}$ **13.** $\frac{3}{4}$ **14.** $\frac{1}{2}$ **15.** $78\frac{3}{4}$ **16.** $38\frac{1}{2}$ **17.** $26\frac{5}{6}$

12. $\frac{7}{8} + \frac{5}{6}$

$\frac{5}{16}$ $\frac{3}{20}$ $37\frac{1}{4}$ $19\frac{7}{8}$ $14\frac{2}{3}$

$\frac{3}{8}$ $\frac{3}{5}$ $5\frac{1}{4}$ $38\frac{3}{4}$

18. $22\frac{2}{9} + 15\frac{2}{3} + \frac{1}{2} + 19\frac{5}{9}$

19. $17\frac{1}{2} + 5\frac{3}{8} + 14\frac{5}{8} + 33\frac{1}{2}$

20. 7 yd. 2 ft.
6 yd.
8 yd. 1 ft.

Subtract and prove:

21. 1938
879

22. 6890
4987

23. 6000
1456

24. 32106
17248

25. 13536
8687

26. 12.3
7.4

27. .07
.068

28. 4.03
2.8

29. 27.463 − 18.574

30. 9.73 − 8.7485

Subtract:

31. $\frac{11}{12} - \frac{1}{3}$ **33.** $38\frac{1}{6}$ **34.** 77   **35.** $486\frac{5}{12}$ **36.** $48\frac{5}{8}$

32. $20 - 4\frac{4}{5}$

$26\frac{5}{12}$ $49\frac{5}{8}$ $249\frac{2}{3}$ $26\frac{3}{4}$

37. 3840
$2951\frac{7}{16}$

38. $47.06 - 5\frac{1}{3}$

39. $121.3 - 85\frac{2}{3}$

40. 14 yd. 2 ft. 8 in.
8 yd. 1 ft. 10 in.

—REVIEW OF THE FUNDAMENTALS OF ARITHMETIC—8—

Multiplication and Division

Multiply and prove:

1. 709
56

2. 604
97

3. 7096
76

4. 108
408

5. 1906
69

6. 478
83

7. 57.9
608

8. 56.72
5.76

9. 474
5.9

10. 63.8
3.5

Multiply:

11. .0468 × 10   **12.** 100 × .89   **13.** 100 × 78.1

14. 24.86 × 10   **15.** .91 × 1000   **16.** .68 × 1000

17. $\frac{5}{6} \times \frac{2}{15} \times \frac{9}{20}$ **18.** $5\frac{1}{2} \times 5\frac{1}{2}$ **19.** $12 \times 8\frac{1}{3}$

20. $72 \times 4\frac{1}{12}$ **21.** $\frac{1}{3} \times \frac{4}{9} \times \frac{1}{2} \times 6$ **22.** $40\frac{1}{5} \times 15\frac{3}{8}$

23. $8\frac{1}{2} \times 14\frac{3}{4}$ **25.** $18\frac{3}{4} \times 140\frac{2}{3}$ **26.** 3 hr. 52 min. 45 sec.

24. $12\frac{2}{3} \times 24\frac{3}{8}$ $\underline{\hspace{4cm}10}$

Divide and prove:

27. 5091 by 32   **31.** 684.5 by .38   **35.** 61 ÷ 10

28. 4003 by 37   **32.** 458.81 by .97   **36.** 45.75 ÷ 100

29. 4500 by 125   **33.** 1792 by .85   **37.** 6.75 ÷ 100

30. 67,446 ÷ 56   **34.** 34.336 by 148   **38.** .4 ÷ 1000

Divide:

39. $\frac{3}{10} \div \frac{2}{5}$ **42.** $2\frac{1}{4} \div 1\frac{1}{8}$ **45.** $6\frac{2}{3} \div 5\frac{1}{3}$ **48.** $10\frac{4}{5} \div 18\frac{3}{4}$

40. $\frac{3}{4} \div \frac{1}{2}$ **43.** $8\frac{1}{2} \div 4\frac{1}{4}$ **46.** $11\frac{7}{9} \div 5\frac{1}{3}$ **49.** $34\frac{1}{2} \div 5\frac{3}{4}$

41. $\frac{5}{6} \div \frac{2}{3}$ **44.** $9\frac{1}{7} \div 4\frac{4}{5}$ **47.** $12\frac{3}{4} \div 5\frac{2}{3}$ **50.** $3\overline{)8 \text{ bu. 1 pk.}}$

—REVIEW OF THE FUNDAMENTALS OF ARITHMETIC—9—

Percentages

Express each of the following numbers as (1) a common fraction, (2) a decimal, (3) a percentage:

1. $\frac{1}{3}$ **6.** $\frac{3}{8}$ **11.** $12\frac{1}{2}\%$ **16.** 1.5

2. $\frac{1}{5}$ **7.** .01   **12.** .35   **17.** $16\frac{2}{3}\%$

3. 50%   **8.** $3\frac{1}{3}\%$ **13.** $\frac{1}{25}$ **18.** .005

4. $\frac{3}{5}$ **9.** 28%   **14.** .075   **19.** 220%

5. .72   **10.** .875   **15.** 175%   **20.** $2\frac{3}{8}$

Find the following percentages:

21. 5% of 2,549   **27.** 2% of $1256   **33.** 8% of $47.50

22. 150% of .186   **28.** $1\frac{3}{4}\%$ of 52   **34.** $5\frac{1}{2}\%$ of $250

23. $14\frac{2}{7}\%$ of 49.84   **29.** 12% of $88.50   **35.** 9% of 67

24. 12% of 12,012   **30.** $16\frac{2}{3}\%$ of 4728   **36.** $4\frac{1}{2}\%$ of $80

25. 9% of 50,064   **31.** $3\frac{1}{3}\%$ of 93   **37.** $12\frac{1}{2}\%$ of $25.44

26. 120% of 25.5   **32.** $1\frac{1}{2}\%$ of 169.4   **38.** $\frac{2}{3}\%$ of 480

Fill in the following:

39. 10% of ? = 50   43. ?% of 64 = 12   47. 72% of 19 = ?
40. ?% of 40 = 30   44. 3% of ? = 22½   48. 15% of ? = 13.5
41. 2¾% of 8 = ?   45. ?% of 120 = 8   49. ?% of $6 = $9
42. 2% of ? = 16¢   46. ½% of 150 = ?   50. ¾% of 500 = ?

Solve the following:

51. 4 is what per cent of 50?   55. 1 is what per cent of 6?
52. What per cent of 25 is 75?   56. What per cent of 15 is 6?
53. 6 is what per cent of 45?   57. 9 is what per cent of 12?
54. What per cent of 10 is 1½?   58. 60 is what per cent of 40?

DENOMINATIONS OF CURRENCY

In order for you to have each denomination of currency issued by the United States today you would need to have:

$10,000.00 Bill
5,000.00 "
1,000.00 "
500.00 "
100.00 "
50.00 "
20.00 "
10.00 "
5.00 "
2.00 "
1.00 "
.50 Coin
.25 "
.10 "
.05 "
.01 "

Total $16,688.91

POSITION AND FORM OF OBJECTS

VOCABULARY

1. position	4. slanting	7. meridian	10. geometry
2. horizontal	5. parallel	8. longitude	
3. vertical	6. perpendicular	9. latitude	

134. Lines — horizontal, vertical, and slanting. People are interested in sports. They need to know where to put the guidelines for baseball or football fields. For shuffleboard and other court games, lines must be drawn in a certain relationship to each other. Nets for tennis are stretched between posts that have been erected to fulfill some of these relationships. All of these are found in a part of mathematics known as geometry.

Lines that are in the same relative position as the horizon are said to be *horizontal*. Such lines as the ones on your tablet paper, boards in a floor and the line formed by the meeting of a wall and ceiling in a room are horizontal lines. Locate six more horizontal lines to be found in the classroom. Write six that you recall seeing outside the classroom.

Lines that are at right angles to the horizon are *vertical*. A vertical line points to the center of the earth. Such lines as telephone poles and tree trunks are vertical. The line formed by the joining of the front wall with a side wall is a vertical line. Locate six other vertical lines.

Any straight line that is not horizontal or vertical is a *slanting* line (figure 1). The edge of a ramp is a slanting line. List five other examples of slanting lines. Hold a pencil in a horizontal position, in a vertical position, in a slanting position.

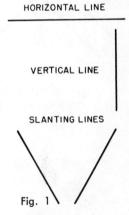

HORIZONTAL LINE

VERTICAL LINE

SLANTING LINES

Fig. 1

135. Parallel lines. The lines in a bar of music are all drawn in the same position and are the same distance apart. Such lines are said to be parallel to each other. Notice the vertical parallel lines in the building of figure 2. By holding two pencils, illustrate each of the three positions of parallel lines in figure 3. Parallel

259

Fig. 2. Parallel Lines
in Buildings.

lines may be extended indefinitely, and they will always remain the
same distance apart throughout their entire length. The edges of a
pencil are parallel. The pencil may be placed in vertical, horizontal,
or slanting positions and its sides will remain parallel. (See figure 4.)
Name six examples of parallel lines.

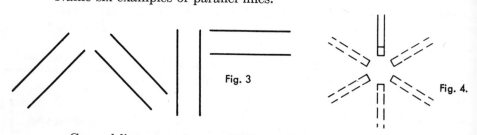

Fig. 3

Fig. 4.

Curved lines may be parallel to each other, as illustrated in the
picture of the large hotel in figure 5. Also notice the curved lines
outlining the plots of grass.

Fig. 5. Curved Parallel Lines in a Building

1. In what position are the hands of a clock when they point: (a) to 3 o'clock? (b) To 6 o'clock? (c) To a quarter to 3? (d) To 9 o'clock? (e) To 12 o'clock? (f) To 3:15? (g) To 8:45?

2. What curved lines can you name that are parallel to each other?

3. (a) Find out how parallel lines can be drawn on paper with only a ruler and pencil. (b) Draw parallel lines by this method.

4. (a) Find out how horizontal or vertical parallel lines are drawn with a T-square. (b) Make a simple T-square and then draw parallel lines by this method.

5. (a) Find out how slanting parallel lines are drawn with a T-square and a triangle. (b) Illustrate this method of drawing parallel lines.

136. Perpendicular lines. All horizontal and vertical lines that meet are perpendicular to each other. (See figure 6.) The angle formed by the meeting of a horizontal and a vertical line is a

Fig. 6. Perpendicular Lines.

A   B   C

right angle. Whenever two straight lines meet so as to form a right angle, the lines are perpendicular to each other. This being true, slanting lines may be perpendicular to each other. The adjoining edges of your book are perpendicular to each other. It makes no difference if the book is in a horizontal, a vertical, or a slanting position. Perpendicular lines are illustrated by picture frames, edges of window panes, and so forth. Name six illustrations of perpendicular lines.

1. How can a perpendicular line be drawn (a) to a line from a point on the line with a T-square? (b) to a line from a point outside the line? (c) Illustrate (a) and (b).

2. How can a perpendicular be drawn from a point to a line with ruler and pencil? Illustrate.

3. How can a carpenter tell when a wall is plumb (perpendicular)?

4. How can a nail on a string be used to tell when a post is vertical?

137. Straight-line designs. Designs are much used for ornamentation. Straight-line designs are often found in towel ends, handkerchief borders, dress patterns, and tiling.

————————— EXERCISES —————————

1. On squared paper, draw the straight-line designs illustrated. Keep clear-cut corners. Use a sharp pencil and a good ruler.

2. Copy straight-line designs found elsewhere.

***3.** Make original straight-line designs suitable for the border of a handkerchief, for wallpaper, and for a rug. The designs may be colored or shaded.

138. Position of places on a map. Places on the surface of the earth are located by means of imaginary lines running north and south and east and west. (See figure 7.) The lines running north and south are called *meridians*. They extend from pole to pole. The meridian which is used as the guide line is the one passing through Greenwich, near London, England. Any place

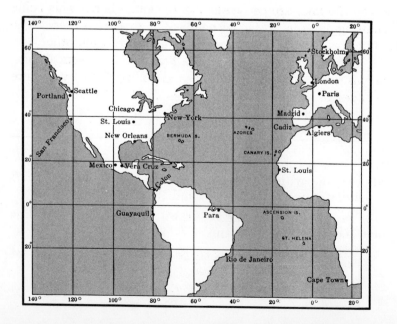

Fig. 7

that is east of this meridian (the *prime meridian*) is said to be so many degrees *east longitude*, while a place west of the prime meridian is so many degrees *west longitude*. Degrees of longitude are read at the top and bottom of a map.

The lines running east and west are called *parallels*. The parallel that is used as the guide line is the equator. Any place north of the equator is said to be so many degrees *north latitude*, while a place south of the equator is so many degrees *south latitude*. Degrees of latitude are read at the sides of a map.

Any number of meridians or parallels may be drawn on the map, but they are usually placed 5°, 10°, or 20° apart.

It is especially important for ships at sea, airplanes, and places to be located in terms of longitude and latitude.

Let us determine the longitude and latitude of Para.

EXAMPLE

Para is close to $\frac{1}{2}$ way between 40° and 60° W. longitude. By measuring the distance with an edge of paper, then folding the paper to locate the center of the distance, you can see that Para falls short of the 50°. A good estimate is about 48° W. longitude. By measuring for the latitude, you find that Para is about 2° S. of 0° latitude.

EXERCISES

Use figure 7 in solving the following exercises:

1. Give the approximate location of each of the following places:

Place	Longitude	Latitude
Para............................	48°W.	2°S.
Vera Cruz.....................	_____	_____
San Francisco.................	_____	_____
Stockholm.....................	_____	_____
Guayaquil.....................	_____	_____
Azores........................	_____	_____
New Orleans...................	_____	_____
New York......................	_____	_____
Colón.........................	_____	_____
Paris.........................	_____	_____
Chicago.......................	_____	_____

2. What city is approximately 5°W. longitude and 42°N. latitude?

3. What city is near 90°W. longitude and 38°N. latitude?

4. Name an island near 5°W. longitude and 18°S. latitude.

5. Name the city not far from 18°E. longitude and 35°S. latitude.

Fig. 8. The Surface of Quiet Water Is a Plane.

THE FORM OF PLANE FIGURES

VOCABULARY

1. plane figure
2. quadrilateral
3. parallelogram
4. rectangle
5. square
6. triangle

7. trapezoid
8. hexagon
9. octagon
10. pentagon
11. decagon
12. regular figure

13. circle
14. circumference
15. diameter
16. radius
17. radii
18. arc

139. Plane figures. Anything drawn on the blackboard would be flat. It would have two dimensions, length and width—no thickness. Such figures are called *plane figures.* Shadows on a wall are plane figures because they have only those of length and width—no thickness. Any figure cut from paper or printed on cloth may be considered a plane figure, since it has only two dimensions, length and width. Most paper or cloth is so thin that its thickness may be disregarded. The surface of quiet water is a plane. (See figure 8.)

To make cloth attractive to the eye, decorative designs are often woven into it. Or, if the cloth is woven plain, a design may be printed or stamped on. This practice has grown until today we find shops filled with lovely prints, many of which have designs based on geometric figures. Consider a few common geometric designs as found in cloth.

264   POSITION AND FORM OF OBJECTS

Figure 9 illustrates a plane figure bounded by four straight lines. Any such figure is called a *quadrilateral*. Look up the meaning of *quad* and *lateral*.

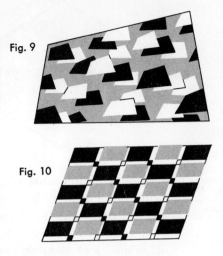
Fig. 9

Figure 10 illustrates a special kind of quadrilateral, called a *parallelogram*. In this figure both pairs of opposite sides are parallel and equal. Why are the quadrilaterals in figure 9 not parallelograms? All parallelograms are quadrilaterals, but not all quadrilaterals are parallelograms. Explain why this statement is true.

Fig. 10

Figure 11 shows a special kind of parallelogram, called a *rectangle*. The angles of a rectangle are all right angles. Why is a rectangle also a parallelogram and a quadrilateral? What is true about a rectangle that need not be true about a parallelogram?

Figure 12 is a cloth pattern composed of *squares*. A square is a rectangle with all the sides equal in length. What kind of angles has a square?

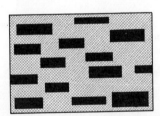

Fig. 11

Fig. 12

The *trapezoid*, figure 13, has only one pair of parallel sides. How does a trapezoid differ from a parallelogram? Why is a trapezoid also a quadrilateral? Are the parallel sides equal in length?

In what way are figures 9, 10, 11, 12, and 13 all alike? They are classed as what kind of a plane figure? Which of the figures mentioned is the most general? Which is the most restricted?

The design of figure 14 is composed of *triangles*. "Tri" means "three." A triangle is a plane figure containing three angles. How many sides has a triangle?

Fig. 13

Fig. 14

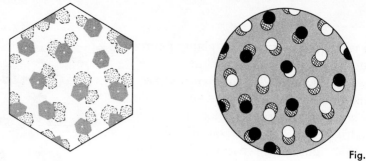

Fig. 15   Fig. 16

Figure 15 illustrates a *hexagon*, a six-sided plane figure. A plane figure of eight sides is called an *octagon;* a *pentagon* has five sides; and a *decagon* has ten sides. In design work, these figures usually have equal sides. Such figures are called *regular* hexagons, *regular* octagons, and *regular* pentagons. See figure 17 for a *regular* pentagon.

The *circle*, figure 16, forms the basis of many an interesting design.

The circle is a curved line all points in which are equidistant from a fixed point within, called the *center.* The length of the curved line is called the *circumference.* A *diameter* is a line that passes through the center of the circle and whose ends are on the circle. A *radius* is a line drawn from the center to a point on the circle. *Radii* is the plural of *radius.*

Fig. 17. The Pentagon houses the Department of Defense. It contains more than 16 miles of corridor and employs more than 32,000 workers.

1. Make a drawing of each of the plane figures illustrated and write the correct name under each. List a number of examples of each that are found in your home. Which shape is the most common?

2. A door is the shape of a rectangle. List ten other parts of buildings and name the geometric shape represented by each. (Find as many different shapes as possible.)

3. Point out some rectangles found in the classroom. Name any squares in the room. Any triangles. Circles. Other plane figures.

4. In what shape is a rug usually made? A saucepan lid? A towel? A checkerboard? Tiling in the bathroom? The front of a doghouse with a hip roof? A handkerchief? The end of a flower box?

5. What geometric forms do the outlines of these forms of nature suggest: snowflakes, top view of cells of honeycomb and wasp's nests, starfish, clover leaf, spruce trees, wild rose, pansy, and trillium?

6. The symbol used by the Y-Teens is a triangle. List other insignia, emblems, or trade-marks that are geometric forms.

140. Plane-figure designs. Borders and other decorations often contain attractive plane-figure designs.

1. Make a copy of some of the designs shown in figure 18.

2. (optional) Make some original designs. The designs may be colored or shaded.

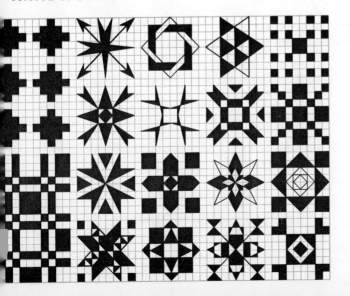

Fig. 18.
Plane-Figure
Designs.

141. How to draw a circle, using the compasses. Learn to adjust the *compasses* to different distances between the pencil point and the steel point. For best results when drawing a circle with compasses, follow this order of procedure:

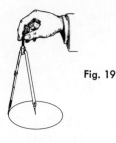

Fig. 19

(a) Adjust the distance between the points of the compasses so that it will equal the length of the radius of the circle that is to be drawn.

(b) Hold the compasses at the top, between the thumb and the forefinger. (See figure 19.)

(c) Stick the steel point into the paper, bearing down lightly.

(d) Starting with the pencil point far to the left, swing it clockwise around the point as an axis, thus drawing the circle.

―――――――――――――― *EXERCISES* ――――――――――――――

1. Practice drawing circles until you can make good ones easily.

2. Draw a circle whose radius is 1 in.

3. Using the same center that was used in the above circle, draw circles whose radii are $1\frac{1}{2}$ in., 2 in., and $2\frac{1}{2}$ in. Circles drawn so as to have the same center are *concentric circles*. Give some examples of concentric circles.

4. What are the diameters of the circles in exercise 3?

5. On a line 6 in. long, draw a continuous design similar to the one shown in figure 20.

Fig. 20

Fig. 21

6. Draw a continuous design similar to the one shown in figure 21.

7. Draw a regular hexagon in the following manner:

(a) Draw a circle.

(b) Keep the points of the compasses to a distance equal to the radius of the circle.

(c) Place the steel point of the compasses at any point upon the circle.

(d) Mark off, using the compasses and starting from this point, six successive points on the circle.

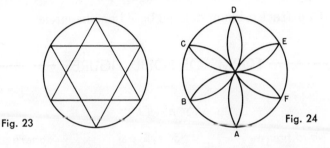

Fig. 22

(e) Draw a line connecting the successive points of division.

The figure thus formed is a regular hexagon, as shown in figure 22.

8. Draw an equilateral triangle. Use the preceding method, joining every other point on the circle.

9. Study figure 23. Construct it.

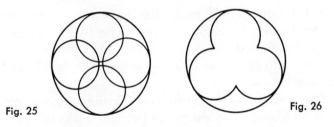

Fig. 23

Fig. 24

10. Draw figure 24. *Hint:* From any point on the circle, as A, and using the same radius as the radius of the circle, draw the arc BF. (An *arc* is a part of a circle, such as the curved line AE.) From B draw the arc CA. Continue in this manner.

Fig. 25

Fig. 26

11. Copy the designs in figures 25 and 26. *Hint:* In the first design, the centers of the small circles are on perpendicular diameters. In the second design, divide the large circle into three equal arcs. Draw radii to these points.

Fig. 27.
Circle Designs.

Fig. 28. Border Designs.

12. Copy the circle designs in figure 27.

13. Copy the border designs in figure 28.

*14. Construct original designs based on the circle.

FORMS OF SOLID FIGURES

VOCABULARY

1. solid figure	5. cylinder	9. sphere
2. rectangular prism	6. cone	10. hemisphere
3. cube	7. pyramid	11. thickness
4. triangular prism	8. frustum	12. height

142. Solid figures. Figures that have three dimensions are called *solid figures*, or merely *solids*. The three dimensions are commonly designated *length, width,* and *thickness,* as of a book; *length, width,* and *height,* as of a room; or *length, width,* and *depth,* as of an excavation.

143. Observing solid geometric forms. Geometric solids are found all about us in nature and in the works of man. Solid figures have *faces,* which are the upright sides of the figure. Most solids also have a *base*—sometimes two bases—upon which the solid may rest. The shape of the faces determines the name of the solid. The shape of the bases gives the description of the solid. For instance, figure 29 is a solid commonly seen in buildings. It is called a *prism.* A prism is a solid which has rectangles for faces. It is a *rectangular prism.* It is *rectangular* because the bases are both rectangles. There are two special rectangular prisms: (a) the square prism whose bases are square, as in a stick of butter, and (b) the *cube,* whose faces and bases are all square, as a child's A B C block. Name another square prism. Name another cube.

POSITION AND FORM OF OBJECTS

Fig. 29
Rectangular
Prism

Fig. 30
Triangular
Prism

Why is a cube also a rectangular prism? Why is not every rectangular prism a cube?

The chicken coop, when stood on end, is seen to have three rectangles for faces and a triangle for each base. Such a figure is a *triangular prism*. What other triangular prisms can you name?

Figure 31 illustrates a *cylinder*. It has a curved surface with two equal circles for bases.

Figure 32 is a combination of a *cone* and a *frustum* of a *cone*. They both have curved surfaces. How many bases has a cone? What is the shape of the base? Name some cone-shaped objects.

The frustum of a cone has two unequal circles for bases. You may recognize the shape as that of a megaphone. There are many other objects that are this shape. Which ones can you name?

Fig. 31
Cylinder

Fig. 32
Cone

Frustum
of Cone

A solid having triangles for its faces, like the upper part of figure 33, is called a *pyramid*. Its base is a plane figure having any number of straight lines for sides. If the top of the pyramid were cut off parallel to its base, the lower portion would be called the *frustum* of the pyramid. Some footstools are good examples.

The *sphere* (figure 34) is frequently used as an ornament on the tops of buildings, posts, and pedestals. Very often one half of a sphere, a *hemisphere*, is used as a dome on a building.

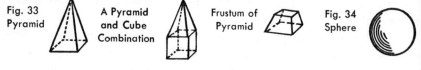

Fig. 33 Pyramid | A Pyramid and Cube Combination | Frustum of Pyramid | Fig. 34 Sphere

EXERCISES

1. Make a drawing of each of the preceding solids and write the correct name under each. List under each drawing several examples of that solid. Which shape is by far the most common?

2. In figure 35 list: (a) the plane figures to be found; (b) the solid figures.

3. An icicle has the shape of a cone. List five other cones.

4. List ten other objects in nature (trees, fruits, flowers, vegetables, and so forth), naming the geometric shape of each.

5. Illustrate a cylinder and a cone, each by a paper model. (Leave bases open. For the cone, draw a circle and cut out a portion between two radii.)

6. Make a paper model of a rectangular prism. (Bases need not be made.)

Fig. 35. Tiros II Weather Satellite

7. Make a paper model of a triangular prism. (Leave ends open.)

8. Make a paper model of a cube.

*9. Make other models of the prism and pyramid, using bases of different shapes.

**10. Make a set of closed cardboard models. (*Hint:* Use the patterns in figure 36 enlarged).

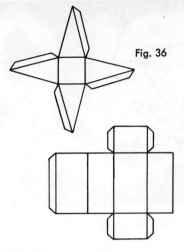

Fig. 36

─────── REVIEW OF CHAPTER XII ───────

1. Draw four parallel lines using only a ruler and pencil.

2. Draw a rectangle using a T-square.

3. Draw a square using a T-square.

4. Draw a parallelogram using a T-square and a triangle.

5. Figure 37 illustrates a court on which a number of games can be played. How many games do you discover can be played? The four corners of the court form right angles. What is the shape of the court? What different shapes are outlined in the court?

In what position are the (a) power poles, (b) the nets? How long is the court? How wide? How many square feet are there in the court? How many square yards?

Fig. 37. Combination Game Court.

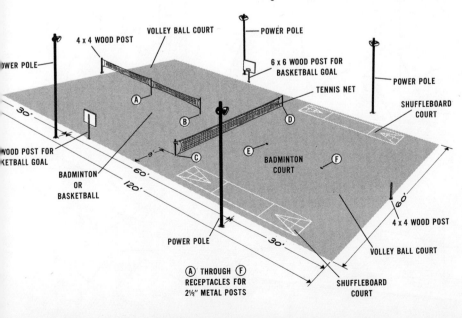

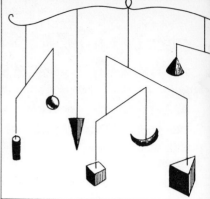

Fig. 38. A Poster of Geometric Forms.   Fig. 39. A Mobile of Solid Geometric Figures.

PLAYOFF FOR CHAPTER XII

1. Make an interesting poster by drawings or by cutouts of various geometric forms.   See figure 38.

2. Make a set of large designs and mount for a display.

3. Make a border for the bulletin board.

4. Make a mobile of geometric shapes studied.   See figure 39.

5. Make a model of a stained-glass window (large or small) using geometric shapes.

6. Form geometric designs by drawing one continuous line. See figure 40.

Fig. 40

Addition

1. 145
   278
   186
   324

2. $26\frac{3}{8}$
   $18\frac{1}{12}$

3. $6.24 + 7.8 + 9. =$

4. $\frac{2}{3} + \frac{5}{6} + \frac{1}{2} =$

Subtraction

5. 3001
   1567

6. $27\frac{3}{4}$
   $18\frac{2}{3}$

7. 2 yd. 1 ft. 15 in.
   1 yd. 2 ft. 10 in.

Multiplication

8. 2.8
   .46

9. $\frac{4}{15} \times \frac{10}{11}$

10. $2\frac{4}{5} \times 75$

Division

11. $7.2\overline{).1728}$

12. $.54\overline{)12.042}$

13. $\frac{9}{10} \div \frac{6}{7}$

Per Cent

14. $16\frac{2}{3}\%$ of 52.2

15. 16% of $? = 20$

16. $?\%$ of $15 = 12$

17. $6:10 = ?:25$

18. $?:8 = 8:32$

Find simple interest:

19. On $320 at 8% for 9 mo.

20. On $1500 at 6% for 90 da.

Find the annual premium on:

21. An $8,000 policy @ $44.07 per $1,000.

22. A $4,500 policy @ $56.82 per $1,000.

If the scale is:

23. $\frac{1}{4}$ in. to 1 ft., what is the real size of a room if the drawing is 4 in. by 6 in.?

24. $\frac{1}{8}$ in. to 1 ft. and the drawing is 5 in. by 7 in., what is the actual size of the room?

25. $\frac{1}{10}$ in. to 1 ft. and the actual dimensions are 20 ft. and 25 ft., find the size of the drawing.

THE SIZE OF PLANE AND

SOLID FIGURES

—— AREA AND PERIMETER OF PLANE FIGURES ——

144. The meaning of "area." In the rectangle $WXYZ$, figure 1, imagine that the sides of each small square measure one inch. The length of the rectangle will measure how many inches? The width how many inches? Each of the small squares is a *square inch*. The square inch is the *unit of area* in this case. The number of these squares (units of area) contained in the rectangle represents its *area*. Since there are 5 rows of squares and 8 squares to the row, there are 5×8 squares, or 40 squares. The area, then, is 40 times the unit of area, or 40 square inches.

Now think of each small square as measuring 1 ft. on a side, and the length and width of the rectangle as being 8 ft. and 5 ft., respectively. Each square is a *square foot*. The square foot is the unit of area in this case. Using this unit of area, find the area of the rectangle. The square inch and the square foot are common units of area. Others frequently used are the square yard, the square rod, the square mile, and the square centimeter.

Fig. 1

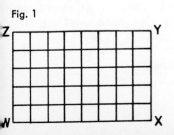

The *area* of any surface is the number of square units of a given kind that it contains. The surface $WXYZ$, when we thought of the squares as being one inch wide, was said to have an area of 40 square inches; but when it was thought of as containing 40 of the square-foot units, its area was said to be 40 square feet. Area is always expressed in square units, such as square inches, square feet, and so on.

145. Perimeter of a rectangle. To find the *perimeter* of $WXYZ$, or the distance around it, add the lengths of the lines that bound it: $WX + XY + YZ + ZW$. How long is the perimeter if the unit of length is 1 in.? The length of a perimeter is always expressed in linear units, such as inches, feet, yards, centimeters, and so forth.

———————————————— *EXERCISES* ————————————————

1. Using squared paper, show that a rectangle that is 6 units long and 4 units wide has an area of 6×4 square units, or 24 square units.

2. Illustrate the area of a rectangle 7 units long and 5 units wide.

3. In the rectangle $ABCD$, figure 2, let each side of the small squares represent 1 in.

(a) What is the unit of area?

Fig. 2

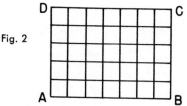

(b) How many of these units of area are contained in the rectangle?

(c) What, then, is the area of the rectangle?
(d) How do you find the perimeter?
(e) What is the unit of length for the perimeter?
(f) Find the perimeter.

In finding the perimeter of the rectangle in Fig. 2, Tom added $5 + 7 + 5 + 7 = 24$. Jack said that to find the perimeter he could add 5 and 7 and multiply their sum by 2. Will this give the correct perimeter? This can be written as $2 \times (5 + 7) = 2 \times 12 = 24$. Judy said she thought it would be better to multiply 5 by 2 and multiply 7 by 2, and then add these two products. To write this we write $(2 \times 5) + (2 \times 7) = 10 + 14 = 24$. The fact that Jack's method and Judy's method are both correct is an important idea in mathematics. For the numbers in the problem above this idea can be written as: $2 \times (5 + 7) = (2 \times 5) + (2 \times 7)$.

This rule will work for multiplying any number by any sum. For example: $8 \times (15 + 12) = (8 \times 15) + (8 \times 12)$

that is: $8 \times 27 = 120 + 96$

or: $216 = 216$

This rule is called the Distributive Law. It is used in arithmetic, in algebra, and in all other branches of mathematics.

4. Find in two different ways the perimeters of the rectangles having the following dimensions: (a) length—10″; width—6″. (b) length—17″; width—14″. (c) length—35″; width—15″.

5. On squared paper, let the squares represent 1 sq. in. Then:

(a) Draw a rectangle 6 in. long and 4 in. wide. Find its area. Find its perimeter.

(b) Draw a rectangle 11 in. long and 9 in. wide. Find its area. Find its perimeter.

(c) Draw three rectangles of different dimensions, each having an area of 36 sq. in. Compare the perimeters of the rectangles. The perimeter of which rectangle is the longest? Which the shortest? Do all rectangles of the same area have the same perimeter?

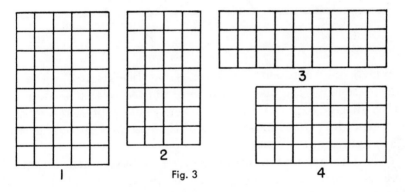

Fig. 3

6. In figure 3, let each side of each of the small squares of the rectangles represent each of the following, in turn: (1) 1 yard, (2) 1 rod, (3) 1 inch, (4) 1 foot.

(a) Find the area of each rectangle.

(b) Find the perimeter of each rectangle.

7. Using squared paper, let one side of each square represent 1 in. Then draw a square proving that 1 sq. ft. contains 144 sq. in.

8. Using squared paper, let one side of each square represent 1 ft. Draw a square proving that 1 sq. yd. contains 9 sq. ft.

9. On squared paper, let the side of each small square represent 1 ft. Using this scale, draw five rectangles, the perimeter of each being 20 ft. (*Hint:* Use 1 ft., 2 ft., 3 ft., 4 ft., and 5 ft. for the respective widths.) Find and compare the areas of the rectangles. Do all rectangles having the same perimeter have the same area?

The preceding exercise illustrates the following truth:

> *For a perimeter of any given length, the square will inclose an area greater than any other rectangle of the same perimeter.*

146. Base and altitude of plane figures. The base of a plane figure is the line upon which the figure rests. Any one of the bounding lines may be used for the base if the position of the figure is shifted.

The *altitude* (height or depth) of a figure is the perpendicular distance from the highest point in the figure to its base. For illustrations of base and altitude, see figure 5.

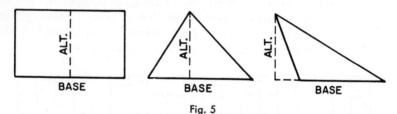

Fig. 5

Which line represents the base of the blackboard? The altitude? Imagine the blackboard to be shifted so that it stands up on its shorter edge. Which line then would represent the base? The altitude? Find illustrations of the base and altitude of other plane figures in the classroom.

147. The area of a rectangle. You have learned that the area of a rectangle is the product of the length and the width. This rule can be expressed in a much shorter way if initial letters are used for the words *area, length,* and *width* and signs for the words *equals* and *times.* Let A represent *area,* and let l and w denote *length* and *width,* respectively. The rule then becomes: $A = l \times w$. A rule written in this way is called a *formula.* The times sign is usually omitted in formulas to avoid confusion with the letter x. Letters written side by side in formulas are to be multiplied. The formula for the area of a rectangle may be written:

$$A = lw.$$

Since the length of a figure is usually called its *base* and the width its *altitude*, we can let *b* stand for *base* and *h* for *altitude*. The formula $A = lw$ then becomes:

$$A = bh.$$

——— EXAMPLE ———

To find the area of a rectangle whose base is 10 ft. and altitude 8 ft., solve as follows:

$$A = bh \qquad b = 10 \text{ ft.}$$
$$A = 10 \times 8 \qquad h = 8 \text{ ft.}$$
$$\text{Area} = 80 \text{ sq. ft.}$$

Note: In substituting numbers for letters in formulas, it is important to remember two things:

(a) To write merely the number, omitting the letter that it replaces.

(b) To be sure that the numbers are expressed in the same unit of measurement, that is, all measurements expressed in feet, or all expressed in inches—not some measurements expressed in feet and others expressed in inches.

——— EXERCISES ———

A. Oral

State the area of each of the following rectangles, using short cuts when possible:

1. $b = 6'$, $h = 12'$
2. $b = 10''$, $h = 7.5''$
3. $b = 20'$, $h = 24''$
4. $l = 24.5'$, $w = 100'$
5. $b = \frac{1}{4}'$, $h = \frac{2}{5}'$

6. $b = \frac{3}{8}'$, $h = \frac{2}{3}'$
7. $l = 24$ rd., $w = 12\frac{1}{2}$ rd.
8. $l = 66$ cm., $w = 16\frac{2}{3}$ cm.
9. $b = 50$ cm., $h = 80$ cm.
10. $b = 7.2'$, $h = .33\frac{1}{3}'$

B. Written

Find the area of each of the following rectangles:

11. $b = .32'$, $h = 14'$
12. $b = 100'$, $h = 88.8''$
13. $l = 2.86'$, $w = 7.2''$

14. $b = 35$ cm., $h = 3.8$ cm.
15. $l = 10\frac{1}{5}'$, $w = 1\frac{2}{3}'$
16. $b = 12\frac{1}{2}''$, $h = 88''$

17. How many square feet are in a lot 180 ft. long and 60 ft. wide? How many square yards are in the lot?

18. How many square rods are there in a rectangular field 86 rd. long and 75 rd. wide? How many acres?

19. How many rods of fencing will be needed to enclose the farm in exercise 18?

20. A farm in the shape of a rectangle is 80 rd. long and 56 rd. wide. How many acres does it contain?

21. How many rods of fencing will be needed to inclose the farm in exercise 20? What will be the total cost of the fence at $.75 per rod?

22. If a floor contains 288 sq. ft. and is 18 ft. long, how wide is it? ($w = A \div l$)

23. A table top contains 864 sq. in. and is 36 in. long. What is the width of the table?

*24. A pattern plan is pictured. How many square inches are there in the surface?

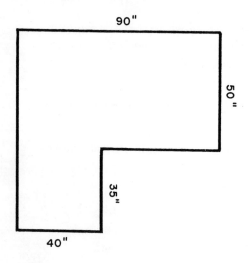

90"
50"
35"
40"

*25. It has been suggested that on a playground 30 sq. ft. of space should be allowed for each pupil. At this rate, how many pupils can safely play at one time on a ground 180 ft. by 120 ft.?

*26. Find the cost of covering a lot 40 ft. by 120 ft. with sod at 12½ cents a square yard.

*27. A railway box car is to be painted gray on the sides and black on the ends. How many square feet are painted in each color, if the sides are 40½ ft. long by 10 ft. high and the ends are 9½ ft. wide and 10 ft. high?

*28. A building foundation has the shape pictured. How many square feet of floor space does it cover?

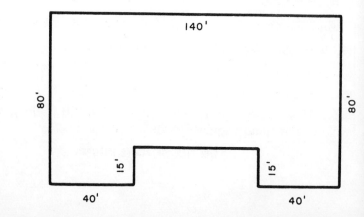

140'
80'
80'
15'
15'
40'
40'

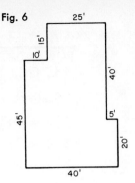

Fig. 6

*29. Two boys out camping built a fire which, through their carelessness, spread to the forest. It burned an area 120 rd. long and 80 rd. wide. How much was the loss if the timber was worth $500 per acre?

**30. A house plan has the shape pictured in figure 6. Find the number of square feet of floor space it contains.

**31. Mr. Sands has a rectangular surface 140 ft. by 30 ft. to paint. Which is more economical and how much more: to use paint at $5.80 per gallon that will cover 300 sq. ft. of surface, or paint at $5.15 per gallon that will cover 210 sq. ft. of surface?

**32. Determine the number of square feet of painted surface in your classroom. Which will be cheaper and how much cheaper: to buy paint for this surface at $2.96 per half-gallon that covers 150 sq. ft., or paint at $2.45 per half gallon that covers 100 sq. ft.?

**33. A plot of ground extending 120 rd. along a highway and 20 rd. deep was divided into building lots of 90-ft. frontage by 165 ft. deep. How many lots were thus formed? If the plot of ground cost $600 per acre and each lot sold for $28 per foot frontage, what was the profit on the ground?

**34. How many square meters are there in the floor of the classroom?

148. The area of a square. Since the lengths of all four sides of a square are equal, you can find its area by multiplying the length of one side by itself. If the side of a square is 6 units, the square has an area of 6 × 6 square units, or 36 square units. Let s represent the length of one side of the square; then $A = s \times s$.

6 × 6 may be written: 6^2 (*six squared*); and the formula $A = s \times s$ may be written:

$$A = s^2.$$

It is read, "A equals s squared."

EXAMPLE

To find the area of a square whose side is 10 in. long, solve by the following method:

$$A = s^2 \qquad\qquad s = 10''$$
$$A = 10^2$$
$$A = 10 \times 10$$
$$\text{Area} = 100 \text{ sq. in.}$$

A. Oral

State the area of each of the following squares:

1. $s = 40$ in.
2. $s = 25$ ft.
3. $s = .3$ in.

4. $s = 4\frac{1}{2}$ cm.
5. $s = 100$ mm.
6. $s = .4$ rd.

7. $s = .02$ ft.
8. $s = 1.1$ ft.
9. $s = 1.5$ in.

B. Written

Find the area of each of the following squares:

10. $s = 18$ in.
11. $s = 24$ ft.
12. $s = 3.5$ rd.
13. $s = 2.8$ yd.
14. $s = 6.3$ in.

15. $s = 8.25$ ft.
16. $s = 14\frac{1}{2}$ cm.
17. $s = 8.8$ yd.
18. $s = 7\frac{1}{2}$ yd.
19. $s = 17\frac{1}{2}$ in.

20. $s = 27\frac{1}{3}$ yd.
21. $s = 4.25$ in.
22. $s = 4\frac{5}{6}$ ft.
23. $s = 4'\ 8''$
24. $s = 9'\ 3''$

25. A checkerboard is 15 inches on an edge. How many square inches are there in the checkerboard?

26. One of the large pyramids of Egypt has a square base 764 ft. long. How many square feet of ground does it cover?

*27. Some boys were given a square lot for a garden. It measured 72 ft. on a side. How many square feet were there in the lot? If they divided it off into plots 6 ft. by 8 ft., how many plots of ground were there?

*28. A square has an area of 10,000 sq. ft. What is the length of each side? (What number multiplied by itself equals 10,000?)

*29. A building 48 ft. by 60 ft. was built on a lot 90 ft. square. How many square feet were left for the lawn?

**30. A plot of ground 1 mile square is divided into four equal square farms. How many acres has each farm? How many pounds of fertilizer are required for each farm if 20 lb. will fertilize 1 acre?

**31. How many pounds of fertilizer (20 lb. to the acre) will be required for: (a) A field 80 rd. square? (b) A garden 120 ft. square? (c) A piece of ground containing 2,880 sq. ft.?

**32. What is the difference between a 6-ft. square and 6 sq. ft.?

149. The lateral area of a rectangular prism. A rectangular prism is made up of how many rectangles? What are the dimensions of the base rectangle in figure 7? What is the area of one base? Of both bases together?

The rectangles forming the sides between the bases are called *lateral faces*. The sum of the areas of the lateral faces is called the *lateral area*.

In figure 7, what is the area of each lateral face? What is the lateral area of the rectangular prism?

What is the perimeter of the base? Multiply the perimeter of the base by the height. How does this result compare with the lateral area? They should agree.

The formula for finding the lateral area of a rectangular prism by the shorter method is:

$$S = Ph,$$

S standing for *lateral area*, P for *perimeter*, and h for *height*.

The *total area* of a rectangular prism is the sum of the area of the bases and the lateral area.

What is the total area of figure 7?

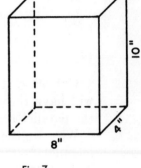

Fig. 7

―――――――――――――――― EXERCISES ――――――――――――――――

*1. Henry made a tool box 38 in. long, 20 in. wide, and 16 in. high. How many square inches of lumber were there in the box, including the top?

*2. Make a paper carton 2 in. long, 1½ in. wide, and 3 in. high. What is its lateral area? Its total area?

*3. How much will it cost at 8 cents per square foot to paint a chest 6 ft. long, 2½ ft. wide, and 18 in. high? (The bottom base is to be left unpainted.)

*4. Find the number of square feet in the total surface of a cubical box 5 ft. on each edge.

**5. Draw the pattern for a carton 4 in. long, 1½ in. wide, and 2 in. high. Find the lateral area and the total area.

**6. Find the cost of covering with paper all sides of ten rectangular boxes each 15 in. long, 8½ in. wide, and 6 in. deep, at 5 cents per square foot.

**7. Find the cost of plastering a room 16 ft. x 12 ft. x 9 ft. at 15 cents per square foot. (Make no allowance for openings.)

**8. Find the area of each lateral face of the classroom. Find the lateral area of the room. Find the total area of the room.

150. The area of a parallelogram. On a piece of squared paper draw a parallelogram 8 units long and 4 units high, as shown in figure 8. The height (altitude) is the perpendicular distance to the base, as DX.

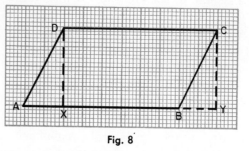

Fig. 8

Cut off $\triangle ADX$ and place it so that AD falls on BC, and you will have the rectangle $XYCD$ of the same base and altitude as the parallelogram $ABCD$.

Why are the bases AB and XY equal? What is the area of the rectangle? Since the area of the rectangle is found by multiplying its base by its altitude, the area of the parallelogram, which is the same, will be found in the same way. What is the area of the parallelogram?

The area of a parallelogram is the product of its base and altitude.

Expressed as a formula, this rule becomes:

$$A = bh.$$

―――――――――――― *EXERCISES* ――――――――――――

A. Oral

State the area of each of the following parallelograms:

1. $b = 20'$, $h = 16'$ 4. $b = 646$ yd., $h = 50$ yd.
2. $b = 100'$, $h = 10'$ 5. $b = 33'$, $h = 66\frac{2}{3}'$
3. $b = 84''$, $h = 25''$ 6. $b = 37\frac{1}{2}''$, $h = 88''$

B. Written

Using the formula, find the area of each of the following parallelograms:

7. $b = 26'$, $h = 18'$ 10. $b = 12$ ft., $h = 8$ yd.
8. $b = 3.8''$, $h = .8''$ 11. $b = 1.8$ cm., $h = 2.6$ cm.
9. $b = 7\frac{1}{3}'$, $h = 5\frac{1}{4}'$ 12. $b = 1\frac{1}{2}$ yd., $h = 4\frac{2}{3}$ yd.

THE SIZE OF PLANE FIGURES

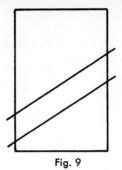

Fig. 9

13. How many acres are there in a field in the shape of a parallelogram with a base 80 rd. long and an altitude of 15 rd.?

14. A state road cut across some Boy Scouts' camping ground, as illustrated in figure 9. The portion of the road crossing the camp ground was 840 ft. long and 18 ft. wide. How many square feet of land did the boys lose?

In each of the following drawings, indicate the altitude by a heavy dotted line:

15. On squared paper draw a parallelogram whose base is 5 cm. and altitude 2 cm. Let 1 square = 1 sq. cm. Find the area and check the result by counting the square centimeters.

16. On squared paper draw a parallelogram with base of 54 mm. and altitude 22 mm. What is the area of the parallelogram?

*17. On paper ruled in square centimeters, draw to a convenient scale a parallelogram with base of 80 ft. and altitude of 16 ft. Indicate the scale used. Find the area. Count squares to verify your result.

*18. Draw to a convenient scale on squared paper a parallelogram 120 yd. long and 60 yd. wide. Indicate the scale used. Find the area. Verify by counting the squares.

151. The area of a triangle. On squared paper draw a rectangle *ABCD* with a base of 10 units and an altitude of 6 units. (See figure 10.) Draw a diagonal, as *BD*, forming two triangles each with a base and altitude equal to the base and altitude of the rectangle. Cut out the triangles and fit one on the other. Since they fit exactly, the two triangles are equal. The area of one triangle is just one-half the area of the rectangle.

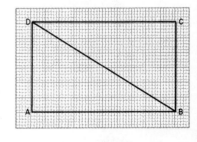

Fig. 10

Draw another rectangle 10 by 6 units. (See figure 11.) Draw the lines *XZ* and *YZ*, forming △ *XYZ* with the base 10 units long and the altitude *ZO* 6 units high. Cut out △ *XYZ* and fit the remaining △ *YNZ* on *OZY* and △ *XZM* on *XZO*. Since they fit exactly, the area of △ *XYZ* is just one-half the area of the rectangle of the same base and altitude.

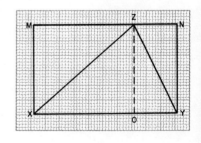

Fig. 11

What is the area of the rectangle? Of the triangle?

The area of a triangle is one-half the product of its base and altitude.

Expressed as a formula, this rule becomes:

$$A = \tfrac{1}{2}bh$$

--- **EXAMPLE** ---

To find the area of a triangle whose base is 16 in. and whose altitude is 13 in., solve as follows:

$$A = \tfrac{1}{2}bh \qquad\qquad b = 16 \text{ in.}$$

$$A = \frac{1}{\overset{}{\underset{2}{2}}} \times \overset{8}{\cancel{16}} \times 13 \qquad h = 13 \text{ in.}$$

$$\text{Area} = 104 \text{ sq. in.}$$

--- *EXERCISES* ---

State the area of each of the following triangles:

1. $b = 14'$, $h = 8'$ /s—'

2. $b = 8''$, $h = 4.2''$ // ''

3. $b = \frac{1}{2}'$, $h = 2.8'$ ⨽'

4. $b = \frac{2}{3}''$, $h = 1''$ /⨽ ''

5. $b = 10$ rd., $h = 40$ rd. ⨽⨽

6. $b = 16$ ft., $h = 9$ in. /⨽'

7. $b = 8$ yd., $h = .3$ yd. ⨽.⨽⨽

8. $b = .2$ cm., $h = .9$ cm.

9. $b = 14'$, $h = 28'$

10. $b = 26''$, $h = 2'$

11. $b = 8\frac{1}{4}''$, $h = 5\frac{1}{3}''$

12. $b = 18$ cm., $h = 14.2$ cm.

13. $b = 12$ mm., $h = 8.5$ mm.

14. $b = 7.2'$, $h = .9'$

*15. A triangular sail with a base of 9′ 6″ and an altitude of 11′ 4″ exposes how many square feet of surface when spread out to the wind?

*16. The gable end of a house has a base of 18′ 8″ and a height of 8′ 6″. How many square feet does it contain?

**17. What is the area of figure 12?

**18. What is the area of figure 13?

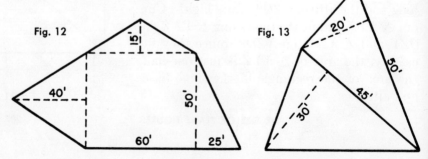

Fig. 12   Fig. 13

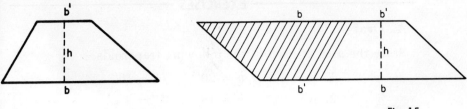

Fig. 14

Fig. 15

152. The area of a trapezoid. Figure 14 is a *trapezoid*. The two opposite sides b and b' (b' is read b *prime*) are parallel and are called the *lower* and *upper* bases, respectively. The non-parallel sides may or may not be the same length. The altitude is the perpendicular distance, h, between the two bases.

Draw and cut out two trapezoids of the same size and shape. Inverting one of the trapezoids, place the two together as in figure 15. The figure thus formed is a parallelogram with the same altitude as the trapezoid and with base equal to the sum of the upper and lower bases of the trapezoid. The area of the parallelogram is $h \times (b + b')$. Why? Since each trapezoid is just one-half of the parallelogram:

The area of a trapezoid equals one-half the product of its altitude and the sum of its bases.

Written as a formula, this rule becomes:

$$A = \tfrac{1}{2}h \times (b + b')$$

Omitting the times sign:

$$A = \tfrac{1}{2}h(b + b')$$

In order to show that b and b' are to be added together before they are multiplied by $\tfrac{1}{2}h$, b and b' are inclosed in parentheses.

EXAMPLE

To find the area of a trapezoid with lower and upper bases 6 in. and 8 in., respectively, and altitude 4 in., solve as follows:

$$A = \tfrac{1}{2}h(b + b') \qquad h = 4 \text{ in.}$$
$$A = \tfrac{1}{2} \times 4(8 + 6) \qquad b = 8 \text{ in.}$$
$$\qquad\qquad\qquad\qquad\quad b' = 6 \text{ in.}$$
$$A = \frac{1}{\cancel{2}} \times \overset{2}{\cancel{4}} \times 14$$

Area = 28 sq. in.

THE SIZE OF PLANE FIGURES

A. Oral

State the area of each of the following trapezoids:

    1. $h = 4''$, $b = 20''$, $b' = 10''$

    2. $h = 2'$, $b = 18'$, $b' = 8'$

    3. $h = 10''$, $b = 12''$, $b' = 8''$

    4. $h = 5$ yd., $b = 6$ yd., $b' = 4$ yd.

    5. $h = 3$ rd., $b = 40$ rd., $b' = 30$ rd.

    6. $h = 8$ cm., $b = 10$ cm., $b' = 8$ cm.

    7. $h = 1'$, $b = 9'$, $b' = 7'$

    8. $h = 20''$, $b = 25''$, $b' = 15''$

B. Written

Using the formula, find the area of each of the following trapezoids:

    9. $h = 10''$, $b = 17''$, $b' = 13''$

  10. $h = 9'$, $b = 28'$, $b' = 20'$

  11. $h = 5$ cm., $b = 16$ cm., $b' = 10$ cm.

  12. $h = 3\frac{1}{2}''$, $b = 8\frac{1}{2}''$, $b' = 7\frac{1}{2}''$

  13. $h = 4'$, $b = 10' \, 6''$, $b' = 8' \, 4''$

  14. $h = 3' \, 4''$, $b = 16' \, 8''$, $b' = 12' \, 4''$

  15. $h = 2' \, 8''$, $b = 15' \, 9''$, $b' = 13'$

  16. $h = 5$ cm., $b = 9.2$ cm., $b' = 6.4$ cm.

*17. A 33-ft. road was cut across one corner of a rectangular field, as shown in figure 16. The owner was offered $7.50 per square rod for the portion of his land that was used. If one side of the road on his field measured 80 rd. and the other side 72 rd., how much did the owner receive for his land?

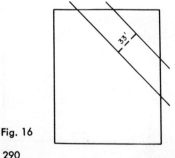

*18. In order to enlarge a room, a bay window with the dimensions shown in figure 17 was added. How many square feet of floor space were added?

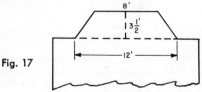

Fig. 16

Fig. 17

**19. Betty is making a lamp shade of parchment. Each of the four sides is the shape of a trapezoid, the bases of which are 15 in. and 12 in., with an altitude of 8 in. Find the area of each side. Find the total area.

153. The circumference and diameter of a circle. Short distances are often more conveniently measured with compasses or dividers than by direct application of the ruler. The sharp points of either instrument are adjusted so as to touch both ends of the line to be measured. Then the distances between the points of the instrument used are measured on the ruler and the length of the line is thus determined. This method is especially good for measuring the radii and diameters of circles and dimensions of other figures.

A good way to measure the circumference of any cylindrical object is as follows:

(a) Place a mark at some point on the circumference of the object to be measured.

(b) Place the one-inch mark of a tapeline on this mark.

(c) Wrap the tapeline around the object until it again touches the marked place on the circumference. The distance between these two points on the tapeline will represent the circumference of the object.

Measure carefully the circumference of several cylindrical objects, such as a pie pan, table top, bucket, and wheel. Also measure the diameter of each. Find the ratio of the circumference to the diameter, expressing the results to the nearest hundredth. Arrange the results as follows:

Object	Circumference	Diameter	Ratio
Plate	29.75"	9.5"	3.13+

Fig. 18. Observe the circular forms in the Telstar telemetry antenna.

Find the average of the Ratio column. It should be about 3.14. This shows us that:

The circumference of a circle is about 3.14 times the length of its diameter.

For more accurate results, 3.1416 is used; however, even this ratio is only approximate.* For ordinary purposes, the ratio $3\frac{1}{7}$ ($\frac{22}{7}$) is used.

Letting C stand for *circumference,* d for *diameter,* and the Greek letter π (pronounced $p\bar{\imath}$) for *ratio,* the formula for the circumference is:

$$C = \pi d$$
$$\text{or, } C = 2\pi r. \quad \text{(Why?)}$$

--- EXAMPLE ---

To find the circumference of a circle whose diameter is 35 in., solve as follows:

$$C = \pi d \qquad \qquad \pi = 3\frac{1}{7}$$
$$\qquad \qquad \qquad d = 35 \text{ in.}$$
$$C = \frac{22}{\cancel{7}} \times \cancel{35}^{5}$$
$$\qquad \quad 1$$

Circumference = 110 in.

--- EXERCISES ---

Using the ratio $3\frac{1}{7}$, find the circumference of each of the following circles:

1. $d = 14$ in.   4. $d = 3\frac{1}{2}$ ft.   7. $r = 4$ yd.

2. $d = 21$ yd.   5. $d = 7$ in.   8. $d = 5.6$ ft.

3. $d = 49$ cm.   6. $r = 28$ in.   9. $r = 2.1$ in.

Using the ratio 3.14, find the circumference of each of the following circles:

10. $d = 10$ in.   12. $r = 20$ ft.   14. $d = 35$ in.

11. $d = 100$ ft.   13. $r = 140$ yd.   15. $d = 70$ in.

16. How do the circumferences of the circles in exercises 14 and 15 compare? How do you account for this relation?

---

* The ratio of the circumference to the diameter will never divide out evenly. It divides like this: 3.14159265358979323846426433832, and on and on.

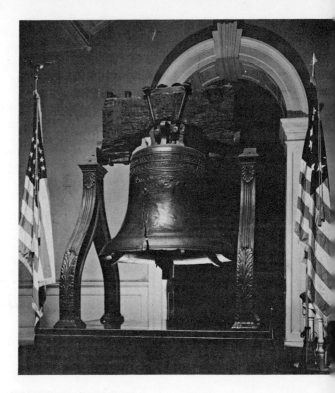

Fig. 19. The Liberty Bell As Seen in Independence Hall in Philadelphia.

17. The diameter of a circular boiler is 105 in. What is its circumference?

18. A garden is in the form of a circle 26 ft. across. How many feet of fencing are required to inclose it?

19. The cross-section of a tree has an outside diameter of 16 in. Find the circumference.

20. A flywheel in a power plant is 14.14 in. in diameter. What is the circumference?

21. The diameter of a steel boiler is 57.4 in. What is its circumference?

22. If the circumference of a circular piece of oilcloth is to be 132 in., what must be its diameter? $(d = C \div \pi)$

23. The circumference of a tree is 88 in. Find its diameter.

24. The circumference around the lip of the Liberty Bell is 12 ft. 6 in. What is the diameter at the lip? (See figure 19.)

25. What is the diameter of a boiler whose circumference is 121 in.?

26. The circumference of a cylindrical tank is 66 in. What is the diameter?

27. The flywheel of a steam engine is 16.8 in. in diameter. How many feet does a point on the circumference travel in one revolution?

To find the *velocity* (sometimes called the *surface speed*) of pulleys and wheels, multiply the circumference in feet by the number of revolutions per minute (r.p.m.).

$$V = \pi \times d \times \text{r.p.m.}$$

EXAMPLE

Find the velocity in feet per minute of an emery wheel 9 in. in diameter turning at 500 r.p.m.

$$V = \pi \times d \times \text{r.p.m.}$$

$$V = 3.14 \times \frac{\overset{3}{\cancel{9}}}{\underset{4}{\cancel{12}}} \times \overset{125}{\cancel{500}}$$

$$V = 1177.5 \text{ ft. per minute.}$$

Solve for velocity in feet per minute:

	Diameter	*r.p.m.*
*28.	6′	400
*29.	18″	1,100
*30.	2′	750
*31.	6″	1,800
*32.	7½′	350

**33. Draw a circle with a radius of 3 in. Draw a diameter and construct another diameter perpendicular to it. Cut out ¼ of the circle and form the remaining ¾ into a funnel. Find the circumference of the base of the funnel by using the formula. Check your result by actual measurement.

**34. What is the length of a paper wrapper that fits around a can of 2-in. diameter, if ½ in. extra is allowed for pasting?

**35. The diameter of each wheel over which a band saw runs is 3.5 ft. The distance between the centers of the two wheels placed one above the other is 3.9 ft. How long is the band saw?

**36. A cylindrical lamp stand 8 in. in diameter is cut down in a lathe in the manual-training shop to a diameter of 6 in. What is the new circumference?

154. The area of a circle.

An interesting method of discovering the rule for the area of a circle is illustrated in figure 20. This circle has a radius of 10 units. The lower right-hand fourth has a square drawn on the radius. As the square is 10 units long, the area of the square on the radius, r^2, is 100 square units.

The square units in the circle are more difficult to count, because of the many fractions of a square unit. In the marked fourth, the number of squares in each row is estimated and listed as

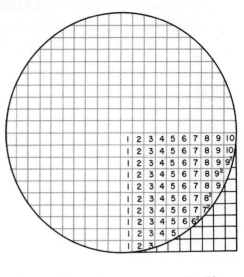

Fig. 20

follows: 10, 10, 9½ (written as 9^2), 9½, 9, 8½, 7½, 6½, 5, 3—making a total of approximately 78½ square units in each one-fourth of the circle, or approximately 314 square units in the whole circle.

When the approximate area of the circle is compared with the area of the square on the radius, it is found that the former is about 3.14 times as large as the latter ($314 \div 100 = 3.14$).

This leads to the rule:

The area of a circle is about 3.14 (or 3⅐) times the square of the radius.

$$A = 3.14 \times r^2$$

Using π for 3.14, the formula becomes:

$$A = \pi r^2$$

EXAMPLE

To find the area of a circle whose radius is 3½ in., solve as follows:

$$A = \pi r^2 \qquad\qquad \pi = 3\tfrac{1}{7}\ \left(\tfrac{22}{7}\right)$$
$$\qquad\qquad\qquad r = 3\tfrac{1}{2}\text{ in.}$$

$$A = \frac{\overset{11}{\cancel{22}}}{\cancel{7}} \times \frac{\cancel{7}}{\cancel{2}} \times \frac{7}{2}$$

Area = $\tfrac{77}{2}$, or $38\tfrac{1}{2}$ sq. in.

Using the ratio $3\frac{1}{7}$, find the area of each of the following circles:

1. $r = 70$ ft.   4. $r = 2\frac{1}{3}$ yd.   7. $d = 6$ in.

2. $r = 140$ in.   5. $d = 5.6$ rd.   8. $r = 7$ ft.

3. $r = 2.1$ ft.   6. $d = 8$ cm.   9. $r = 14$ ft.

10. In exercises 8 and 9, how do the radii compare in length? How do the areas compare in size?

Using the ratio 3.14, find the area of each of the following circles:

11. $r = 100$ rd.   13. $d = 8.6$ cm.   15. $r = 10$ ft.

12. $r = 80$ yd.   14. $d = 7.8$ mm.   16. $r = 20$ ft.

17. How do the radii in exercises 15 and 16 compare in length? How do the areas compare in size?

18. A wigwam has a diameter on the ground of $3\frac{1}{2}$ yd. How many square yards of floor space does it cover?

19. A circular flower bed has a radius of $4\frac{1}{5}$ ft. How many square feet are there in the flower bed?

20. Morning Glory Pool in Yellowstone Park is about 23 ft. across. Approximately how many square feet does the surface of the pool cover? What is the distance in feet around the pool?

*21. Find the perimeter and area of figure 21.

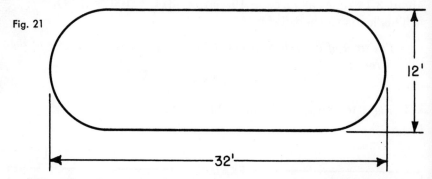

Fig. 21

12'

32'

*22. The diameter of a circle is $\frac{1}{2}$ in. Find its area to the nearest thousandth of a square inch; to the nearest ten-thousandth of a square inch. (Use $\pi = 3.1416$.)

*23. Which has the larger surface, and how much larger: a circular pool 70 ft. in diameter, or a square pool 70 ft. on a side?

*24. If a city with a radius of $2\frac{1}{2}$ mi. doubles its radius to 5 mi., how much has it increased its area in sq. mi.?

*25. Find the area of figure 22.

*26. How many circles 3 in. in diameter can be cut from a strip of decorative paper 9 in. by 60 in.?

*27. What is the area of the largest circle that can be cut from a rectangle 6 in. by 9 in.? Make either a full-size or a scale drawing to show how the circle would be cut. Label the dimensions.

*28. A girl cuts two doilies each 18 in. in diameter, 4 doilies each 9 in. in diameter, and 4 doilies each 7 in. in diameter from a square yard of lace. How many square inches of lace are in the doilies? How many square inches are left?

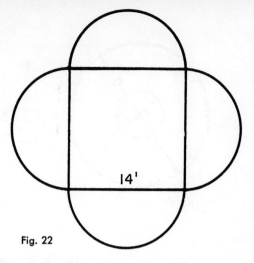

14'

Fig. 22

*29. Using the correct formula in each case, find the area of each of the forms in figure 23 after making the necessary measurements.

Fig. 23

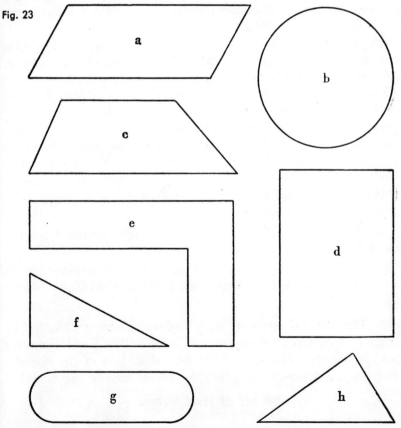

a

b

c

d

e

f

g

h

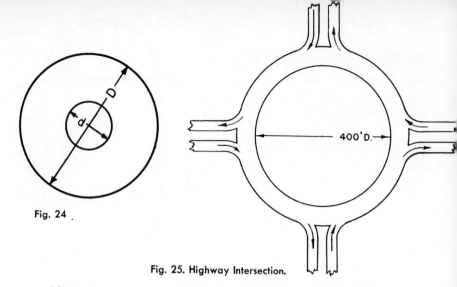

Fig. 24.

Fig. 25. Highway Intersection.

**30. A steel rod 3.125 in. in diameter must be turned down to a 2.287 in. diameter. How deep must the cut be?

**31. The outside diameter of a pipe is 3.475 in. and the thickness of the wall is .388 in. Find the inside diameter.

**32. The top of a steam table is a metal plate 2′ 3″ by 5′ 4″. Six holes each 9 in. in diameter are cut in the plate. What is the area of the plate remaining?

**33. There is a walk 3 ft. wide around a circular fountain whose diameter is 21 ft. (a) What is the area of the fountain base? (b) What is the area of the fountain and the walk together? (c) Now that you know these two areas, how can you find the area of the walk? (d) Find the area of the walk.

**34. The outside diameter of a circular plate is 22 in. A circular hole in the center is 7 in. across. What is the area of the metal ring? (Use $\pi = 3\frac{1}{7}$.) Area of ring $= \pi \times (R^2 - r^2)$. (R = radius of plate; r = radius of hole.)

**35. Find the area of figure 24, if $D = 1\frac{1}{2}$ in. and $d = \frac{1}{2}$ in. (Use $\pi = 3\frac{1}{7}$.)

**36. How many square rods of sod will be required for the circle in the center of the highway, figure 25?

**37. At 75 cents per square yard, what will a contractor charge for paving a circular walk whose inside diameter is 35 ft. and whose width is 7 ft.?

155. The lateral area of a cylinder. Form a cylinder by rolling a rectangular piece of paper as in figure 26. Let the shorter edges just touch. The area of the curved surface of the cylinder formed by the rectangle is called the *lateral area* of the cylinder.

The total surface of the cylinder is the sum of the areas of the two bases and the lateral area.

How does the width of the rectangle compare with the altitude of the cylinder? The length of the rectangle becomes what of the cylinder? Since the rectangle forms the curved surface of the cylinder, the area of the rectangle is the same as the lateral area of the cylinder.

As the area of the rectangle is equal to the product of the length and the width, the lateral area of the cylinder is equal to the product of the circumference (length of rectangle) and the altitude (width of rectangle).

Fig. 26

This leads to the rule:

The lateral area of a cylinder is the product of its circumference and altitude.

If S stands for lateral area, C for circumference, and h for altitude, the formula for the lateral area of the cylinder is:

$$S = Ch.$$

――――――――――――――― *EXERCISES* ―――――――――――――――

1. What is the lateral area of a cylinder which has a circumference of 24 ft. and an altitude of 8 ft. 6 in.?

2. A large roller is a cylinder 70 in. long and 96 in. in circumference. What area of ground is rolled in one revolution (lateral area)?

*3. How many square feet of lumber are there in a water tower 21 ft. in diameter and 20 ft. high?

*4. How many square feet of metal are there in a hot water tank $1\frac{1}{4}$ ft. in diameter and 6 ft. high?

*5. At 5 cents per square foot, what would it cost to paint a cylindrical smokestack 40 ft. high and $3\frac{1}{2}$ ft. in diameter?

*6. A cylindrical tank has a radius of 7 ft. and an altitude of 20 ft. Find the area of the two bases. Find the lateral area; the total area.

**7. How many square feet of surface exposed to the air has a steam-heating pipe 18 ft. long and 3 in. in diameter?

**8. A cylinder has a radius of $3\frac{1}{2}$ in. and an altitude of 4 in. What is the circumference? What is the lateral area? Roll a piece of paper to make a cylinder with the above dimensions. Measure the circumference to verify your answer.

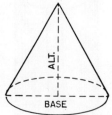

156. Base and altitude of solid figures. The *base* of a solid figure is the side or face upon which it stands. Any one of the sides may be used for the base if the position of the figure is shifted. The *altitude* of a solid figure is the perpendicular distance from the highest point in the figure to its base.

Place your book on your desk. Which side is its base? What is its altitude? Change its position so that it will have a different base. Now which side is the base? What is the altitude? Find illustrations of the base and altitude of other solid figures in your classroom.

157. The volume of a solid figure. The *volume* of a solid figure is determined by the number of cubic units that it contains. The unit of measure may be a cubic inch, a cubic foot, or a cubic yard, depending upon the size of the solid to be measured. A *cubic inch* is a cube one inch long, one inch wide, and one inch high, like figure 27. What are the dimensions of a cubic foot? Of a cubic yard?

What unit of measure would be convenient to use in finding the volume of a shoe box? Of a coal bin? Of a room?

158. The volume of a rectangular prism. In figure 28, imagine each small cube to measure 1 inch on an edge. The length of the rectangular prism measures how many inches? The width measures how many inches? The height is how many inches? Each of the small cubes is called a *cubic inch*. The cubic inch is the unit of volume in this case. The number of these cubes contained in a rectangular prism represents its volume.

Since each layer of cubes is made up of 3 rows of cubes with 7 cubes in each row, there are 3 × 7 cubes, or 21 cubes, in one layer. Four such layers will contain 4 × 21 cubes, or 84 cubes. The volume, then, is 84 times the unit of volume, or 84 cubic inches.

Fig. 28

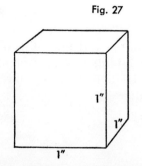

Fig. 27

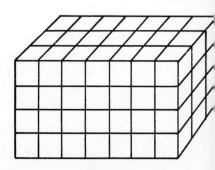

Now think of each small cube in figure 28 as measuring 1 ft. on an edge, and the length, width, and height as 7 ft., 3 ft., and 4 ft., respectively. The unit of measure now becomes a cubic foot. Using this unit of measure, find the volume of the rectangular prism.

By determining the total number of cubic units in any rectangular prism, you find its volume.

EXERCISES

1. In figure 29, let the edge of each cube represent 1 in.

   (a) What is the unit of volume?
   (b) How many of these units of volume are contained in the rectangular prism?
   (c) What, then, is its volume?

2. In the same figure, let the edge of each cube represent 1 ft.

   (a) What is the unit of volume?
   (b) What is the volume of the rectangular prism?

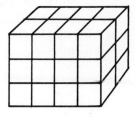

Fig. 29

3. In the rectangular prisms of figure 30, let one edge of each small cube be represented as follows:

  In No. 1 = 1 in.   In No. 2 = 1 ft.   In No. 3 = 1 yd.

Find the volume of each rectangular prism.

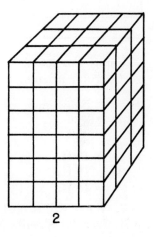

2

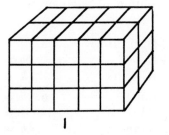

1

Fig. 30

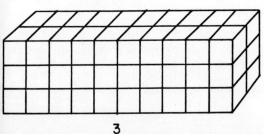

3

301

4. Draw a rectangular solid containing 24 cu. in., letting the length be 3 in.

The volume of a rectangular prism can always be found by the following rule:

The volume of a rectangular prism is the product of its three dimensions.

If V stands for *volume*, l for *length*, w for *width*, and h for *height* or *altitude*, the formula for this rule will then become as follows:

$$V = lwh.$$

Since the base is a rectangle with the dimensions l and w, the area of the base is lw.

Letting B represent the area of the base, and substituting B for lw in the above formula, we have:

$$V = Bh.$$

EXAMPLE

To find the volume of a box 4 ft. long, 3 ft. wide, and $2\frac{1}{2}$ ft. high, solve as follows:

$$V = lwh \qquad l = 4 \text{ ft.}$$
$$V = \overset{2}{\cancel{4}} \times 3 \times \frac{5}{\cancel{2}} \qquad w = 3 \text{ ft.}$$
$$\qquad\qquad\qquad h = 2\frac{1}{2} \text{ ft.}$$
$$\text{Volume} = 30 \text{ cu. ft.}$$

EXERCISES

Using the formula, find the volume of each of the following rectangular prisms:

1. $l = 8$ in.   **3.** $l = 3$ ft. 6 in.   **5.** $l = 7.8$ cm.
$w = 2$ in. $w = 4$ ft. $w = 4.1$ cm.
$h = 9$ in. $h = 3$ ft. 4 in. $h = 2.5$ cm.

2. $l = 12$ ft.   **4.** $l = 8$ mm.   **6.** $l = .6$ ft.
$w = 16$ ft. $w = 2$ mm. $w = 1.9$ ft.
$h = 18$ ft. $h = 2.8$ mm. $h = .7$ ft.

7. What will it cost to dig a trench 40 ft. long, $2\frac{1}{2}$ ft. wide, and 6 ft. deep, at 8 cents per cubic foot?

8. A freight car is 38 ft. long and 8 ft. wide and is filled with sand to a depth of 3 ft. 9 in. How many cubic feet of sand are in the car? How many cubic yards?

9. A box 8.8 cm. long, 5 cm. wide, and 4.2 cm. deep contains how many cubic centimeters?

10. A coal bin is 15 ft. long and 12 ft. wide. How many cubic feet of coal will it hold when filled to a depth of 5 ft.? There are 63 lb. in 1 cu. ft. of coal. How many pounds of coal will the bin hold?

***11.** A coal bin 14 ft. long, 9 ft. wide, and 6 ft. 4 in. high is half full of coal. How many cubic feet of coal are in the bin? How many tons at 32 cu. ft. per ton?

***12.** How many bars of soap measuring 4 in. by 2 in. by 1 in. are there in a stack of soap 2 ft. by 1 ft. by 8 in.?

***13.** Carl is making a box 16 in. long and 9 in. wide. He wants it to hold 720 cu. in. How high must he make it? $\left(h = \dfrac{V}{lw} \right)$

***14.** Mr. Cooper wishes to make an icehouse that will hold 6,000 cu. ft. of ice. He has decided to make the ground plan 20 ft. by 20 ft. How high must he make the house?

****15.** A porch pillar 27 ft. high has for its base the shape illustrated in figure 31. How many cubic feet are there in the pillar?

****16.** A square chimney 8 ft. high has a base as pictured in figure 32. Find the number of cubic feet of material in the chimney.

****17.** Find the number of cubic feet of air space in your classroom. How many cubic feet of air does this allow per pupil in your class? How many cubic feet would there be per pupil if the room were: (a) twice as long; (b) twice as wide; (c) two times as high; (d) twice as long and twice as wide; (e) with twice as many pupils; (f) with half as many pupils; (g) twice as long and with twice as many pupils; (h) twice as long and with half as many pupils?

****18.** The swimming pool of a certain school is 50 ft. long and 30 ft. wide, and is filled to an average depth of 3 ft. 6 in. How many gallons of water are in the pool? (One cubic foot = $7\frac{1}{2}$ gal., approximately.) If the water costs $1.25 per one thousand cubic feet, what does it cost to fill the pool? If the tank is filled once a month with fresh water for the nine months, find the cost of the water for the school year.

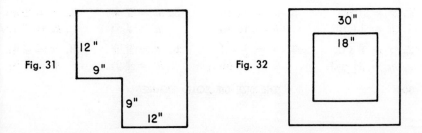

Fig. 31   Fig. 32

**19. (optional) Get the necessary measurements of your school pool and find the number of gallons of water required to fill it. Find the cost of each filling at your local rates.

159. The volume of a cylinder. The cylinder in figure 33 is 20 in. high and its base contains 154 sq. in.

$$\pi r^2 = \tfrac{22}{7} \times 7 \times 7 = 154.$$

At a distance 1 in. high on the cylinder there are 154 cu. in. Then, at a distance 20 in. high, there will be 154 cu. in. × 20, or 3,080 cu. in.

From the above, we derive the following rule:

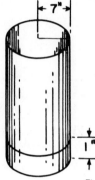

The volume of a cylinder is equal to the product of the area of the base and the altitude.

As a formula, the rule may be written:

$$V = Bh.$$

Since the cylinder B represents the area of the circle, $B = \pi r^2$. Then the formula may be written:

$$V = \pi r^2 h.$$

Fig. 33

EXAMPLE

To find the volume of a hot water tank whose diameter is 1 ft. and altitude 5 ft., solve in this manner:

$$V = \pi r^2 h \qquad\qquad \pi = 3\tfrac{1}{7}$$

$$V = \frac{\overset{11}{\cancel{22}}}{7} \times \frac{1}{\cancel{2}} \times \frac{1}{2} \times \frac{5}{1} \qquad r = \tfrac{1}{2}\text{ ft.}$$

$$h = 5\text{ ft.}$$

$$V = \tfrac{55}{14}$$

Volume $= 3\tfrac{13}{14}$ cu. ft.

EXERCISES

Using the formula, find the volume of each of the following cylinders:

1. $r = 5$ in.   **3.** $r = 4$ cm.   **5.** $d = 7$ ft.   **7.** $r = 2$ in.
    $h = 14$ in. $h = 14$ cm. $h = \tfrac{1}{2}$ ft. $h = 7$ in.

2. $r = 8$ yd.   **4.** $r = \tfrac{1}{2}$ in.   **6.** $d = 1$ ft.   **8.** $r = 4$ in.
    $h = 3\tfrac{1}{2}$ yd. $h = 14$ in. $h = \tfrac{2}{3}$ ft. $h = 7$ in.

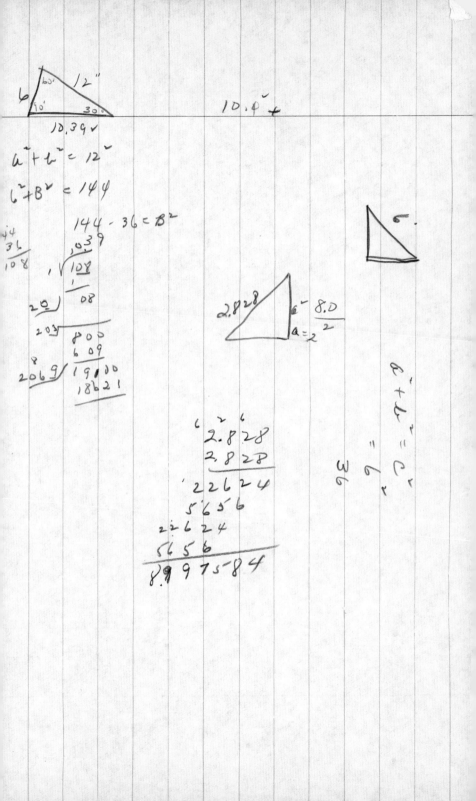

6 $60°$ $12"$

$10°$ $30°$

$10.39\sqrt{}$ $10.4"$ +

$a^2 + b^2 = 12^2$

$b^2 + B^2 = 144$

$144 - 36 = B^2$

44
36
108   ,√108
             1
             08

20) 08

203) 800
       6 09

2069 / 19000
          18621

2.828 $b = 8.0$
              $a = 2$ 2

$a^2 + b^2 = c^2$ 36 $= b^2$

  6 2 6
2.828
2.828
22624
5 6 5 6
22624
5 6 5 6
8.9 9 7 5 84

9. In exercises 7 and 8, how was the volume of the cylinder affected by doubling the radius? How do you account for this result?

10. A silo 42 ft. in height has an inside diameter of 14 ft. What is its capacity in cubic feet?

11. How many cubic inches of tomatoes are there in a can whose diameter is 4 in. and depth $4\frac{1}{2}$ in.?

*12. What would it cost to dig a cistern $3\frac{1}{2}$ ft. in diameter and 16 ft. deep at 12 cents per cubic foot?

*13. What fractional part of a cubic foot can be contained in an iron pipe 14 ft. long and 2 in. across?

*14. How many gallons are there in a barrel $3\frac{1}{2}$ ft. deep and 2 ft. across?

*15. How many gallons of water will a street sprinkler hold if it is 15 ft. long and 4 ft. across?

*16. An automobile gasoline tank that is cylindrical has a diameter of 12 in. and is 35 in. long. How many gallons will it hold when filled? How many gallons are in it when the instrument on the dashboard shows the tank to be three-fourths full?

*17. A lawn sprinkler has a $\frac{1}{8}$-in. stream and spreads about 100 gallons of water per hour. What will it cost to operate the sprinkler for three hours at the rate of $1.50 per thousand cubic feet of water used?

*18. What is the weight of a concrete roller $8\frac{1}{2}$ ft. long and 4 ft. in diameter if one cubic foot of concrete weighs 147 lb.?

**19. Bring an empty cylindrical can from your home. Measure its diameter and height. How many square inches are in the bottom of the can? How many cubic inches of vegetables would be required to fill it? How many if the can were twice as tall? How many if the diameter of the can were doubled? How many if the height of the can and the diameter were both doubled?

**20. How many cubic inches does a No. 1 can of corn contain, if it has a diameter of 3 in. and a height of $4\frac{5}{8}$ in.? How many cubic inches are there in a No. $2\frac{1}{2}$ can of corn if the diameter is 4 in. and the height is $4\frac{11}{16}$ in.?

**21. Tiros II, the weather observation satellite, was in the form of a cylinder with a diameter of 42 inches and a height of 19 inches. It weighed 280 pounds. (a) What was its volume? (b) What was its weight per cubic inch?

160. The volume of a cone and pyramid.

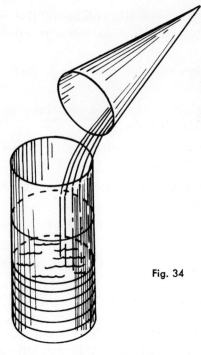

Fig. 34

Figure 34 shows a cone and a cylinder of the same height, with bases of the same size. Estimate how many times as much will be contained in the cylinder as in the cone.

It is interesting to check your estimate by the following experiment. Obtain a cylinder of convenient size. Make a cone of stiff paper the same height and with its base the same size as that of the cylinder.

Fill the cone with sand, sawdust, or any other suitable material and pour it into the cylinder. Continue filling the cone and pouring into the cylinder until the cylinder is filled. If the work is accurately done, the capacity of the cylinder will be found to be three times the capacity of the cone.

Since the volume of a cylinder is equal to the product of the area of the base and the altitude, we arrive at the following rule:

The volume of a cone is equal to one-third the product of the area of the base and the altitude.

The formula for this rule is:

$$V = \tfrac{1}{3}Bh$$

or,
$$V = \tfrac{1}{3}\pi r^2 h$$

A similar experiment may be tried with a prism and a pyramid that have the same bases and equal altitudes. It will be found that the capacity of the prism is three times that of the pyramid. Hence:

The volume of a pyramid is equal to one-third the product of the area of the base and the altitude.

That is:

$$V = \tfrac{1}{3}Bh$$

To find the volume of a cone whose height is 8 in. and radius of base $3\frac{1}{2}$ in., solve as follows:

$$V = \tfrac{1}{3}\pi r^2 h \qquad\qquad r = 3\tfrac{1}{2}\text{ in.}$$

$$V = \frac{1}{3} \times \frac{\overset{11}{\cancel{22}}}{\cancel{7}} \times \frac{7}{\cancel{2}} \times \frac{7}{\cancel{2}} \times \frac{\overset{4}{\cancel{8}}}{1} \qquad h = 8\text{ in.}$$

$$V = \frac{308}{3}$$

Volume $= 102\frac{2}{3}$ cu. in.

To find the volume of a pyramid whose altitude is 9 in. and whose base is a rectangle 4 in. by 3 in., solve as follows:

$$V = \tfrac{1}{3}Bh \qquad\qquad l = 4\text{ in.}$$

$$V = \frac{1}{\cancel{3}} \times 4 \times \cancel{3} \times 9 \qquad \begin{aligned} w &= 3\text{ in.} \\ h &= 9\text{ in.} \end{aligned}$$

Volume $= 36$ cu. in.

1. Find the volume of a cone if the radius of the base is 3 in. and the altitude is 7 in.

2. How many cubic feet are there in a cone if its altitude is 15 ft. and its diameter at the base is 7 ft.?

3. What is the volume of a pyramid if its altitude is 18 in. and its base is a square 4 in. on each side?

Fig. 35

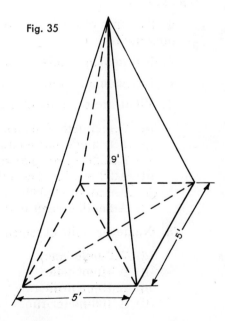

4. How many cubic feet are there in a pyramid if its height is 5 ft. and its base is a triangle with an area of 42 sq. ft.?

5. How many cubic feet of space are there in a conical tent if its height is 12 ft. and its diameter on the ground is 14 ft.?

6. A stone pyramid of the dimensions in figure 35 contains how many cubic feet?

7. If a certain tepee has a diameter on the ground of 9 ft. and is 11 ft. in height, what is its volume?

Fig. 36

*8. Some putty is molded in the shape of a rectangular prism with a base 3 in. by 3 in. and an altitude of 5 in. How many pyramids with the same base and altitude can be molded from the same amount of putty? Why?

**9. A cylindrical tank is topped with a cone as shown in figure 36. Find the capacity of the tank if the inside diameter is 15 ft. and the heights of the cylinder and cone are 12 ft. and 2 ft., respectively.

**10. The Great Pyramid of Egypt (see page 106) was originally 481 ft. high and its base was 756 ft. square. What was its volume?

────────── *REVIEW OF CHAPTER XIII* ──────────

1. The area of a square that is one inch long on each side is called a ____.

2. The area of a square that is one foot long on each side is a ____.

3. The number of squares contained in a plane figure represents its ____.

4. The sum of the lengths of the lines that enclose a plane figure represents its ____.

5. List as many units of an area as you know.

6. List as many units of length as you know.

7. What are the units of area of the following plane figures?

    (a) A rectangle that has an area of 60 sq. ft.
    (b) A triangle that contains 72 sq. yd.
    (c) A 2500-sq. rd. playground.
    (d) A 225-sq. in. checkerboard.
    (e) A state of 86,000 sq. mi.
    (f) A handkerchief of 144 sq. in.

8. Name the unit of length of these lines:

    (a) A 2-mile lane.
    (b) A 4-foot pole.
    (c) A 12-inch ruler.
    (d) A 100-meter run.

9. For a 16-inch perimeter of a rectangle, what shape will enclose the greatest number of square inches?

10. In the formula $A = lw$, what does lw represent?

11. You wish to find the area of a rectangle that is 2 feet long and 6 inches wide. What is the first step in solving for the area?

12. What does $A = s^2$ mean?

13. What does $P = 4s$ mean?

14. What is the difference between S^2 and $2s$?

15. (a) What are lateral faces?
(b) What is lateral area?
(c) What is total area?

**16. Why is $3\frac{1}{7}$ (3.1416) called a *ratio?*

17. What is the meaning of *r. p. m.?*

18. Altitude is the _____ distance from the highest point in the figure to its base.

19. Base is _____.

20. (a) What are the dimensions of a cubic inch? (b) A cubic foot? (c) A cubic centimeter?

21. Name the unit of measure that would be convenient to use in finding the volume of (a) a chalk box, (b) a refrigerator, (c) a breakfast room, (d) a school auditorium, (e) the earth.

22. What does $V = Bh$ mean?

23. The volume of an ice cream cone is what fractional part of the volume of an ice cream container in the shape of a cylinder of the same size base and height?

24. What is the difference between a 2-ft. square and 2 sq. ft.?

25. How many square feet are there in a rectangular garden 40 ft. by 30 ft ?

*26. In the preceding garden, there are two circular flower beds each 5 feet across. How much area do these flower beds occupy? How much area is left for grass?

*27. A square green felt emblem measuring 24 in. on a side has a triangular white felt piece in the center which has a base and an altitude of 18 in. each. Find the number of square inches in the square and in the triangle. How many square inches of the green are exposed?

*28. How many acres are there in a field in the shape of a parallelogram with a base of 76 rd. and an altitude of 40 rd.?

*29. The top of a wall seat in a bay window is the shape of a trapezoid with the parallel sides 9 ft. and 7 ft., respectively, and the depth 1 ft. 6 in. How many square feet are there in the top of the seat?

*30. A triangular sail has a base of 9 ft. 6 in. and a height of 11 ft.

(a) The sail exposes how many square feet of surface when spread out to the wind?

(b) If the wind is blowing with a pressure of 3.5 pounds to the square foot, how much is the pressure on the sail?

(c) If, by reefing, the height of the sail is reduced 1 ft. and the base is reduced 6 in., what is the area of the part that is then exposed to the wind?

(d) What would the pressure on the sail of the reduced size be at 3.5 pounds per square foot?

*31. An automobile wheel is $24\frac{1}{2}$ in. in diameter. What distance does it cover in making one complete revolution?

*32. Find the area of the surface of a plastic tube which has a circumference of 4 in. and a length of 14 in.

*33. A box 9.2 cm. long, 6 cm. wide, and 3.4 cm. deep contains how many cubic centimeters?

*34. What is the weight of a concrete roller 8 ft. long and $3\frac{1}{2}$ ft. in diameter if one cubic foot of concrete weighs 147 lb.?

*35. A candy cone is $1\frac{1}{2}$ cm. high and has a base 1 cm. across. What fraction of a cubic centimeter of candy does it contain?

**36. A $34\frac{1}{2}$-ft. square-based pyramid tops the Washington Monument. As it is 25 ft. high, how many cubic feet of space does the pyramid occupy?

———————— PLAYOFF FOR CHAPTER XIII ————————

1. Glue colored sticks together to make the outline of one or more solid figures.

2. The Great Pyramid of Egypt (p. 106) is now 451 ft. high and the square base is 750 ft. long. How much space does it occupy?

3. *An easy one? How may 100 be expressed with four nines?

---

* Courtesy of Burroughs Corp.

Addition

1. 5678
1295
2837

2. $37\frac{5}{6}$
$78\frac{3}{4}$

3. 2.8
.6
6.7

4. 8T. 1800 lb.
6T. 1560 lb.

Subtraction

5. 61203
48729

6. 7
2.156

7. 126
$78\frac{7}{8}$

8. 7 hr. 40 min.
3 hr. 48 min.

Multiplication

9. 307
108

10. 80
70

11. $75\frac{2}{3}$
18

12. 4 yd. 2 ft.
9

Division

13. $.18\overline{)3618}$

14. $\frac{7}{12} \div \frac{2}{3} =$

15. $.6 \div 100 =$

16. $\frac{1}{2}$ of 7 hr. 15 min.

Per Cent

17. $66\frac{2}{3}\%$ of 84 =

18. $3\frac{1}{3}\%$ of 96 =

19. 6% of ? = 252

20. ?% of 36 = 4

21. Round off (a) 4.617 to the nearest tenth; (b) 7.286 to the nearest hundredth.

22. How many pounds of apples can be bought for $1.20 at 15¢ per pound?

23. What is the cost of 48 pencils at 90¢ per dozen?

24. $\frac{7}{8} \times \frac{6}{11} \times \frac{2}{3} \times \frac{33}{8} =$

25. 309^2

CONSTRUCTIONS

VOCABULARY

1. right triangle
2. acute triangle
3. obtuse triangle
4. isosceles triangle

5. equilateral triangle
6. compasses
7. bisect
8. △ symbol for triangle

161. Kinds of triangles.   One method of classifying a triangle is by the kind of angles that it contains.

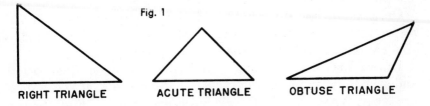

Fig. 1

RIGHT TRIANGLE   ACUTE TRIANGLE   OBTUSE TRIANGLE

A *right triangle* is a triangle that contains one right angle.

An *acute triangle* is a triangle all the angles of which are acute.

An *obtuse triangle* is a triangle that contains one obtuse angle.

A second method of classifying a triangle is by the relationship of its sides.

Figures 2 and 3 are special kinds of acute triangles.   In figure 2, measure AC and CB.   How do they compare in length?   A triangle having two equal sides is called an *isosceles* triangle.   Measure $\angle A$ and $\angle B$, the *base angles*.   How do they compare in size?

In figure 3, measure and compare the lengths of XY, YZ, and XZ.   A triangle having three equal sides is called an *equilateral triangle*.   What does the word "equilateral" mean?   Compare the number of degrees in each angle.   What is the size of each angle of an equilateral triangle?

A triangle that has no two sides equal in length is a *scalene* triangle.

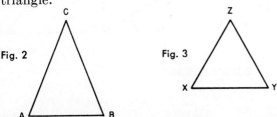

Fig. 2

Fig. 3

313

1. Draw:

(a) A right triangle that is also a scalene triangle.
(b) A right triangle that is also an isosceles triangle.
(c) An isosceles triangle that is also an acute triangle.
(d) An isosceles triangle that is an obtuse triangle.
(e) A scalene triangle that is also an acute triangle.

2. Name one or more examples of: (a) a right triangle; (b) an acute triangle; (c) an obtuse triangle; (d) an isosceles triangle; (e) an equilateral triangle; (f) a scalene triangle.

162. The sum of the angles of a triangle. Draw a 2-in. line *AB*. At *A* draw a 50° angle and at *B* draw a 40° angle. Extend the sides of these angles until they meet, forming △ *ABC*. Measure the angle at *C*. What kind of triangle is *ABC*? Find the sum of the degrees in ∡ *A, B,* and *C*.

On a 2½-in. line *XY*, draw ∡ *X* and *Y* equal to 30° and 70°, respectively. Complete △ *XYZ*. Measure ∠ *Z*. What kind of triangle is △ *XYZ*? Find the sum of the three angles.

Draw a line *MN* 3 in. long. At *M* draw an angle equal to 110° and at *N* draw an angle equal to 20°. Complete △ *MNO*. Measure ∠ *O*. What kind of triangle has been formed? Find the sum of the angles in △ *MNO*.

What do you observe about the sum of the three angles of the above triangles?

An important geometric truth:

The sum of the angles of any triangle equals 180°.

━━━━━━━━━━━━━━ *EXERCISES* ━━━━━━━━━━━━━━

1. Cut from paper a triangle of any convenient size. Tear off the three angles and put them together, as in figure 4. How does this prove that the sum of the angles of a triangle equals 180°?

Fig. 4

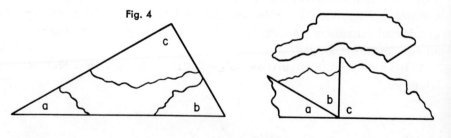

2. If the sum of two angles of a triangle equals 70°, what is the size of the third angle?

3. The sum of two angles in a triangle equals 148°. Find the size of the third angle.

4. In △ *XYZ*, ∠ *X* equals 60° and ∠ *Y* equals 35°; ∠ *Z* equals how many degrees?

5. In △ *MNO*, ∠ *M* = 48° and ∠ *N* = 75°; ∠ *O* = ?

6. Why can you not draw a triangle containing more than one right angle? More than one obtuse angle?

163. A practical use of triangles. You have no doubt noticed the many uses of triangles in construction work of carpenters and engineers. The trusses on bridges, brackets for shelves, diagonals across box ends and gates, and the supports of a roof are all uses made of one or more triangles. The triangle is used in these instances because of its rigid form. Once a triangle is made, its shape or size cannot be changed by pressure applied to any of its sides or angles. This is not true of quadrilaterals. Fasten four sticks together with one nail at each corner and note how the size and shape of the quadrilateral thus formed can be changed by a little pressure on its sides or angles. Then fasten three sticks together with one nail at each corner and note how the triangle thus formed cannot be changed in size or shape by any amount of pressure. A triangle once formed retains its shape and hence is rigid. What instances have you noticed in which the triangle has been used to make objects rigid?

164. How to bisect a line, using the compasses. Draw a line *MN*. From *M* as center, with a radius greater than ½ *MN*, draw two arcs, one above and one below *MN*. Using the same radius and with *N* as a center, draw two other arcs. Connect the points at which the arcs intersect. Line *OP* is the bisector of line *MN*. Prove by measuring. Why must the radius of the arcs be greater than ½ *MN*?

The resulting line *OP* not only bisects line *MN* but also is perpendicular to it. You can prove this by measuring the angles at the intersection of the two lines.

Can you suggest practical uses for this construction?

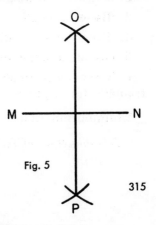

Fig. 5

1. Draw a line 3 in. long. Using compasses, bisect the line. Measure the halves.

2. Bisect a 4-in. line, a 5-in. line, and a $4\frac{1}{2}$-in. line. Measure the parts in each case.

3. Divide a 6-in. line into 4 equal parts, using compasses.

4. Erect a perpendicular bisector to each side of the following: (a) an acute triangle, (b) an obtuse triangle, (c) a right triangle.

An important rule:

> *The perpendicular bisectors of the sides of any triangle intersect at the same point.*

165. How to bisect an angle, using the compasses. To bisect an angle, as $\angle MON$, place the steel point of the compasses on the vertex O and draw an arc cutting the sides of the angle,

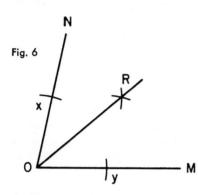

Fig. 6

as at x and y. From x and y as centers, draw two arcs intersecting, as at R. Join R and O with a straight line. The line OR bisects $\angle MON$. Prove by measuring $\angle MOR$ and RON.

1. Draw a 90° angle. Bisect it. Test with a protractor.

2. Draw a 150° angle. Bisect and test.

3. Bisect an angle of 70°. Test.

4. How would you divide an angle into 4 equal parts?

5. Divide an angle of 160° into 4 equal parts, using compasses.

6. Bisect each angle of: (a) an acute triangle; (b) an obtuse triangle; (c) a right triangle.

An important rule:

> *The bisectors of the angles of any triangle intersect at the same point.*

166. How to erect a perpendicular to a line from a given point in the line. On the line AB it is required to erect a perpendicular at the point O. From O as a center, draw arcs cutting AB in points X and Y, making $OX = OY$. From X and Y as centers, draw arcs of equal radii intersecting at point Z. Draw ZO. ZO is perpendicular to the line AB at the point O. What kind of angles are ∡ YOZ and ZOX? Prove by measuring.

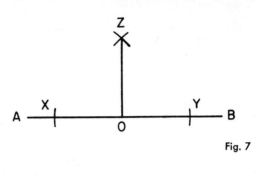

Fig. 7

─────────────── EXERCISES ───────────────

1. Draw a line MN. At a point O in MN, erect a perpendicular line KO.

2. Copy figure 8. At M erect a perpendicular line RM above the line AB. At N erect a perpendicular line SN below the line AB.

$$A \bullet\!\!-\!\!-\!\!-\!\!\underset{M}{\bullet}\!\!-\!\!-\!\!-\!\!\underset{N}{\bullet}\!\!-\!\!-\!\!-\!\! B$$

Fig. 8

3. Draw a slanting line AB. At a point O on AB, erect a perpendicular MO.

167. How to drop a perpendicular to a line from a given point outside the line. On the line AB it is required to drop a perpendicular from the outside point O. Using O as center, draw an arc intersecting the line AB in two points, x and y. With x and y as centers, draw two arcs of equal radii below the line AB, intersecting at point Z. Draw OZ. OZ is perpendicular to the line AB. Prove by measuring the angles thus formed.

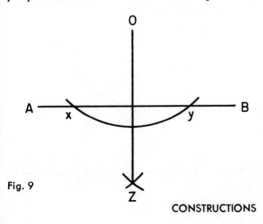

Fig. 9

CONSTRUCTIONS

317

1. Draw a line *MN*. From a point *O* outside the line, drop a perpendicular to *MN*.

2. Copy figure 10. Drop perpendiculars to the line *AB* from points *M* and *N*.

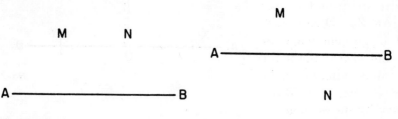

Fig. 10   **Fig. 11**

3. Copy figure 11. Drop perpendiculars to the line *AB* from points *M* and *N*.

4. Draw a slanting line and drop a perpendicular to it from any point outside the line.

168. How to construct with compasses an angle equal to a given angle. It is required to construct an angle equal to ∠ *AOB*. (See figure 12.) Draw line *PM* to correspond to line *OA*. With *O* as a center, and with any radius *Ow*, draw an arc intersecting the lines *OA* and *OB* at points *w* and *x*, respectively. With the same radius and *P* as center, draw an arc intersecting *PM* at *y*. Using *y* as center and *wx* as radius, draw an arc cutting the previous arc at point *z*. Draw *PN* through *z*. ∠ *MPN* = ∠ *AOB*. Prove by measuring the angles with a protractor.

Fig. 12

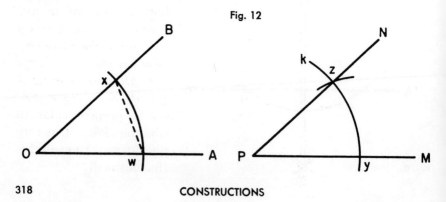

1. Draw an acute angle. Using compasses and ruler, construct an angle of the same size. Prove by measuring the angles with a protractor.

2. Draw an obtuse angle. Construct an angle of equal size. Test with protractor.

3. Draw segment AB 2″ long. At A draw an angle less than 45°. At B construct an angle the same size as $\angle A$, using compasses and ruler. Extend the sides of these angles to meet at C. Measure AC and BC. How do they compare in length? What name is given to the acute triangle ABC? Why?

4. On a base XY make an acute angle X greater than 45°. Construct $\angle Y$ equal to $\angle X$. Complete $\triangle XYZ$. How do XZ and YZ compare in length? What kind of a triangle is XYZ?

5. On a 2″ line MN draw a 60° angle at M, using the protractor. At N construct with compasses and ruler an angle equal to $\angle M$. Extend the sides of the angles to form $\triangle MNO$. What is the size of $\angle O$? Why? Measure and compare the lengths of the 3 sides. What name is given to the acute triangle MNO?

6. A line AB is 3″ long. With AB as base, construct an equilateral triangle.

7. Why can you not make an equilateral triangle containing obtuse angles?

169. How to construct a triangle with sides equal to three given lines. Let the lines a, b, and c in figure 13 be the given lines. Draw the line MN equal to line a. With M as center, draw an arc with radius equal to line b. With N as center, draw an arc with radius equal to line c. From O, the intersection of the two arcs, draw the lines OM and ON. $\triangle MNO$ is the required triangle.

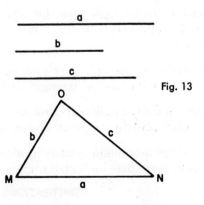

Fig. 13

170. How to construct a triangle when two sides and the included angle are given. Let lines m and n be the given sides and $\angle x$ the included angle. (See figure 14.) Draw the line AB equal to the line m. At B construct $\angle B = \angle x$ and draw the side BC equal to the line n. Now connect A and C. $\triangle ABC$ will then be the required triangle.

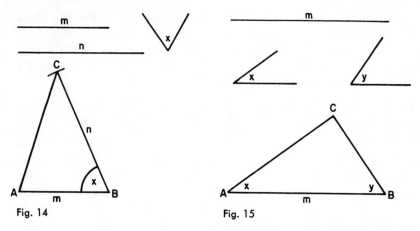

Fig. 14   Fig. 15

171. How to construct a triangle when two angles and the included side are given. Let $\angle x$ and $\angle y$ be the given angles and line m the included side. (See figure 15.) Draw the line AB equal to the line m. At A construct an angle equal to $\angle x$. At B construct an angle equal to $\angle y$. Extend the sides of the angles until they meet at C. $\triangle ABC$ is the required triangle.

──────────────*EXERCISES*──────────────

1. Construct a triangle with sides equal to $2''$, $1\frac{1}{2}''$, and $2\frac{1}{2}''$.

2. Construct a triangle with the sides a, b, and c equal to 4 cm., 5 cm., and 5 cm., respectively. What kind of triangle have you constructed?

3. Construct a triangle all three of whose sides are 4 cm. in length. Name the kind of triangle that has been formed.

4. Construct a triangle with side AB equal to $3''$, the angle at A equal to 120°, and the angle at B equal to 20°.

5. Construct a triangle with two sides equal to 4 cm. and 6 cm., respectively, and their included angle equal to 65°.

1. (a) What does the word *acute* mean? (b) How is the word appropriate when used in an *acute* triangle?

2. (a) What is the meaning of *obtuse?* (b) In what way is it appropriately used in an *obtuse* triangle?

3. (a) In the word *isosceles,* what does the *isos* mean? (b) *skelos (celes)* means ____?

4. What is the meaning of the prefix *equi?* *Lateral* comes from *latus (lateres)* which means ____? The word *equilateral* means ____ ____?

5. In the word *bisect, bi* means ____, *sect* means ____. Hence, *bisect* means ____.

6. Name some practical uses of the triangle for the sake of rigidity.

7. Draw a 3½-in. line. Bisect the line, using compasses.

8. Bisect a 100° angle.

9. Draw a 3-in. line. Erect a perpendicular one inch from the end of the line.

10. Draw a line *AX*. Drop a perpendicular to *AX* from a point *O* outside the line.

11. Draw an 80° angle. Using compasses, construct an angle equal to the 80° angle.

12. Construct a triangle with sides equal to 3″, 2″, and 2″.

13. Construct a triangle with two sides equal to 2½″ and 2″ and the included angle equal 35°.

14. Construct a triangle with its base equal to 1½″ and its base angles 15° and 30°.

PLAYOFF FOR CHAPTER XIV

A. How many of the following geometric words can you make out:

1. An 8-letter word meaning "earth measure."

2. An 8-letter word meaning three angles.

3. A 7-letter word meaning six angles.

4. A 9-letter word meaning "to measure around."

5. A 6-letter word meaning to cut into two equal parts.

6. A 10-letter word meaning on a plane parallel with the horizon.

7. A 7-letter word meaning side.

8. A 5-letter word meaning "sharp."

9. A 6-letter word meaning "dull."

10. An 11-letter word meaning equal sides.

11. A 9-letter word meaning equal legs.

12. A 7-letter word meaning eight angles.

13. A 13-letter word meaning four sides.

14. A 9-letter word meaning "right angle."

15. An 8-letter word meaning five sides.

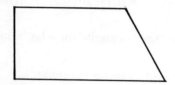

B. In a trapezoid the same shape as the one pictured, draw lines that divide the trapezoid into four equal parts all the same shape.

ACHIEVEMENT TEST IV

Addition

1. 9	2. 87	3. $\frac{3}{4}$	4. 42.66	5. 286
7	46	$\frac{7}{8}$	.96	375
5	32		3.77	421
4	59		58.96	189
8				674
6				822
				358

6. $8.92 + .7 + 9$ 8. $38\frac{1}{8}$ 9. $37\frac{4}{5}$ 10. 7 gal. 3 qt.   173

7. $\frac{5}{9} + \frac{2}{3} + \frac{1}{6}$ $62\frac{1}{6}$ $68\frac{2}{3}$ 9 gal. 1 qt.   636

811

Subtraction

11. 508   12. 7005   13. 815.9   14. $3.17 − $.59
    59   786   698.8   15. $2 − 35¢

16. $32\frac{1}{8} − 15.7$ 18. $42\frac{2}{3}$ 19. $81\frac{1}{4}$ 20. 40° 30 min.

17. $\frac{3}{8} − \frac{3}{16}$ $18\frac{1}{6}$ $38\frac{3}{5}$ 10° 40 min.

Multiplication

21. 29
    76

22. 204
    708

23. 290
    80

24. 7.9
    .09

25. $\frac{1}{5} \times \frac{1}{5}$

26. $5\frac{1}{3} \times 21$

27. $\frac{1}{7} \times 4\frac{2}{3}$

28. $\frac{5}{6} \times 180$

29. $72\frac{3}{5}$
    $35\frac{1}{3}$

30. 2 hr. 10 min.
    8

Division

31. $4\overline{)387}$

32. $.19\overline{)1.216}$

33. $6.25 \div 100$

34. $2.4\overline{)4.32}$

35. 137
   $.057\overline{)7.809}$

36. 137
   $5.7\overline{)78.09}$

37. $\frac{3}{4} \div \frac{5}{8}$
  38. $1\frac{2}{3} \div 10$
  39. $14 \div 3\frac{1}{2}$
  40. $\frac{1}{3}$ of 16 lb. 4 oz.

Per Cent

Write as fractions:

41. $66\frac{2}{3}\%$ **42.** 2%

Write as decimals:

43. 7%   **44.** $1\frac{1}{4}\%$

Write as per cents:

45. $\frac{9}{25}$ **46.** .1

47. 40% of 125 = ?

48. 14% of ? = 70

49. ?% of 45 = 15

Arrange in order of size—largest first:

50. $.033\frac{1}{3}$, $3.33\frac{1}{3}$, $\frac{34}{100}$, $33\frac{1}{3}\%$

Record your scores on the Achievement Chart.

This is your last test. Calculate your percentage of improvement over the scores you made on Achievement Test I.

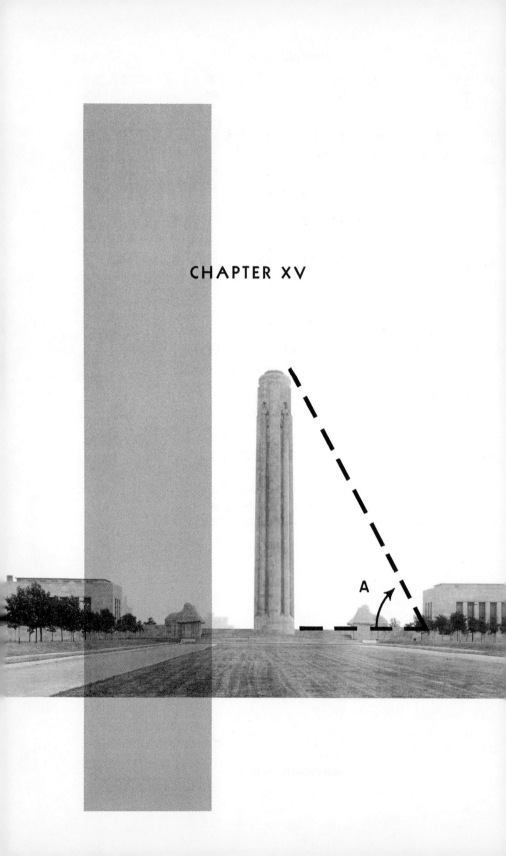

CHAPTER XV

A

INDIRECT MEASUREMENT OF LINES

VOCABULARY

1. indirect measurement
2. opposite side
3. square

4. square root
5. radical sign
6. hypotenuse

172. Distinguishing between direct and indirect measurement. Direct measurement is used whenever a ruler, tapeline, protractor, or any other measuring instrument is applied directly upon whatever is to be measured. Often it is inconvenient, and sometimes impossible, to measure a line or an angle by direct measurement. At such times some indirect method must be used. The width of a river, the breadth of a hill, and the height of trees, buildings, chimneys, flagpoles, and mountains are usually found by indirect measurement.

If one is familiar with certain truths, indirect measurement can easily be done by any one of several methods. In this chapter you will learn some of these truths and apply them in finding distances by indirect measurement.

173. Squares and square roots. Suppose that the square $WXYZ$ measures 8 in. on a side. The area, then, is $(8 \text{ in.})^2$, or 64 sq. in.

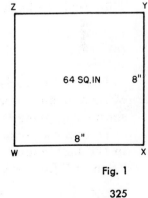

Fig. 1

Now, suppose you know the area to be 64 sq. in. and wish to know the length of one side. Since the area, 64 sq. in., is obtained by multiplying the length by the length, one side of the square can be found if we know what number multiplied by itself equals 64. Since 8 × 8 = 64, 8 in. is the length of one side of the square.

64 is the *square* of 8.

8 is the *square root* of 64.

The square root of a number is one of its two equal factors. The sign of square root is $\sqrt{\ }$. It is called the *radical* sign. Thus, $\sqrt{64} = 8$ and is read, "The square root of 64 equals 8."

EXERCISES
---

1. Write the squares of all the numbers from 0 through 15.

2. Find the square of 25, of 16, and of 18.

3. Find the value of 21^2, 17^2, 50^2, 24^2, 70^2.

4. (a) $(\frac{1}{3})^2 = \frac{1}{3} \times \frac{1}{3} = ?$ (b) $(\frac{2}{5})^2 = ?$
   (c) $(\frac{3}{4})^2 = ?$ (d) $(\frac{7}{8})^2 = ?$ (e) $(\frac{4}{7})^2 = ?$

5. What is the square root of 16? Of 36? Of 81?

6. Find:

(a) $\sqrt{100}$	(e) $\sqrt{625}$	(i) $\sqrt{3600}$	(m) $\sqrt{\frac{1}{9}}$
(b) $\sqrt{225}$	(f) $\sqrt{121}$	(j) $\sqrt{2500}$	(n) $\sqrt{6\frac{1}{4}}$
(c) $\sqrt{144}$	(g) $\sqrt{196}$	(k) $\sqrt{\frac{4}{9}}$	(o) $\sqrt{11\frac{1}{9}}$
(d) $\sqrt{4900}$	(h) $\sqrt{6400}$	(l) $\sqrt{\frac{16}{25}}$	(p) $\sqrt{2\frac{1}{4}}$

7. What is the length of one side of a square if its area is 25 sq. in.?

8. Find the length of the sides of the squares whose areas are:

(a) 196 sq. in.   (c) 1600 sq. rd.   (e) 400 sq. in.   (g) 1 sq. ft.
(b) 900 sq. ft.   (d) 169 sq. yd.   (f) .25 sq. ft.   (h) 81 sq. yd.

To save time, scientists, mechanics, and others often use a table of squares and square roots, as on the next page. This table is shortened, giving the squares and square roots through 75 only.

To find the square of the number 23 in the table, locate the 23 in the first column headed "No." Then, in the column headed "Square," just to the right of the 23 is the number 529. $23^2 = 529$.

Using the table, find the squares of: 18, 24, 28, 33, 42, 48, 69, 57, 75, 46.

To find the square root of the number 23, look to the column headed "Square Root," the second column to the right of the 23. $\sqrt{23}$ = 4.795. The square roots in this table are to thousandths, but not necessarily to the nearest thousandths.

Find: $\sqrt{75}$, $\sqrt{43}$, $\sqrt{28}$, $\sqrt{51}$.

You can find the square root of the figures in the "Square" column by finding the number on the same line in the column headed "No." just to the left. For instance, the square root of 2116 is 46.

Find: $\sqrt{1849}$, $\sqrt{1156}$, $\sqrt{3969}$, $\sqrt{5329}$.

TABLE 1
TABLE OF SQUARES AND SQUARE ROOTS

No.	Square	Square Root	No.	Square	Square Root	No.	Square	Square Root
1	1	1.000	26	676	5.099	51	2601	7.141
2	4	1.414	27	729	5.196	52	2704	7.211
3	9	1.732	28	784	5.291	53	2809	7.280
4	16	2.000	29	841	5.385	54	2916	7.348
5	25	2.236	30	900	5.477	55	3025	7.416
6	36	2.449	31	961	5.567	56	3136	7.483
7	49	2.645	32	1024	5.656	57	3249	7.549
8	64	2.828	33	1089	5.744	58	3364	7.615
9	81	3.000	34	1156	5.831	59	3481	7.681
10	100	3.162	35	1225	5.916	60	3600	7.746
11	121	3.316	36	1296	6.000	61	3721	7.810
12	144	3.464	37	1369	6.082	62	3844	7.874
13	169	3.605	38	1444	6.164	63	3969	7.937
14	196	3.741	39	1521	6.245	64	4096	8.000
15	225	3.873	40	1600	6.324	65	4225	8.062
16	256	4.000	41	1681	6.403	66	4356	8.124
17	289	4.123	42	1764	6.480	67	4489	8.185
18	324	4.242	43	1849	6.557	68	4624	8.246
19	361	4.358	44	1936	6.633	69	4761	8.306
20	400	4.472	45	2025	6.708	70	4900	8.366
21	441	4.582	46	2116	6.782	71	5041	8.426
22	484	4.690	47	2209	6.855	72	5184	8.485
23	529	4.795	48	2304	6.928	73	5329	8.544
24	576	4.899	49	2401	7.000	74	5476	8.602
25	625	5.000	50	2500	7.071	75	5625	8.660

A number whose square root is an integer is called a *perfect square*.

If you wish to find the square root of a number that is not in the table, you can compute the square root for yourself.

────────────────── **EXAMPLE** ──────────────────

Find $\sqrt{1049.76}$

1. Starting at the decimal point, and working to the left and to the right, set down the digits in pairs.

2. Place the decimal point in the quotient directly above the decimal point in the dividend. There will be as many digits in the quotient as there are pairs in the dividend. In this quotient there will be two digits to the left and one digit to the right of the decimal point.

$$
\begin{array}{r|l}
 & \quad 3 \;\; 2 \;.\;\; 4 \\
 & \overline{10\ 49\ .\ 76} \\
3^2 & 9 \\
\hline
60 & 1\ 49 \\
62 & 1\ 24 \\
\hline
640 & \quad 25\ 76 \\
644 & \quad 25\ 76 \\
\hline
\end{array}
$$

3. Find the largest integer that, when squared, will be contained in 10. It is 3. $3^2 = 9$. ($4^2 = 16$ is too large.) Place the 3 in the quotient just above the zero in the first pair.

4. Put the 9 under the 10 and subtract, $10 - 9 = 1$. Bring down the next pair, 49. This makes the new dividend 149.

5. Trial divisor: To find the trial divisor, the part of the square root already found is always doubled and then multiplied by 10. This is the same as multiplying by 20. Hence, the part of the square root already found (3) $\times$ 20 = 60, the trial divisor. Put the 60 on a line with and to the left of the 149. $149 \div 60 = 2+$. Place the 2 in the quotient above the 9 in the second pair. Then add 2 to the 60.

6. Real divisor: $60 + 2 = 62$, the real divisor. $62 \times 2 = 124$. Subtract and bring down the next pair. 2576 is the new dividend.

7. Trial divisor: $32 \times 20 = 640$. 2576 divided by $640 = 4+$. Put the 4 in the quotient above the 6 in the third pair. Add 4 to 640.

8. Real divisor: $640 + 4 = 644$, the real divisor. $644 \times 4 = 2576$. There is no remainder.

9. The square root of $1049.76 = 32.4$.

10. Check: $32.4 \times 32.4 = 1049.76$, the original square.

Find the square root of:

1. 14.44	6. 16.81	11. 1267.36	16. 10.7584
2. 26.01	7. 43.56	12. 17.2225	17. 9216
3. 12.96	8. 10.24	13. 46.24	18. 1004.89
4. 21.16	9. 50.41	14. 18.0625	19. 37.9456
5. 31.36	10. 72.25	15. 739.84	20. 219.04

Many numbers have no exact square roots, yet an approximate square root can be found for any number.

EXAMPLE

Find $\sqrt{326.149}$

1. In setting off 326.149 into pairs, there is only one digit (3) for the first pair to the left. This is all right. There is also just one digit (9) for the last pair to the right of the decimal point. In this case annex a zero, and the pair becomes 90.

2. Proceed as usual until the second trial divisor (360) will not be contained in the dividend (214). Put a zero in the quotient and bring down the next pair. The new trial divisor is 3600.

```
                    1  8. 0  5
                    3 26.14 90
        1²  |  1
        20  |  2 26
        28  |  2 24
       360  |    2 14 90
      3600  |
      3605  |    1 80 25
           |      34 65
```

3. The square root to hundredths is 18.05. To the nearest tenth, it is 18.1. The nearest hundredth can be found by carrying the quotient to thousandths. Annex a pair of zeros for each additional digit desired in the quotient.

4. Check: 18.05^2 = 325.8025
   Add remainder =   .3465
   Original square = 326.1490

EXERCISES
---

*1. Find the square root to tenths:

(a) 147.06   (b) 238.84   (c) 7245.8   (d) 6925.6   (e) 573.1

**2. Find to the nearest tenth:

(a) $\sqrt{64.8274}$ (b) $\sqrt{936.745}$ (c) $\sqrt{1512.94}$

**3. Find to the nearest hundredth:

(a) $\sqrt{86.4528}$ (b) $\sqrt{3.7}$ (c) $\sqrt{25.623}$

4. Find the value of:

(a) $\sqrt{\frac{25}{64}} = \frac{5}{8}$. Why?

(b) $\sqrt{\frac{3 - \frac{3}{4}}{9}} = \sqrt{\frac{2.25}{9}} = \frac{1.5}{3} = .5$

(c) $\sqrt{\frac{49}{225}}$

(e) $\sqrt{\frac{81}{2500}}$

(g) $\sqrt{\frac{7 - \frac{3}{4}}{16}}$

(d) $\sqrt{\frac{324}{625}}$

(f) $\sqrt{\frac{289}{576}}$

5. Find to the nearest tenth after expressing as decimals:

(a) $\sqrt{\frac{4}{5}}$

(c) $\sqrt{\frac{1}{8}}$

(e) $\sqrt{\dfrac{12 + \frac{1}{4}}{6}}$

(b) $\sqrt{\frac{1}{3}}$

(d) $\sqrt{1\frac{1}{2}}$

6. If the area of a square is 5,184 sq. ft., what is the length of one side of the square?

7. A square garden contains 7,744 sq. ft. Find the length of one side of the garden.

8. A mechanic needs a square board whose cross-section area is 60.84 sq. in. What must be the length of the cross-section?

*9. A square kitchen contains $90\frac{1}{4}$ sq. ft. How long is the kitchen?

*10. A regulation baseball diamond is a square containing 8,100 sq. ft. How far is it between consecutive bases?

**11. A square table cover contains 1,089 sq. in. How many inches of fringe will be needed around the edge? Allow $1\frac{1}{2}$ extra inches for each corner.

**12. The area of a square garden is 6,724 sq. ft. How much will fencing cost to inclose the garden at $1.59 per yard?

**13. A square field contains 40 acres. How many rods of fencing will be needed to inclose it?

*174. Uses of square root. We have seen how square roots are used to find the length of one side of a square when the area is known. Square roots may be used also to find the length of one side of a right triangle when the lengths of the other two sides are known.

More than two thousand years ago a Greek philosopher, Pythagoras, made the discovery that is illustrated in figure 2. Triangle ABC is a right triangle with a right angle at C. a represents the altitude, b the base, and c the side opposite the right angle, called the *hypotenuse*. What is the area of the square on a, the square on b, and the square on c? Add the areas of the squares on a and b. How does this sum compare with the area of the square on c?

In any right triangle, the square on the hypotenuse is equal to the sum of the squares on the other two sides.

Put into a formula, this truth becomes:

$$c^2 = a^2 + b^2$$

INDIRECT MEASUREMENT OF LINES

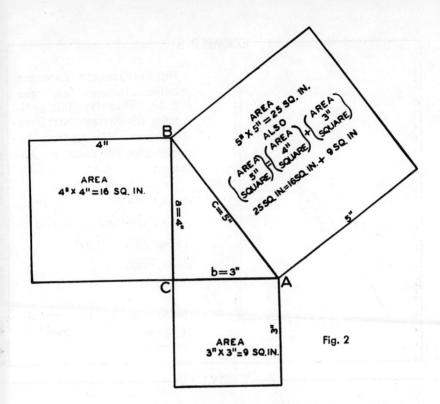

Fig. 2

From this formula we get two other formulas:

$$a^2 = c^2 - b^2 \quad \text{and} \quad b^2 = c^2 - a^2$$

From these three formulas we get three other formulas, which we use in finding the hypotenuse, the base, and the altitude of a right triangle:

$$c = \sqrt{a^2 + b^2} \qquad a = \sqrt{c^2 - b^2} \qquad b = \sqrt{c^2 - a^2}$$

EXAMPLE A

If your classroom is 36 ft. long and 27 ft. wide, what is the diagonal distance from one corner to the opposite corner?

$$c = \sqrt{a^2 + b^2} \qquad a = 36 \text{ ft.}$$
$$c = \sqrt{36^2 + 27^2} \qquad b = 27 \text{ ft.}$$
$$c = \sqrt{1296 + 729}$$
$$c = \sqrt{2025}$$
$$c = 45$$

Hence, the diagonal is 45 ft.

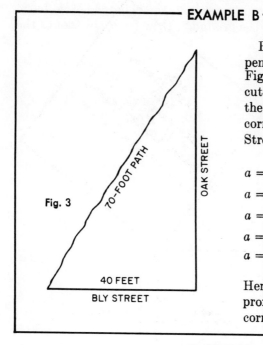

Fig. 3

70-FOOT PATH

OAK STREET

40 FEET

BLY STREET

Bly and Oak streets are perpendicular to each other. (See Fig. 3.) There is a 70-ft. path cutting Bly Street 40 ft. from the corner. How far from the corner does the path cut Oak Street?

$a = \sqrt{c^2 - b^2}$ $c = 70$ ft.

$a = \sqrt{70^2 - 40^2}$ $b = 40$ ft.

$a = \sqrt{4900 - 1600}$

$a = \sqrt{3300}$

$a = 57.4$

Hence, Oak Street is cut approximately 57.4 ft. from the corner.

EXERCISES

Sketch, label, and then solve:

1. The base of a right triangle is 21 ft. and its altitude is 28 ft. Solve for the hypotenuse.

2. An iron gate which has a length of 10 ft. and a height of 4 ft. is to be braced diagonally from corner to corner. Find the length of the brace.

3. A lot is in the shape of a rectangle. Its length is 32 ft. and its diagonal distance from the northwest corner to the southeast corner is 40 ft. Find the width of the lot.

4. An automobile travels directly west 20 miles. If it then turns and travels directly north for 25 miles, how far is it from its starting point by a straight line?

5. On a regulation baseball diamond, it is 90 ft. from any base to the next. What is the distance from home plate to second base?

6. Plane A leaves an airport and flies directly south for 120 miles. Plane B leaves at the same time and flies directly east for 160 miles. How far apart are the planes by the shortest route?

7. The diagonal of a rectangle is 36 in. long and its width is 14 in. Find the length of the rectangle.

8. A 32-ft. ladder is leaning against the window of a barn. The window is 25 ft. above the ground. How far is the foot of the ladder from the barn?

9. A flagstaff 72 ft. high casts a shadow 30 ft. long. How far is it from the top of the flagstaff to the tip of the shadow?

10. A 75-ft. rope is stretched from the second-story window of a building until it reaches the ground 40 ft. from the base of the building. Find the height of the window from the ground.

11. A 70-ft. brace wire on a telephone pole touches the ground 24 ft. from the foot of the pole. What is the approximate height of the pole?

12. A 180-ft. rope of a circus tent is stretched so that it is fastened to the ground at a point 100 ft. from the base of the center pole. Find the height of the pole.

*13. What is the diameter of the largest wheel that can be taken through a door that is $4\frac{1}{2}$ ft. wide and $8\frac{1}{2}$ ft. high?

**14. Measure the length and width of your classroom to the nearest foot. Compute the length of the diagonal from one corner to the opposite corner of the floor. Check your result by measurement.

**15. Compute the distance around a room, to the nearest tenth of a foot, if its length is 16 ft. and the distance between the opposite corners is 24 ft.

**175. Making similar triangles by scale drawings. The triangle in figure 4 is drawn similar to a triangular plot of ground. It is drawn to the scale $1'' = 10'$. Measure the lengths of the sides in inches. As AB is $2''$ long, it represents $20'$. How many feet does BC represent? AC?

As $10' = 120''$, $1''$ in the drawing represents $120''$ in the plot of ground. Hence the ratio of the corresponding sides is $1:120$.

─────────────────────── EXERCISES ───────────────────────

1. Some Boy Scouts were given a piece of ground in the shape of $\triangle XYZ$ in figure 5. They wanted to know the distances XZ and YZ, but a stream of water was in the way. So they made a scale drawing, using the scale $1'' = 80$ rd. Make the scale drawing and determine the lengths of XZ and YZ.

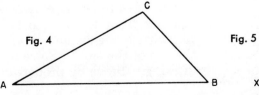

Fig. 4

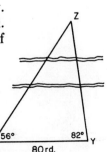

Fig. 5

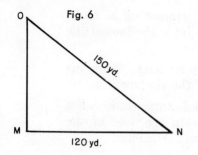

Fig. 6

2. Make a scale drawing of △ *MNO* in figure 6. *OM* is perpendicular to *MN*. Let 1 cm. represent 30 yd. *MN* will be represented by how many centimeters? *ON*? Measure *OM* in the scale drawing. How long is it in centimeters? How many yards does it represent?

3. Some Boy Scouts wish to extend a wire from camp *A* to camp *B* straight across a pond. (See figure 7.) They make a scale drawing similar to △ *ABC* in order to find the distance *AB*. They let 1″ represent 40 yd. They find that ∠ *C* measures 75°. Make the scale drawing and determine the length of *AB*.

Fig. 7

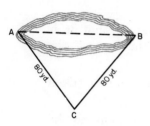

4. Floyd wishes to know the height of a column. He finds it by the following method: He measures a line of convenient length, as *AB*, on the ground out from the base of the column. At *B* he imagines a line *BT*, the *line of sight*, drawn to the top of the column. He measures ∠ *B*, the *angle of elevation*, with a large protractor. He knows that ∠ *A* is a right angle. Knowing the length of *AB* and the size of ∡ *A* and *B*, he constructs a similar triangle on a much smaller scale.

Fig. 8

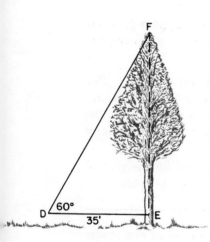

Suppose the distance *AB* to be 30′, and ∠ *B* to be 50°. Draw a similar triangle, letting 1″ represent 10′. How high is the column?

5. Using ⅛″ = 5′, make a scale drawing of figure 8. Find the height of the tree.

6. Figure 9 shows how Henry measures the height of a tree. He erects a 10′ rod, *MN*, in a vertical position (parallel to the tree). The line *AT* which passes through the tip of the rod and the top of the tree is the line of sight. If Henry's eye at *A* is 1′ above the ground and the distance from Henry's eye to the tree, *AE*, is 90′, and the distance from the rod to his eye, *MA*, is 15′, what is the distance from the ground to the top of the tree? Solve by a small scale drawing. Prove by proportion.

Fig. 9

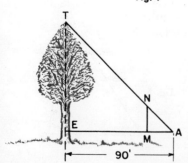

7. Figure 10 pictures Lee flying his kite. How high is the kite above ground if the string is let out 300′ and Lee is holding the string 3′ above the ground? ∠ A measures 35°. Sketch the figure, using a suitable scale.

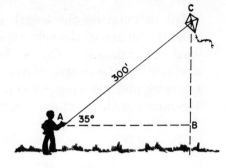

Fig. 10

8. How high is a flagstaff if the angle of elevation measures 40° at 120′ from the base of the flagstaff?

9. Draw △ MNO, letting MN = 3″, ∠ M = 60°, ∠ N = 40°. Make a similar triangle, using the scale 1:2 for its sides.

10. Draw △ RST, letting RS = 6 cm., ST = 9 cm., ∠ S = 80°. Make a similar triangle, using for its sides the scale 1:3.

**176. The right-triangle method of indirect measurement. This method of indirect measurement is the one used by surveyors in measuring distances. It is the quickest and most accurate method, as the number of measurements to be made and the number of lines to be drawn are fewer than in the other methods studied.

Let us do a little experimenting to see upon what "truth about right triangles" this method is founded.

On a piece of squared paper draw ∠ A of 35°, extending its sides to an indefinite length. At various points on the slanting line, drop perpendiculars to the base line. Avoid fractions by dropping the perpendiculars from a point where the horizontal and vertical lines on the squared paper cross each other. (See figure 11.) You now have a number of right triangles each having an acute angle of 35°.

Fig. 11

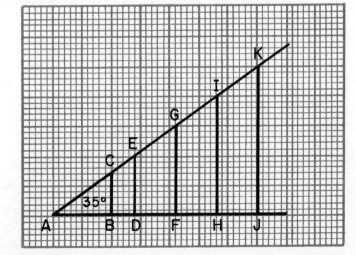

Let us compare the length of the side opposite the 35° angle with the length of the side adjoining (*adjacent to*) the 35° angle in each right triangle. That is, let us divide the length of the opposite side by the length of the adjacent side in each of the right triangles and see what we can learn about the ratio of the sides. By counting the number of squares in each side we find:

In $\triangle ABC$, $\dfrac{CB}{AB} = \dfrac{7}{10} = .70$ In $\triangle AFG$, $\dfrac{GF}{AF} = \dfrac{15}{21} = .71$

In $\triangle ADE$, $\dfrac{ED}{AD} = \dfrac{10}{14} = .71$ In $\triangle AHI$, $\dfrac{IH}{AH} = \dfrac{20}{28} = .71$

You will notice that in each of the right triangles having an acute angle of 35°, the ratio of the opposite side to the adjacent side is .7, to the nearest tenth. It makes no difference whether the triangle is large or small; the ratio remains the same as long as the acute angle is the same size.

Try the same experiment, but use 30° for one of the acute angles, and find to the nearest hundredth the ratios of the sides opposite the 30° angle to the sides adjacent to the 30° angle. How do these ratios compare? If the work is accurately done, the ratios should be approximately the same. If any of your ratios differs greatly from the others, recheck your measurements and division.

Try the same experiment, using 60°, 70°.

From the preceding experiments you have discovered the following important truth about right triangles:

> *In right triangles the ratio of the opposite side to the adjacent side is always the same for equal angles.*

Let us see how this truth can be used in calculating distances.

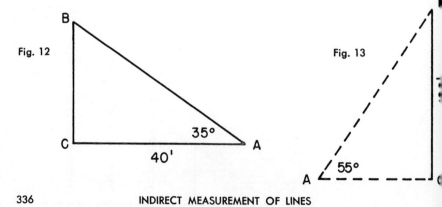

Fig. 12

Fig. 13

Suppose in the right triangle ABC, figure 12, the angle of elevation is 35° and the distance AC is 40′. We know from the above truth that BC (the side opposite the 35° angle) divided by AC (the side adjacent to the 35° angle) equals .7 (the ratio found in figure 11). In other words:

$$\frac{BC}{AC} = .7$$

As $AC = 40′$, substitute 40 for AC:

$$\frac{BC}{40 \text{ ft.}} = .7$$

If we multiply both sides of the ratio by the same number, the resulting products will be equal:

$$\frac{BC}{40 \text{ ft.}} \times \frac{40 \text{ ft.}}{1} = .7 \times 40 \text{ ft.}$$

$$BC = 28.0 \text{ ft.}$$

Either acute angle of the right triangle may be used. However, it is easier for us to use the angle that is opposite the unknown side; the ratio is formed by the side opposite the angle divided by the side adjacent to the angle.

EXAMPLE

In figure 13, the unknown distance is opposite $\angle B$.

Therefore, use $\angle B$ instead of $\angle A$.

As $\angle A = 55°$, $\angle B = 35°$

$$\frac{\text{Opposite side}}{\text{Adjacent side}} = \frac{AC}{BC}$$

$BC = 100$ ft.

$$\frac{AC}{100 \text{ ft.}} = .7$$

$AC = .7 \times 100$ ft.
$AC = 70$ ft.

EXAMPLE

Find the value of the unknown in the following ratio:

$$\frac{M}{6} = .7$$

Multiplying by 6:

$$\frac{M}{6} \times 6 = .7 \times 6$$

$$M = 4.2$$

Proof:

Substituting 4.2 for M:

$$\frac{4.2}{6} = .7$$

$$.7 = .7.$$

Solve:

1. $\dfrac{w}{9} = \dfrac{1}{3}$ **3.** $\dfrac{t}{9} = \dfrac{2}{3}$ **5.** $\dfrac{K}{10} = 1.2$ **7.** $\dfrac{BC}{50} = .18$

2. $\dfrac{S}{6} = \dfrac{5}{2}$ **4.** $\dfrac{m}{60} = .8$ **6.** $\dfrac{AC}{20} = .42$ **8.** $\dfrac{AB}{25} = 1.19$

9. To find the height of the post BC in figure 14, some boys measured the distance AC to be 60′ and the angle of elevation to be 35°. What is the height of the post?

10. A rope is stretched from the second-story window of a building until it reaches the ground 40′ from the base of the building, where it forms an angle of 30° with the ground. Using the ratio of the opposite side to the adjacent side of the 30° angle (.58), find the height of the window from the ground.

11. Using the ratio of the opposite side to the adjacent side of a 60° angle (1.73), find the distance NO in figure 15.

In the preceding exercises, we have considered only angles of 35°, 30°, and 60°. However, there is a constant ratio between the opposite side and the adjacent side for acute angles of any size in right triangles. This unchanging ratio is called the *tangent* of the angle. For instance, we say that the tangent of a 35° angle is .7, or that the tangent of 35° is .7. This statement is usually abbreviated to: tan 35° = .7.

The table of tangents shown on page 339 gives the tangent ratios of angles from 1° to 89°, to the nearest hundredth.

1. Using the table of tangents, find the following: tan 8°; tan 13°; tan 25°; tan 38°; tan 45°; tan 64°; tan 80°; tan 86°; tan 88°; tan 89°.

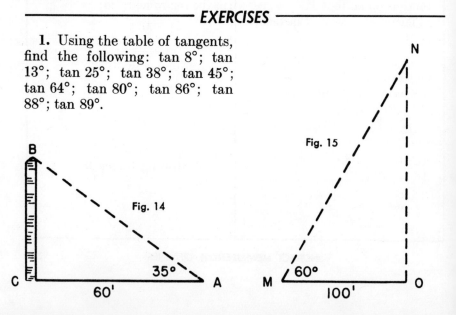

Fig. 14

Fig. 15

B

C

60′

35°

A

N

M

60°

100′

O

2. Find the angle corresponding to each of the following tangent ratios: .36; .58; .73; 1.03; 1.38; 1; 2.75; 8.14.

3. Estimate the tangent of $26\frac{1}{2}°$, of $49\frac{1}{2}°$, of $61\frac{1}{2}°$, of $45\frac{1}{3}°$, and of $57\frac{2}{3}°$.

4. Henry is at the top edge of a 200-foot wall overlooking a lake. He observes Paul swimming in the lake. He wonders how far Paul is from the foot of the wall. (See figure 16.)

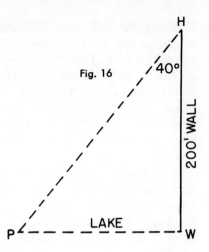

Fig. 16

TABLE 2
TABLE OF TANGENTS

Angle	Tangent	Angle	Tangent	Angle	Tangent
1°	.02	31°	.60	61°	1.80
2°	.03	32°	.62	62°	1.88
3°	.05	33°	.65	63°	1.96
4°	.07	34°	.67	64°	2.05
5°	.09	35°	.70	65°	2.14
6°	.10	36°	.73	66°	2.25
7°	.12	37°	.75	67°	2.36
8°	.14	38°	.78	68°	2.48
9°	.16	39°	.81	69°	2.61
10°	.18	40°	.84	70°	2.75
11°	.19	41°	.87	71°	2.90
12°	.21	42°	.90	72°	3.08
13°	.23	43°	.93	73°	3.27
14°	.25	44°	.97	74°	3.49
15°	.27	45°	1.00	75°	3.73
16°	.29	46°	1.03	76°	4.01
17°	.31	47°	1.07	77°	4.33
18°	.32	48°	1.11	78°	4.70
19°	.34	49°	1.15	79°	5.14
20°	.36	50°	1.19	80°	5.67
21°	.38	51°	1.23	81°	6.31
22°	.40	52°	1.28	82°	7.12
23°	.42	53°	1.32	83°	8.14
24°	.45	54°	1.38	84°	9.51
25°	.47	55°	1.43	85°	11.43
26°	.49	56°	1.48	86°	14.30
27°	.51	57°	1.54	87°	19.08
28°	.53	58°	1.60	88°	28.64
29°	.55	59°	1.66	89°	57.29
30°	.58	60°	1.73		

Henry can calculate this distance if he first determines the size of the angle of elevation, $\angle WPH$. In $\triangle WPH$, the line HP extending from Henry to Paul is called the "line of sight." This line forms with the horizontal line WP the angle of elevation, WPH. (Paul looks up to Henry to form this angle with the horizontal line.) Henry can find its size by first measuring $\angle PHW$, which is found to be 40°. The angle that is the size of $\angle WPH$ is the angle formed by PH and a horizontal line drawn from H parallel to PW.

This angle is called the "angle of depression." (Henry looks down to Paul to form this angle with the horizontal line.) This angle is 50° (90° − 40°). The angle of elevation always equals the angle of depression for the same line of sight. Hence, $\angle WPH$ is 50°. In the right triangle WPH, the distance PW can be found as follows:

$$\frac{\text{Opposite side}}{\text{Adjacent side}} = \frac{WH}{WP} \qquad \frac{WH}{WP} = 1.19$$
$$WH = 200 \text{ ft.} \qquad 1.19WP = 200 \text{ ft.}$$
$$\tan 50° = 1.19 \qquad WP = 168.06 \text{ ft.}$$

Hence, Paul is 168.06 ft. from the foot of the wall.

5. The angle of elevation of a flagstaff at a point 60′ from its base is 42°. How high is the flagstaff?

6. A pole is braced by a certain length of wire which is anchored 10 ft. from the foot of the pole. If the wire is fastened to the pole 9 ft. from the ground, what is the angle of elevation?

7. A plane is directly above a flagpole. A searchlight on the ground 2,000 ft. from the pole spots the plane, making the angle of elevation 33°. How high up is the plane?

8. A paratrooper drops from a plane 1,800 ft. in the air directly over a farmhouse. His line of drop makes an angle of 64° with the ground. How far does he land from the farmhouse?

9. John stands 35′ from the base of a telegraph pole and finds the angle of elevation to be 32°. If John's eye is 5′ above the ground, what is the height of the telegraph pole?

10. Leaning against a house is a ladder whose base is 15′ from the house. The ladder makes an angle of 72° with the ground. To what height on the building does it extend?

11. A building casts a shadow 25′ long when the angle of elevation is 66°. Find the height of the building.

12. The angle of elevation of an airplane from point A is 65°. Tom, who is standing directly under the airplane, is 150 yd. from A. Find the height of the plane in the air.

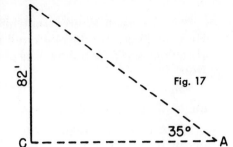

Fig. 17

13. In figure 17, find the length of side AC. (*Hint:* Use the tangent ratio of $\angle B$.)

14. The rope of a circus tent is stretched so that it is fastened to the ground at a point 100′ from the base of the pole. The angle of elevation to the top of the pole is 40°. Find the height of the pole.

15. The brace wire on a telephone pole touches the ground 24′ from the foot of the pole and makes an angle of 61° with the ground. What is the approximate height of the pole?

──────────── **REVIEW OF CHAPTER XV** ────────────

*1. Find the square root of (a) 253,009, (b) 156.25, (c) 6.6 to the nearest tenth.

*2. Find the diagonal of a floor 12 ft. by 15 ft.

*3. Leaning against a house is a 24-ft. ladder whose base is 15 ft. from the house. To what height on the building does the ladder extend?

**4. A ladder placed 10′ from the base of a barn reaches a point on the barn 30′ above the ground. What is the approximate size of the angle of elevation?

**5. The angle of elevation of a lighthouse from a boat at point A is 52°. If the lighthouse is known to be 110′ high, how far is the boat from the lighthouse?

**6. In exercise 5, as the boat comes nearer to the lighthouse, how would the size of the angle of elevation be affected? What is the largest size that the angle of elevation could become?

**7. In a certain city, a highway runs under a railroad bridge. There is a clearance of 15 feet under the bridge. Ninety feet from the bridge, the road starts to dip to the underpass. What is the degree of slope of the approach to the underpass?

Fig. 18

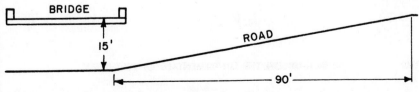

**8. Joe is so located that his eyes are 5 feet from the ground. He is looking from level ground at a mark on a limb 60 feet away. If the mark is 5 feet above the ground, what is its angle of elevation from Joe's eyes?

**9. A road rises 3.9′ in a level distance of 200′. Find the angle of elevation of the road.

**10. Find the angle of elevation of Blue Hill if it rises 6.5′ for every 10′ on the horizontal.

**11. At a certain time of day, a 5-ft. boy casts an 8-ft. shadow. At that time of day, what is the sun's elevation (the angle that the sun's rays make with the ground)?

─────────── PLAYOFF FOR CHAPTER XV ───────────

1. If possible, find the height of your flagpole, or some other high object, by indirect measurement.

2. Calculate by indirect measurement a distance on the ground by laying off a triangle and making a scale drawing.

3. The restless family. In how many ways may a family of ten persons seat themselves differently at dinner?

─ CHECK-UP ON THE FUNDAMENTALS OF ARITHMETIC ─

Addition

1. 276
138
314
282
617
888
413
979

2. $35\frac{7}{16}$
$28\frac{5}{8}$

3. $7.24 + 6.2 + 17 =$

4. $\frac{4}{5} + \frac{1}{10} + \frac{8}{15} =$

Subtraction

5. 4002
2678

6. $34\frac{2}{3}$
$19\frac{3}{4}$

7. 3 hr. 10 min. 21 sec.
1 hr. 28 min. 35 sec.

Multiplication

8. 7.6
.48

9. $\frac{7}{16} \times \frac{24}{49} =$

10. $3\frac{1}{4} \times 69 =$

Division

11. $3.8\overline{)102.6}$ **12.** $.63\overline{)6.552}$ **13.** $\frac{7}{8} \div \frac{3}{4} =$

Per Cent

14. $37\frac{1}{2}\%$ of $.336 =$ **15.** 24% of $? = 2.16$

16. $?\%$ of $18 = 3$ **17.** $5:8 = 12\frac{1}{2}:?$

18. $3:8 = ?:12$ **19.** $?:6 = 9:32$

Find the square root of:

20. $199,809$ **21.** 702.25 **22.** $\frac{121}{144}$

Find the area of:

23. A rectangle: **24.** A triangle:

$l = 27$ ft. $b = 42$ yd.
$w = 6$ yd. $h = 17$ yd.

25. A square: **26.** A circle:

$s = 102$ in. $\pi = 3\frac{1}{7}$
    $r = 21$ cm.

27. Find the interest on $720 at 4% for 150 days.

28. Find the interest on $1280 at $4\frac{1}{2}\%$ for 8 mo.

29. Find the sales tax on the following purchases:

(a) $240 at 3%.   (b) $18 at 2%.
(c) $16.50 at 1%.   (d) $5.40 at $2\frac{1}{2}\%$.

30. Out of 150 baseball players in the Allen school, 90 were from the 9th grade. What per cent of the players were from the 9th grade?

31. Mr. Reed purchases 10 gallons of gas at 32¢ per gallon. He gives the attendant $5. Count the change to Mr. Reed.

32. If the diameter of a circular race track is 840 ft., what is the distance around the track?

CHAPTER XVI

THE FORMULA

VOCABULARY

1. symbol
2. factor
3. numerical factor

4. literal factor
5. coefficient
6. terms

7. similar terms
8. dissimilar terms
9. evaluate

177. Writing formulas. In Chapter XIII you shortened geometric rules by the use of letters and other symbols. In the formula $A = lw$, the A, l, and w are called *symbols*. In this formula the w does not stand for the word "width"; but w does stand for the number of units in the width. The l stands for the number of units in the length. What does the A represent? The letters are used to represent numbers and not words.

The signs (symbols) for the fundamental operations in algebra are: $+$, $-$, $\times$, and $\div$, as used in arithmetic. However, the times sign, $\times$, is usually either replaced by a dot or omitted entirely, as in such expressions as $a \cdot x$, lw, $3b$, and $4xy$.

The division of numbers in algebra is more often expressed in the form of a fraction than by the use of the division sign $\div$. That is, $\dfrac{a}{b}$ is a more common form of division in algebra than $a \div b$.

Here, for example, are a few expressions stated in terms of symbols and numbers:

(a) The expression "2 more than a" may be written "$a + 2$" or "$2 + a$."

(b) The expression "5 times y" may be written "$5y$."

(c) The expression "the quotient of 2 and 3" may be written "$\frac{2}{3}$."

(d) The expression "the quotient of s and t" may be written "$\frac{s}{t}$."

(e) The expression "one-third x" may be written "$\frac{1}{3}x$" or "$\frac{x}{3}$."

(f) The expression "4 times a divided by 5" may be written "$\frac{4}{5}a$" or "$\frac{4a}{5}$."

EXERCISES

1. State each of the following expressions in terms of symbols and numbers:

(a) y increased by 4.

(b) The sum of m and n.

(c) 8 times r.

(d) The product of l and w.

(e) a less b.

(f) a divided by b.

(g) m divided by r.

(h) 4 y's added together.

(i) One-half g decreased by 3.

(j) t divided by 4.

(k) The sum of x, y, and z.

(l) The difference of c and d (c being the larger).

(m) The quotient of $3a$ and $4b$.

(n) 5 decreased by e.

(o) Three times the product of e and f.

(p) Twice x divided by 4.

(q) The square of x.

(r) Three times the square of a.

(s) The square of d minus the square of m.

*(t) The product of the square of a and the square of b.

*(u) The sum of the square of x and the square of y.

*(v) The quotient of five times the square of w and 4 times the square of x.

*(w) The product of b and c divided by the product of d and e.

**(x) The square of r minus the product of s and t plus the square of x.

**(y) Four times the product of w and x minus the sum of the square of y and the square of z.

**(z) Twice the product of the square of x and the square of t divided by the sum of a and b.

2. Change the following formulas into sentences, orally:

$$A = bh \qquad V = lwh \qquad V = \pi r^2 h \qquad A = s^2$$
$$C = 2\pi r \qquad A = \pi r^2 \qquad P = 2b + 2h \qquad P = 4s$$

3. State the fundamental operations called for in the following expressions: bh, lwh, $2b$, $2h$, s^2, πr^2, $2\pi r$, $6xy$, $l + w$, $2l + 2w$, $a + b + c$, $\dfrac{bh}{2}$, $\dfrac{A}{w}$, $\dfrac{V}{lw}$, $c - e$, $\dfrac{n}{2}$, $\dfrac{9c}{2}$, $\frac{1}{2} y$, $2d - 3$.

4. State the following expressions in a shorter way: $l + l$, $s + s + s$, $2 \times a$, $3 \times b$, $a \times b$, $e \times e$, $\pi \times r \times r$, $e \times e \times e$, $2 \times w \times w$, $6 \times s \times s$, $A \div l$, $V \div wh$, $3c + 4c$, $\frac{1}{2} d$.

5. What is the difference in meaning between $l + w$ and lw? $a + b + c$ and abc? $2l$ and l^2? $2r$ and r^2? $3e$ and e^3? $3s$ and s^3?

6. If the length of a pencil is represented by l, tell what each of the following expressions mean: $2l$, $3l$, $4l$, $5\frac{1}{2}l$, $\frac{1}{3}l$, $\frac{1}{4}l$, $2.5l$, $\dfrac{l}{2}$, $l \div 5$, $l \div 10$, $l - 1$ in., $2l - 3$ in., $l + \dfrac{l}{2}$, $l - \frac{1}{4}l$.

7. Let the width of the room be called w. What is the meaning of: $8w$, $\frac{1}{2}w$, $3\frac{1}{3}w$, $1.5w$, $w + 6$ ft., $w - 3$ ft., $2w - 1$ ft.?

***8.** Let h denote the height of a wall. What is the height of a wall 3 times as high? $\frac{1}{3}$ as high? $\frac{2}{3}$ as high? $\frac{1}{3}$ higher? $\frac{1}{3}$ lower? $\frac{2}{3}$ higher? $\frac{2}{3}$ lower? $\frac{1}{4}$ as high?

***9.** Draw a line the length of your thumb. Letter it l. What does $2l$ mean? Explain the meaning of $3l$. Of $2\frac{1}{2}l$. Draw each length.

****10.** Let d represent the diameter of a penny. Draw lines representing $2d$, $5d$, $1\frac{1}{2}d$, $3\frac{1}{2}d$, $\dfrac{d}{2}$, $d + 1$ in., $2d - \frac{1}{2}$ in., $\dfrac{2d}{3}$.

178. Some common algebraic terms. In the simple exercise $3 \times 4 = 12$, what do you call the 12? The 3 and 4? As in arithmetic, you call the 12 the *product* and the 3 and the 4 the *factors*. In the formula $p = 4s$, p is called the product and 4 and s the factors; 4 is known as the *numerical factor* and s as the *literal factor*. Can you explain why? The numerical factor is usually called the *coefficient*. In such expressions as a, x, k, mn, yz, the coefficient or numerical factor is understood to be 1.

Algebraic expressions such as $4a$, $7b$, and $3x$ are called *terms*. Two or more terms having the same literal factor are said to be *similar*. For instance, $4m$, $5m$, and $2m$ are *similar terms* because each term contains the literal factor m.

Two or more terms having different literal factors are said to be *dissimilar*. $4x$, $5y$, $4x^2$, and $2z$ are *dissimilar terms*.

1. State orally (1) the numerical factors, (2) the literal factors, of the following terms: $4a$, $7b$, $2k$, ax, $8r$, $\frac{1}{2}t$, $6s$, $3.5c$, $5.8b$, $3\frac{1}{4}m$, $6ab$, $2mn$, $\frac{1}{3}xy$, $4abc$, $8xyz$, mn, $.6c$, $1\frac{1}{2}az$, d^2, ef.

2. Name orally the coefficients in the following terms: $2l$, $5m$, $\frac{1}{10}n$, $7ab$, $5t$, y, $3.4r$, $.6f$, $.4e$, $1.2k$, $\dfrac{n}{6}$, $14axy$, $\dfrac{n}{6}$, $\dfrac{2n}{4}$, $2x^2$.

3. List the following terms in two groups, (1) those similar to $4a$, and (2) those dissimilar to $4a$: $7a$, $6x$, $5a$, $4a$, a, $3y$, $2n$, $6a^2$, $\frac{1}{2}a$, $2b$, $4a^3$, $3.2a$, $4ab$, $\dfrac{a}{2}$, $.4a$, $16a^2$, $8a$.

4. Is $6n$ similar or dissimilar to n? To n^2? To mn? To $5n$? To $6an$?

5. Make a list of five terms similar to $6x$ and five terms dissimilar to $6x$.

6. List five terms similar to $2mn$ and five terms dissimilar.

7. List five terms similar to $3l$ and five terms dissimilar.

8. List five terms similar to a^2 and five dissimilar to a^2.

9. List five terms similar to $25xyz$ and five dissimilar to $25xyz$.

179. Combining similar terms. You may add or subtract similar terms by finding the sum or difference of the coefficients of the given terms and multiplying this result by the common literal factor. Thus:

$4m + 5m + 2m = 11m$ (that is, $4 + 5 + 2 = 11$; $11 \times m = 11m$).
$8m - 2m = 6m$ (that is, $8 - 2 = 6$; $6 \times m = 6m$).

The addition and subtraction of terms that are not similar can only be indicated by the plus and minus signs. Thus, $4m$ added to $5n$ equals $4m + 5n$, and $3b$ subtracted from $2a$ equals $2a - 3b$.

If more than one set of similar terms appears in an expression, combine them as follows:

1. Group together the terms that are similar to each other.
2. Add or subtract separately each group of similar terms. For example:

$p = 4m + 2y + 3m + 5y + 2m$
$p = 4m + 3m + 2m + 2y + 5y$ (Grouping similar terms together)
$p = 9m + 7y$ (Adding similar terms)

EXERCISES

1. In the following exercises perform the necessary operations:

(a) $3a + 5a + 7a$
   Solution:
   $3a + 5a + 7a = 15a$
(b) $4b + 8b + 6b + b$
(c) $80w + 70w + 40w - 20w$
(d) $100n - 16n + 26n - n$
(e) $60h + 24h - 30h$
(f) $\frac{1}{5}e + \frac{3}{10}e + \frac{1}{2}e$
(g) $\frac{1}{2}y + \frac{2}{3}y + \frac{5}{6}y - y$
(h) $3\frac{1}{4}x - 1\frac{1}{2}x + \frac{1}{4}x$
(i) $2\frac{1}{2}n + 8\frac{3}{4}n - 3\frac{1}{4}n - n$
(j) $8.4m - 2.3m + 4.1m$

(k) $700k - 150k - 275k - 25k$
(l) $.64y + .72y + .35y - .82y$
(m) $3.8z + .4z + 7z + z$
(n) $9.4a - 3.9a + 6.2a - .7a$
(o) $9x + 3\frac{1}{2}x + 7\frac{5}{6}x - 8\frac{1}{2}x$
(p) $42d + 78d + 65d + 37d$
(q) $5.6h + 7.8h - 3.5h + 1.4h$
*(r) $7x + 2y + 3y + 8x - 9x - x$
*(s) $6a + 3a + 2b + 5a - a - 6a$
*(t) $6m + 4n - 2m - n + n$
*(u) $7a + 5b - 3a + b + 4a$
*(v) $4.6x + 3.2y + 5.2x - 1.4y$

(w) $\begin{array}{r} 195c \\ +76c \\ \hline \end{array}$
(x) $\begin{array}{r} 7\frac{2}{3}w \\ +9\frac{1}{6}w \\ \hline \end{array}$
(y) $\begin{array}{r} 15.4l \\ -8.8l \\ \hline \end{array}$
(z) $\begin{array}{r} 24.3m \\ -16.7m \\ \hline \end{array}$

2. The costs of four books are $3c$, $5c$, $8c$, and $2c$, respectively. Find the sum (s) of the costs.

3. The attendance during the first 5 months of a school year was $408a$, $412a$, $460a$, $454a$, and $472a$. Find the total (t) attendance for these months.

4. The savings of Lila, Jean, and Rose are $14s$, $28s$, and $45s$, respectively. Find their total savings (t). How much more are the savings of Rose than those of Lila? How many times the savings of Jean are those of Lila?

5. Find the total length (t) of the sides of a regular pentagon and a regular hexagon, if their perimeters are of length $8e$ and $10e$, respectively.

6. James makes 6 models of cubes from sticks. The sum of their edges is $2e$, $3e$, $4e$, $6e$, $7e$, and $8e$, respectively. What is the total length of sticks used for the 6 models?

7. Two boards the same length (l) are placed together, as in figure 1. What is the total length of the larger rectangle thus formed?

8. John piled three blocks, all of which were the same height (h), one on top of the other, as in figure 2. What is the total height (t) of the three blocks?

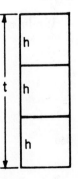

Fig. 2

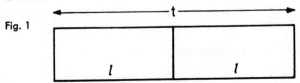

Fig. 1

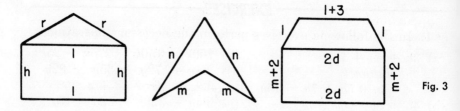
Fig. 3

Fig. 4

9. Draw a regular hexagon. If the length of each side is l, write the formula for the perimeter of the hexagon.

10. Write the formula for the perimeter of a regular octagon. Of a regular pentagon. (Let l represent the length of one side in each case.)

*11. Write the formula for the sum of the lines of each of the shapes in figure 3.

*12. In figure 4, the edges are represented by e and b, as pictured. What is the formula for the length of the total number of edges (t)?

*13. The distance (d) equals the rate (r) multiplied by the time (t). Express this relationship in a formula. $d = ?$

*14. The selling price (s) equals cost price (c) plus gain (g). $s = ?$

*15. The loss (l) equals cost price (c) minus selling price (s). $l = ?$

*16. The gain (g) equals selling price (s) minus cost (c). $g = ?$

*17. Interest (i) equals principal (p) times rate (r) times time in years (t). $i = ?$

*18. Amount (A) equals principal (p) plus interest (i). $A = ?$

*19. The average (a) of a series of numbers is the sum (s) divided by the number (n) in the series. $a = ?$

We have seen that in algebra similar terms are added as follows:

$$4m + 6m + 3m$$
$$4m = 4 \times m$$
$$6m = 6 \times m$$
$$3m = 3 \times m$$
$$\overline{\text{Sum} = 13 \times m = 13m}$$

In arithmetic, sums may be found in a like manner. Thus, if a salesman sells 142 books to one firm at 68¢ each, 134 books to another firm at 68¢ each, and 175 books to a third firm at 68¢ each, he may total his three sales as follows:

$$142 \times 68¢$$
$$134 \times 68¢$$
$$\underline{175 \times 68¢}$$
$$451 \times 68¢ = \$306.68$$

Solve the following exercises by the preceding method:

*20. James sold from his garden 8 qt. of beans to Mr. A @ 15¢; 6 qt. to Mr. B @ 15¢; and 10 qt. to Mr. C @ 15¢. Find the total amount received from his sales.

*21. Florence made doorstops, which she sold at 75¢ apiece. During September, October, November, and December she sold 12, 18, 20, and 32, respectively. Find the amount of her total sales for the four months.

*22. Mr. Kelley borrowed \$1,280 from Mr. Morgan and \$1,500 from Mr. Witte. He paid 8% interest in each case. How much interest does he pay each year?

*23. Mr. Ward bought his coal from three different firms, paying each \$15.75 per ton. Find the total cost of his coal if from one firm he purchased 4 T., from another 5 T., and from the third $3\frac{1}{2}$ T.

*24. For the three weeks preceding Christmas, Jack sold toys that he had made in his workshop. The first week he sold 34, the second week 48, and the third week 65. If his profit on each was 25¢, how much was his total profit?

**25. If the cost of a telegram between two cities is 60¢ for 15 words plus $2\frac{1}{2}$¢ for each additional word, explain the formula $C = 60 + 2\frac{1}{2}(n - 15)$.

**26. If the cost of a 15-word telegram between two stations is 75¢ plus $4\frac{1}{2}$¢ for each additional word, write the formula representing the cost.

**27. If the parcel-post rate to the fifth zone is 26¢ for the first pound plus $9\frac{1}{4}$¢ for each additional pound, explain $C = 26 + 9\frac{1}{4}(n - 1)$.

**28. Write a formula representing the parcel-post charge for the sixth zone, if the rate is 28¢ for the first pound plus 12¢ for each additional pound.

**29. The cost of a 50-word night letter between two cities is 85¢. Five cents is charged for each 5 additional words. Write the formula.

**30. A bus fare (f) is 25¢ for the first mile and 10¢ for each mile (m) thereafter. $f = ?$

**31. On Monday, Bob walked m miles. On Tuesday, he walked 3 mi. farther than on Monday. Find the total distance (t) that Bob walked in the two days.

**32. (optional) Draw, cut, or otherwise make models of various forms; letter the edges; write the formula for the length of the total number of edges in each case.

180. Making algebraic formulas for perimeters and areas. The perimeter of a figure is the distance around its outer boundary. Thus, in figure 5 the perimeter is $a + a + b + a + b + a$, or $4a + 2b$.

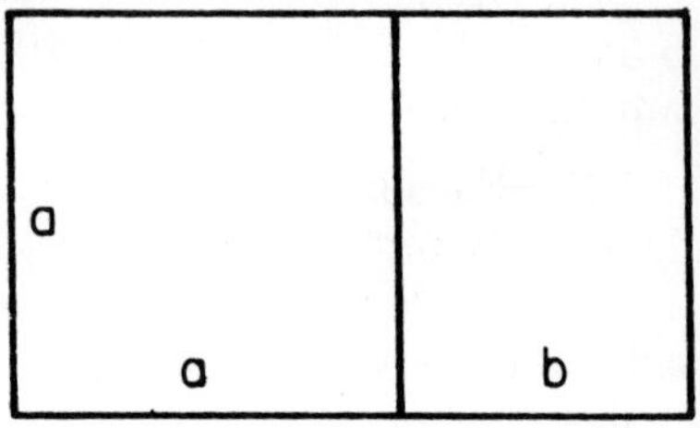

To find the entire amount of space inclosed within the lines (the area), you must add together the two areas inclosed. The area of the square in figure 5 is $a \times a = a^2$. The area of the rectangle in figure 5 is $a \times b = ab$. The area of the entire figure then is $a^2 + ab$.

Fig. 5

──────────────── EXERCISES ────────────────

1. Draw or cut out a rectangle. Label its sides l and w to represent length and width, respectively. What formula will represent its perimeter; that is, $p = ?$ $A = ?$

2. Draw or cut out a triangle. Label its three sides x, y, and z. What formula will represent its perimeter?

3. In an equilateral triangle, let the length of each side be represented by s. Then $p = 3s$. Explain.

4. Draw an isosceles triangle. Represent each of the equal sides by a and the base by b. Write in two different ways the formula for the perimeter of the triangle.

5. Let e represent the length of each edge of a cube. Write the formula for the length of the total number of edges (t). Area of one face = ?   Area of all faces = ?

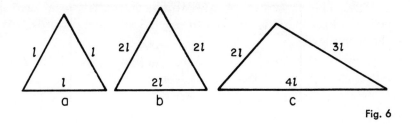

Fig. 6

*6. Find the perimeter of each of the triangles in figure 6.

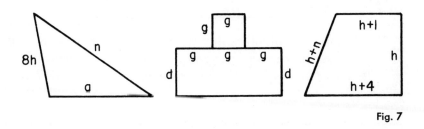

Fig. 7

**7. Write the formula for the perimeter of each figure in figure 7.

Fig. 8

**8. Write the formula for the area of each board in figure 8.

181. Evaluating algebraic expressions. To *evaluate* is merely to put a number in place of a letter in an algebraic expression in order to find the numerical value of the whole expression.

```
                        EXAMPLES
  ┌──────────────────────────────────────────────────┐
  │  A. If:                a = 4                       │
  │                        b = 7                       │
  │                        c = 5                       │
  │        Then:  a + b − c = 4 + 7 − 5               │
  │               a + b − c = 6.                       │
  │                                                    │
  │  B. If:                x = 8                       │
  │                        y = 3                       │
  │        Then:      x² + y² = 64 + 9                │
  │                   x² + y² = 73.                    │
  └──────────────────────────────────────────────────┘
```

If an expression involves multiplication and division as well as
addition and subtraction, *perform the operations of multiplication
and division first, and then perform the operations of addition and
subtraction.*

```
                          EXAMPLES
┌────────────────────────────────────────────────────────────┐
│   A. If:                    x = 5                            │
│                             y = 3                            │
│       Then:          4x + 2y = 4 × 5 + 2 × 3                │
│       Multiplying:   4x + 2y = 20 + 6                        │
│       Adding:        4x + 2y = 26.                           │
│                                                              │
│   B. If:                    a = 2                            │
│                             b = 3                            │
│                             c = 5                            │
│       Then:         6ab − 2bc = 6 × 2 × 3 − 2 × 3 × 5      │
│       Multiplying:  6ab − 2bc = 36 − 30                     │
│       Subtracting:  6ab − 2bc = 6.                          │
└────────────────────────────────────────────────────────────┘
```

EXERCISES

A. Oral

Find the numerical value of each of the following expressions;
let $a = 10$, $b = 6$, $c = 5$, $x = 8$, $y = 2$:

1. $a + b$	**5.** $3x - 2y$
2. $a + b - c$	**6.** $x^2 + y^2$
3. $2a + b$	**7.** $a^2 - b^2$
4. $x - y$	**8.** $ab + c$

9. $abc + xy$

10. $bc - a$

11. $5x + xy$

12. $3ab - bc$

13. $b^2 + c^2$

14. $ax - by$

*15. $2ay + bc - cy$

*16. $\dfrac{a}{c} + \dfrac{x}{y}$

*17. $\dfrac{c}{a} + \dfrac{y}{x}$

*18. $\dfrac{y}{a} + \dfrac{y}{c}$

*19. $\dfrac{2a}{c} + x$

*20. $ay + bx + cy$

*21. $\dfrac{ab}{c} - \dfrac{x}{y}$

**22. $aby - bcy$

**23. $\dfrac{y}{a} + \dfrac{x}{c} - \dfrac{c}{b}$

**24. $\dfrac{12c}{a} - \dfrac{y}{b}$

**25. $\dfrac{y}{x} + \dfrac{c}{b}$

**26. $\dfrac{cxy}{2a} - \dfrac{3c}{b}$

**27. $\dfrac{2c}{2y} - \dfrac{2c}{2b} - \dfrac{y}{a}$

B. Written

Let $a = 3$, $b = 2$, $m = 5$, and $n = 4$. Find the value of each of the following expressions:

1. $4a - 2b + ab$

2. $3m + 8n - m$

3. $a^2 + 2n^2$

4. $3ab + 2mn$

5. $4a^2 - 3b^2$

6. $\dfrac{a}{b} + \dfrac{m}{n}$

7. $\dfrac{a}{m} + \dfrac{b}{n}$

8. $an + ab + 2mn$

9. $6mn - 4ab$

10. $m^2 - n^2 + mn$

*11. $\dfrac{a^2b^2}{n} - \dfrac{bm}{a}$

*12. $2amn - b^2m$

*13. $a^2m^2 - 2b^2m^2$

*14. $4am^2 - 5b^2n$

*15. $\dfrac{a^2n}{2b} + \dfrac{bmn}{8}$

*16. $5am - \dfrac{4ab}{an}$

*17. $3b^2n + 2a^2m$

*18. $10a^2 + 5b^2$

*19. $m^2n - a^2b$

*20. $10am^2 + 4bn^2$

*21. $4abm + 5bmn$

*22. $\dfrac{20}{a} + \dfrac{20}{bn}$

THE FORMULA

**23. $\dfrac{m^2n}{2b^2}$

**24. $\dfrac{3a^2bn^2}{a^2b^2}$

**25. $\dfrac{5mn^2}{b^2m^2}$

**26. $10a^2b - 10b^2n$

**27. $\dfrac{n^2m}{b^2} \div mn$

**28. $2a^2b^2m^2n^2$

**29. $\dfrac{3a^2m}{m} + \dfrac{n^2}{m}$

Let $a = 3,\ b = 5,\ c = 1,\ n = 10,\ t = 4,\ x = 2,\ y = \frac{1}{2}$. Find the value of each of the following expressions:

1. $2ab$

2. $c^2 + cy$

3. y^2

4. $2x + x^2$

5. $6ty + \dfrac{n}{b}$

6. $\dfrac{n^2}{n} + \dfrac{a^2}{a} + \dfrac{b^2}{b}$

7. $\frac{1}{2}a + \frac{1}{2}c + \frac{1}{2}y$

8. $\dfrac{xy}{c}$

9. $\dfrac{a}{c} - \dfrac{n}{b}$

*10. $\dfrac{2ab}{n} + \dfrac{x^2}{t}$

*11. $\dfrac{n^2}{b^2} - \dfrac{t^2}{x^2}$

*12. $\dfrac{xy + t}{b}$

*13. $2a^2 + 2b^2 + 2c^2$

*14. $abc + 5c$

*15. $cy + ac - cx$

*16. $\dfrac{ntx}{b} - 4x^2$

*17. $2t^2 - 2t$

**18. $3nx^2 - 2ny^2$

**19. $\dfrac{2b^2x^2}{n^2}$

**20. $\dfrac{a^2b^2c^2}{n} - xy$

182. Making formulas. The relationship between two numbers may be studied and then expressed in a formula. For instance, May deposits money in the school bank every Tuesday. Her total savings at the close of each Tuesday are shown in the following table:

TABLE A

Number of weeks (w)	1	2	3	4	5	6	10	15	20	52
Total savings in cents (s)	15	30	45	60	75	—	—	—	—	—

Each week the number representing the total savings is how many times the number representing the number of weeks? At this rate how much will May's total savings be for the remaining weeks indicated in Table A? If s represents the total savings and w the number of weeks, $s = ?w$.

What is the relation of b to a in Table B? b is how much more than a? Then $b = a + ?$ Find the missing numbers.

TABLE B

$a =$	1	2	3	4	5	6	8	10	12	18
$b =$	4	5	6	7	—	—	—	—	—	—

EXERCISES

Write the formula expressing the relationship shown in each table from 1 to 8, and find the missing numbers:

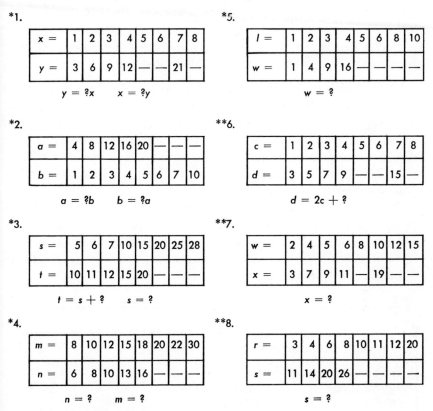

*1.

$x =$	1	2	3	4	5	6	7	8
$y =$	3	6	9	12	—	—	21	—

$y = ?x$ $x = ?y$

*2.

$a =$	4	8	12	16	20	—	—	—
$b =$	1	2	3	4	5	6	7	10

$a = ?b$ $b = ?a$

*3.

$s =$	5	6	7	10	15	20	25	28
$t =$	10	11	12	15	20	—	—	—

$t = s + ?$ $s = ?$

*4.

$m =$	8	10	12	15	18	20	22	30
$n =$	6	8	10	13	16	—	—	—

$n = ?$ $m = ?$

*5.

$l =$	1	2	3	4	5	6	8	10
$w =$	1	4	9	16	—	—	—	—

$w = ?$

**6.

$c =$	1	2	3	4	5	6	7	8
$d =$	3	5	7	9	—	—	15	—

$d = 2c + ?$

**7.

$w =$	2	4	5	6	8	10	12	15
$x =$	3	7	9	11	—	19	—	—

$x = ?$

**8.

$r =$	3	4	6	8	10	11	12	20
$s =$	11	14	20	26	—	—	—	—

$s = ?$

**9. Fred rides straight from his home to a camp, a distance of 50 mi., at the rate of 10 mi. per hour.

Hours traveled (h) =	1	2	—	—	—
Distance traveled (d) =	—	—	—	—	—

Fill in the preceding table. How long will it take Fred to reach the camp? Write the formula showing the relation between the distance traveled and the number of hours traveled ($d = ?h$; $h = ?d$).

**10. George earned $5 a week. Make a table showing his earnings at the close of the first week, second week, fifth week, eighth week, tenth week, and fifty-second week. Write the formula showing the relation between earnings (e) and weeks worked (w).

**11. Sketch plane figures of the following numbers of sides: 4, 5, 6, 7, and 8. Draw as many diagonals as possible from one vertex. How many diagonals are drawn in each figure? Make the table showing the relation between the number of sides (s) and the number of diagonals (d). Write the formula.

**12. How many diagonals can you draw from one vertex in a decagon? A 12-sided figure? A 20-sided figure?

183. Finding the value of a formula. Every symbol in a formula has a definite numerical value when applied to a particular problem. The values of the symbols vary with different problems. For instance, in the formula for the area of the rectangle, $A = lw$, when the rectangle has a length of 10 ft. and a width of 8 ft., $l = 10$ ft., $w = 8$ ft., and $A = 80$ sq. ft. If the rectangle is 7 in. long and 3 in. wide, $l = 7$ in., $w = 3$ in., and $A = 21$ sq. in.

When the numerical value of some one symbol in a formula is to be found, the numerical values of all the other symbols are usually known. To find the value of this one symbol, substitute the numerical values in place of the other symbols and perform the necessary operations of arithmetic.

EXAMPLE 1

In a triangle, the length of side $a = 2$ in., of $b = 4$ in., and of $c = 5$ in. Find the perimeter.

Formula for perimeter: $p = a + b + c$
Substituting: $p = 2 + 4 + 5$
Adding: $p = 11.$

Hence, the perimeter of the triangle is 11 in.

EXAMPLE 2

In a parallelogram whose base equals 8 in. and height equals 3 in., find the area.

The formula for area of parallelogram is:

$$A = bh$$

Substituting: $A = 8 \times 3$

Multiplying: $A = 24.$

Hence, the area of the parallelogram is 24 sq. in.

EXERCISES

Write the formula for each of the following and solve as in the preceding examples.

1. Some Boy Scouts built a surfboard to be used on the lake at their camp. The board was 60 in. long and 30 in. wide. How many square inches did the board contain?

2. A garage roof is 18 ft. long and 12 ft. wide. How many square feet of roofing are needed to cover it?

3. A building contractor may estimate the number of bricks (n) needed for a construction by the formula $n = 22 \, lwh$, if l, w, and h represent the length, width, and height of the building. How many bricks are needed to construct a wall 80 ft. long, $1\frac{1}{2}$ ft. wide, and 6 ft. high?

4. Some Girl Scouts bought a triangular piece of land for a camp. It had a base of 640 ft. and an altitude of 400 ft. How many square feet of land did the girls buy?

5. Clara made for her club a triangular pennant. It had a base of 18 in. and an altitude of 42 in. How many square inches were there in the pennant?

6. A rectangular swimming pool is 38 ft. wide and 54 ft. long. How many cubic feet of water are there in the pool when it is filled to a depth of 5 ft.?

7. Frank's school attendance for five successive years was as follows: 180 days, 175 days, 200 days, 188 days, 198 days. Find his average annual attendance for the five years. $\left(a = \dfrac{s}{n} \right)$

8. For four consecutive weeks, Paul's school lunch cost him as follows: $1.00, $.80, $1.25, $.75. Find his average weekly lunch expenditure.

9. The average score in a test taken by a class of 36 was 78. What was the sum of all the scores? ($s = a \times n$)

10. The average Red Cross contribution of the 38 pupils in a certain room was 27¢. What was the total Red Cross contribution?

*11. A tin cup 4 in. across and 3 in. deep will hold how much water?

*12. How many cubic feet are there in a conical pile of grain that is $3\frac{1}{2}$ ft. high and $4\frac{1}{2}$ ft. in diameter on the ground?

*13. The base of a pyramid contains 90 sq. ft., and its height is 8 ft. How many cubic feet are there in the pyramid?

The formula for determining the average mileage of an automobile tire is $m = 6545d$, m being the distance in miles the tire will probably travel and d the diameter of the tire in feet.

*14. A tire whose diameter is 18 in. should withstand how many miles of travel? A tire of 24 in. should last how many miles of travel?

If p = the number of pounds of pressure the air exerts upon the wings of a moving airplane and V = the speed of the plane in miles per hour, then the formula is $p = .0005V^3$.

Fig. 9.

*15. A plane flying 100 m. p. h. has how many pounds of pressure on its wings? What is the pressure at 150 m. p. h.?

*16. How many square miles are there on the surface of the earth, if the earth is considered to have a diameter of 8,000 mi.? ($S = \pi d^2$)

*17. How many cubic miles are there in the earth? ($V = \frac{4}{3}\pi r^3$)

*18. To find the distance in feet (d) that an object will fall from a height in (t) seconds, use the formula $d = 16t^2$.

A brick falling from the top of a high building will in 5 sec. have fallen a distance of how many feet?

$$d = 16t^2$$
$$d = 16 \times 25$$
$$d = ?$$

*19. Find the distance that a stone will fall from a tower in 3 seconds.

**20. The following formulas are used in the business and scientific world:

a. $d = \dfrac{v^2}{2r}$. (a) Solve for d when $v = 30$ and $r = 10$.

(b) Solve for d when $v = 8$ and $r = 3$.

b. $p = \dfrac{2wh}{S + 1}$. (a) Solve for p when $w = 1500$, $h = 28$, and $S = 3$.

(b) Solve for p when $w = 600$, $h = 15$, and $S = 2$.

c. $l = d + \dfrac{2r^2}{5d}$. (a) Find l if $d = 40$ and $r = 1.5$.

(b) Find l if $d = 6$ and $r = .3$.

d. $h = \dfrac{V}{b^2}$. (a) Find h when $V = 160$ and $b = 4$.

(b) Find h when $V = 200$ and $b = 5$.

e. $r = \dfrac{s^2 + h^2}{2h}$. (a) What is the value of r if $s = 4$ and $h = 3$?

(b) What is the value of r if $s = 15$ and $h = 10$?

f. $C = \dfrac{n(n - 1)}{2}$. (a) Solve for C when $n = 20$.

(b) Solve for C when $n = 12$.

g. $R = \dfrac{l^2}{6d} + \dfrac{d}{2}$. (a) Find R if $l = 3$ and $d = 4$.

(b) Find R if $l = 10$ and $d = 8$.

The speed of an automobile determines the distance in which the automobile can be stopped in case of an emergency. The following formula is approximately true for good brakes and a dry concrete road: $d = .045r^2 + 1.1r$, where d = distance in feet required to stop and r = rate of speed (miles per hour).

**21. Charles is driving at a speed of 30 m. p. h. on a dry concrete road. About how many feet of road will he need to stop the car? When he is driving at 60 m. p. h., in how many feet can he stop?

**22. James notices that the Fahrenheit (F) thermometer records the temperature to be 86°. He wishes to know just what the Centigrade (C) thermometer records at the same time. In his science class he has learned that the relation between the two scales may be expressed by these two formulas:

$$C = \frac{F - 32°}{9} \times 5, \quad \text{and} \quad F = \frac{C}{5} \times 9 + 32°.$$

Determine the Centigrade temperature for him.

**23. On a hot summer day, the Centigrade thermometer read 40°. What was the reading on the Fahrenheit thermometer?

**24. Mabel opened a bank account with a $5 birthday present. Every month thereafter she was able to save $3 from her earnings. Write the formula representing her savings (s) for any number (n) of months, disregarding interest. Find her total savings 10 months later. One year later.

184. Graphing formulas. While a formula shows in symbols the relationship between numbers, the graph of a formula pictures this relationship and thereby gives us the answers to some questions without numerical computation.

Suppose that salt is selling at 5¢ a pound. The relationship between the cost (c) of the salt and the number of pounds (p) may be stated in the formula $c = .05p$. That is, the cost of any amount of salt is .05 times the number of pounds purchased.

To graph the formula $c = .05p$, prepare a table similar to the one at the right, showing the cost of the salt for various numbers of pounds. Then draw the axes for the graph. Mark the vertical guide line for the cost axis, letting one square represent $.05. Mark the horizontal guide line for the amount axis, using one square to each pound. Next plot the pairs of corresponding numbers found in the table.

Pounds	Cost
1	$.05
5	.25
10	.50
15	.75

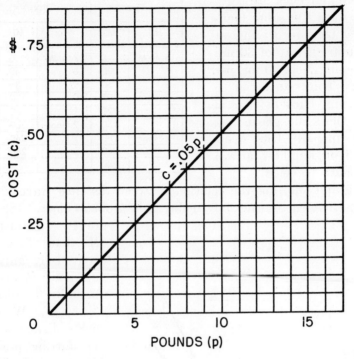

Fig. 10

Since 1 lb. costs $.05, place the first dot on the intersection of the 1-lb. line and the $.05 line. Place the next dot on the intersection of the 5-lb. line and the $.25 line. Where will the third dot be placed? The fourth dot? It is easily seen that the dots lie on a straight line. Let us now draw the straight line through these dots. This line is called "the graph of the formula $c = .05p$."

By graphing this formula showing the relationship between the cost of the salt and the number of pounds purchased, a picture is formed whereby the cost of any number of pounds of salt may be found by merely reading the cost from the graph. It is also possible to read from the graph the number of pounds of salt that can be bought for a given amount of money.

By reading the graph, find the cost of 4 lb. of salt, of 8 lb., and of 11 lb.

From the graph tell how many pounds of salt can be bought for $.15, for $.35, for $.65.

Upon what does the cost (c) of the salt depend?

If the straight line is extended indefinitely, the cost of any number of pounds can be read directly from the graph.

Tom and Dick are traveling over the same highway. Tom is driving at the uniform rate of 30 mi. per hour; Dick, 40 mi. per hour. Tom starts at 6 A. M. and Dick at 7 A. M. from the same place. At what time will Dick overtake Tom, and how far will they have traveled?

Tom		Dick	
Hr.	Mi.	Hr.	Mi.
6 A. M.	0	7 A. M.	0
7	30	8	40
8	60	9	80
9	90	10	120
10	120	11	160
11	150	12 Noon	200
12 Noon	180	1 P. M.	240
1 P. M.	210	2	280
2	240		

A graph showing the relation between distance traveled and hours traveled by each boy makes this problem clear. (See figure 11.) The distance (d) that Tom has traveled by any certain hour (h) is obtained by the formula $d = 30\,h$. W h y? Dick's distance from the starting point is $d = 40h$. Why?

Fig. 11

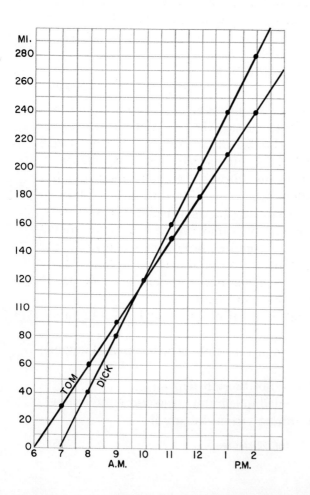

In making the tables, consider that at 6 A. M. Tom is just starting; he is 0 mi. away. At 7 A. M. he is 30 mi. away. At 8 A. M., 60 mi. How far away is he at 9 A. M.? At 7 A. M. Dick is starting and is 0 mi. away, but by 8 A. M. he is 40 mi. on the road. How far away is he at 9 A. M.? At what hour do the lines meet? For how many hours has each boy been traveling? How many miles is this from the starting point?

Consider the rates traveled and prove that each boy will actually be 120 mi. away at 10 A. M. How far apart are they at noon? At 1 P. M.? At 2 P. M.? Which boy is ahead before 10 A. M.? After 10 A. M.? At what time is each boy 240 mi. away? 180 mi. away?

Not all formula graphs form straight lines. Figure 12 illustrates a curved-line graph. It is the graph of the formula for the area of a square, $A = s^2$.

To graph this formula, use the table below. How are the values of A found? The areas, A, are represented on the vertical axis and the lengths, s, on the horizontal axis. A square 0 ft. long evidently contains 0 sq. ft.; hence, the first dot is on the intersection of the 0 area and 0 length lines. A square 1 ft. long has an area of 1 sq. ft.; hence, the second dot is on the intersection of the 1-area and 1-length lines. A square 2 ft. long has an area of 4 sq. ft., making the third dot on the intersection of the 4-area and 2-length lines. The other dots are similarly located. It is evident that these points do not lie on a straight line. Draw the curved line through these points.

Estimate from the graph the area of a square 1.5 ft. on an edge, a square $2\frac{1}{2}$ ft. on an edge, a square $3\frac{1}{4}$ ft. long, and a square $\frac{1}{2}$ ft. long.

By squaring the given lengths, determine how close you came to the correct answer for each of the above areas.

Find from the graph the approximate lengths of squares with the following areas: 6 sq. ft., 8 sq. ft., and 14 sq. ft.

Square each of these approximate lengths and compare the results with the given areas to determine how close you came to the correct answer in each case.

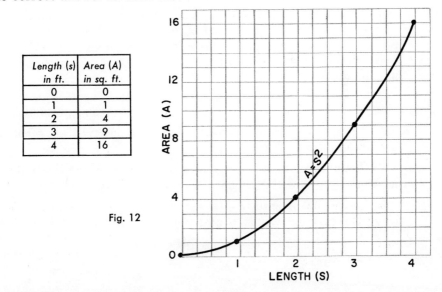

Length (s) in ft.	Area (A) in sq. ft.
0	0
1	1
2	4
3	9
4	16

Fig. 12

*1. Write the formula, make the table, and draw the graph to represent the cost (c) of apples at 12¢ per pound (p).

*2. From the above graph find the cost of 2 lb. of apples. Of $1\frac{1}{2}$ lb. Of 2.5 lb.

*3. From the above graph determine how many pounds of apples can be bought for 36¢. For 6¢. For 15¢. For 30¢.

*4. Cecil earns $20 a month working after school. Let the formula $w = 20m$ represent his wages (w) after any number of months (m). Draw the graph showing his wages after 1 mo., 2 mo., 3 mo., 4 mo., and so on.

*5. From the above graph find the amount of Cecil's wages after 6 mo. After 8 mo.; $3\frac{1}{2}$ mo.; $4\frac{1}{2}$ mo.; $7\frac{1}{2}$ mo.

*6. Determine from the above graph how long Cecil will have to work to earn $80; $50; $110; $90; $175.

**7. Frank and Harold are both starting savings accounts. Frank saves $4 a month and Harold $8 a month. Frank starts in January and Harold in March. Draw the graph showing when Harold will have as much saved as Frank.

**8. Write the formula and draw a graph of the following table.

$t =$	0	2	3	4	6	9
$d =$	0	40	60	80	120	180

REVIEW OF CHAPTER XVI

1. Shorten these expressions, using symbols and numbers:

(a) The sum of the square of a and the product of b and c.

(b) The product of a divided by b and c divided by d.

(c) Twice m decreased by the quotient of $3a$ and $5b$.

(d) Three times the product of the square of w and the square of x divided by y minus z.

(e) $\pi \times r \times r \times h$. (f) $V \div lh$.

(g) $2 \times b + 2 \times h$. (h) 16 times the square of t.

2. Using the formula $i = prt$, find the interest on $540 for 2 years and 6 months at 5%.

3. Using the formula $s = c + g$, find the selling price (s) of a hat that cost (c) $3.50 and was sold at a gain (g) of $2.25.

4. Using the formula $l = c - s$, find the loss (l) on a sale in which the cost (c) was $180 and the selling price (s) was $176.20.

5. Let $a = 2$, $b = 3$, $m = 1$, $n = 4$. Find the value of these expressions:

(a) $a + b + m + n$

(b) $\dfrac{b}{a} + \dfrac{m}{n}$

(c) $5a + 2b - m - n$

(d) $a^2 + b^2 - m^2 + n$

*(e) $3a^2 + 2b^2 + m^2 - n^2$

*(f) $\dfrac{3ab^2}{4mn^2}$

*6. Let the formula $p = 5l$ represent the perimeter (p) of a regular pentagon each side of which is of length l. Prepare the table and make the graph of this formula.

*7. From the above graph determine the perimeter of a regular pentagon each side of which is of length 3 ft. Of length 6 ft. Of length $4\frac{1}{2}$ ft.

*8. According to the above graph, if the perimeter is 20 ft., what is the length of one side of the pentagon? If the perimeter is 15 ft.? $12\frac{1}{2}$ ft.? $22\frac{1}{2}$ ft.?

*9. A package was dropped from a helicopter. It reached the ground 15 seconds later. What was the altitude of the helicopter?

(Use the formula $s = 16t^2$. s represents the number of feet the package fell and t represents the number of seconds used in falling.)

**10. Write the formula and calculate the taxi fare (f) if $f = 30\cent$ for the first mile plus $10\cent$ for each mile thereafter. $f = ?$ for a trip of 9 miles?

──────────── *PLAYOFF FOR CHAPTER XVI* ────────────

1. By experiment, two members of the class or a group may determine the height from a third- or fourth-story window (the higher, the better) by dropping a brick from the window. One person may drop the brick and another on the ground start and stop a stop-watch for exact timing in seconds.

2. *The cats and the rats. If three cats can catch three rats in three minutes, how many cats can catch one hundred rats in one hundred minutes?

──────────

* Courtesy of Burroughs Corp.

CHAPTER XVII

THE EQUATION

185. The meaning and purpose of equations. In algebra, as in arithmetic, we are mostly concerned with finding the value of some *unknown number*. This is done by the use of certain numbers whose values are *known*. For instance, in the formula $P = a + b + c$, P is the unknown number and a, b, and c are the known numbers. The value of P is found if the known values of a, b, and c are added.

The study of *equations* in algebra is concerned with finding the value of the unknown number. By means of equations, the most difficult problems that confront the businessman, the scientist, and the engineer are often greatly simplified.

An equation is a statement in numbers or symbols that two expressions are equal. You have long been familiar with such simple equations as the following: $? + 4 = 6$, $3 \times ? = 12$, $7 - ? = 5$, and $? \div 2 = 5$. Formulas are illustrations of equations. The expressions $3x = 21$, $\frac{1}{3}r = 4$, $m + 2 = 16$, and $n - 1 = 12$ are four simple forms of equations used in the solution of everyday problems.

186. Terms used in equations. In an equation, the expression on the left-hand side of the equals sign is called the *left member* and that on the right-hand side is called the *right member*.

The symbol whose value is to be found is called the *unknown number*, or merely the *unknown*. When equations are written, the letter a, n, x, or any other symbol may be used to represent the unknown number.

In the equation $x - 3 = 8$, $x - 3$ is the left member and 8 is the right member. The symbol x is the unknown number.

187. Writing and solving simple equations. Since many equations cannot be solved orally, it is necessary to learn a few truths that will aid in the solution of the more complex equations.

An equation is like balanced scales. If the scales are to remain perfectly balanced, a change made on one arm must be made also on the other arm. It is the same with equations; a change made in one member of an equation must be made also in the other member.

1. In the figure, **if the salt is divided so that only one-half of it remains on the left arm, for the balance to be maintained the weight must also be divided so that only one-half of the weight remains on the right arm.** One and one-half pounds of salt will balance a $1\frac{1}{2}$-lb. weight.

2. **If 2 lb. of salt are taken from the left arm of the scales, 2 lb. in weight must be taken from the right arm, or the balance will not be maintained.** One pound of salt will balance a 1-lb. weight.

3. **If 2 lb. of salt are added to the left arm of the scales, a 2-lb. weight must be added to the right arm in order that the balance may be maintained.** That is, the 5 lb. of salt and the 5-lb. weight will still balance the scales.

4. **If the amount of salt on the left arm is doubled, the weight on the right arm must also be doubled to keep the balance.** Six pounds of salt will balance a 6-lb. weight.

The truths involved in the preceding illustrations hold good for the solving of equations; that is, these truths are used in finding the value of the unknown.

The equation $4x = 20$ means that some unknown number times 4 equals 20. It is evident that there is 4 times x (the unknown) in the left member of the equation. It is important in solving an equation to have only the unknown number in the left member. In order to have x (no more and no less) in the left member, it is necessary to divide the left member by 4. To keep the left and

Fig. 1

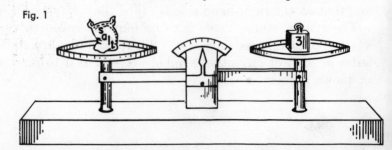

right members of the equation still equal—*balanced*—it is also necessary to divide the right member by 4.

Solution

The equation is: $\quad\quad\quad 4x = 20$
Dividing by 4: $\quad\quad 4x \div 4 = 20 \div 4$
Hence: $\quad\quad\quad\quad\quad x = 5.$
Check: $\quad\quad\quad\quad 4 \times 5 = 20$
$$20 = 20.$$

This illustration leads us to the first truth that we shall need in solving equations:

> **Truth I:** *If both members of an equation are divided by the same amount, the members remain equal.*

EXERCISES

Solve and check the following equations, using Truth I:

1. $4a = 20$
2. $6w = 18$
3. $7x = 28$
4. $5b = 100$
5. $8r = 8$
6. $15c = 900$
7. $10k = 35$
8. $12m = 72$

9. $20d = 800$
10. $6s = 1800$
11. $4y = 25$
12. $25z = 650$
13. $6t = 3$
14. $7e = 32$
15. $30l = 10$
16. $3n = 1$

17. $5a = 18$
18. $4c = 6$
19. $9c = 35$
20. $.6m = 12$
(*Hint:* Multiply the equation by 10 to clear of decimals.)
21. $.12a = 36$

22. A certain number multiplied by 4 equals 84. What is the number?

Solution

Let: $\quad\quad\quad\quad\quad n = $ the number
The equation is: $\quad\quad 4n = 84$
Dividing by 4: $\quad\quad\quad n = 21.$
$\quad$ Hence, the number is 21.
Check: $\quad\quad\quad 4 \times 21 = 84$
$$84 = 84.$$

23. Forty-eight is 3 times a certain number. Find the number.

24. The perimeter of a square is 64 ft. Find the length of one side.

25. Charles said, "My number multiplied by 3 equals 27." Find Charles's number.

26. Jack's home room was selling tickets for a school entertainment. Said Jack, "Four times my sales amounts to 108 tickets." How many tickets has Jack sold?

27. Jean has been earning money for the Junior Red Cross. On returning to school one morning she said, "If I multiply my earnings by 8, I shall have $1.28." How much money has Jean earned?

28. In 6 hours an airplane flew a distance of 840 miles. How many miles did it average per hour?

The equation $x + 4 = 16$ means that some unknown number plus 4 equals 16. It is evident that there is 4 more than x (the unknown) in the left member of the equation. In order to have only x in the left member, it is necessary to subtract 4 from it. To keep the left and right members of the equation still equal, 4 must also be subtracted from the right member, that is, subtract 4 from each member of the equation.

Solution

The equation is:	$x + 4 = 16$
Subtracting 4:	$x + 4 - 4 = 16 - 4$
Hence:	$x = 12.$
Check:	$12 + 4 = 16$
	$16 = 16.$

This illustration leads us to the second truth that we shall need in solving equations:

Truth II: If the same amount is subtracted from both members of an equation, the members remain equal.

EXERCISES

In each of the following exercises, find the value of x, using Truth II. Check results.

1. $x + 10 = 18$	**8.** $5 + x = 15$	**15.** $121 + x = 612$
2. $x + 32 = 67$	**9.** $8 + x = 28$	**16.** $a + 14 = 15$
3. $x + 12 = 45$	**10.** $16 + x = 22$	**17.** $3 + a = 3$
4. $x + 9 = 26$	**11.** $x + 218 = 476$	**18.** $12 + a = 13$
5. $x + 14 = 32$	**12.** $x + 142 = 385$	**19.** $a + 2 = 9$
6. $x + 46 = 78$	**13.** $x + 74 = 191$	**20.** $9 + a = 48$
7. $x + 38 = 43$	**14.** $43 + x = 164$	**21.** $37 + a = 41$

22. A certain number plus 20 equals 35. What is the number?

Solution

Let: $\qquad\qquad\qquad\quad x =$ the number
The equation is: $\quad x + 20 = 35$
Subtracting 20: $\qquad\qquad x = 15.$
$\quad$ Hence, the number is 15.
Check: $\qquad\qquad 15 + 20 = 35$
$\qquad\qquad\qquad\quad\;\; 35 = 35.$

23. Sixteen cents added to Mary's money gives 38¢. Let x stand for Mary's money. Form an equation and solve.

24. If John had 12 more rabbits, he would have 116 rabbits. Form an equation and solve.

25. Joe said, "If I can win 75 points this game, I will have 500 points." How many points has Joe?

26. What number added to 188 equals 391?

27. Said Carol, "If you add 35¢ to my earnings, I will have 62¢." How much money has Carol?

28. Jane said, "I am thinking of a number; if you add 256 to it, the sum is 428." What is the number?

29. Mr. Brown received an increase in salary of $96, making his salary $1500. How much was his salary before the increase?

30. A house sold for $8,500. If the contractor made $1,750 on it, what did it cost him?

In the equation $x - 4 = 16$, it is evident that there is 4 less than x in the left member. In order to have only x in the left member, we must add 4 to it. We must also add 4 to the right member in order to keep the balance. That is, add 4 to each member of the equation.

Solution

The equation is: $\qquad\quad x - 4 = 16$
Adding 4: $\qquad\quad x - 4 + 4 = 16 + 4$
Hence: $\qquad\qquad\qquad\quad x = 20.$
Check: $\qquad\qquad\quad 20 - 4 = 16$
$\qquad\qquad\qquad\qquad\; 16 = 16.$

This illustration leads us to the third truth needed in solving equations:

> ***Truth III:*** *If the same amount is added to both members of an equation, the members remain equal.*

In each of the following exercises, find the value of n. Check results.

1. $n - 2 = 12$	8. $n - 46 = 59$	15. $n - 107 = 211$
2. $n - 8 = 25$	9. $n - 80 = 112$	16. $n - 1 = 1$
3. $n - 7 = 15$	10. $n - 76 = 120$	17. $n - 12 = 0$
4. $n - 14 = 23$	11. $n - 72 = 171$	18. $n - 1 = 9$
5. $n - 10 = 37$	12. $n - 118 = 212$	19. $n - 17 = 18$
6. $n - 24 = 62$	13. $n - 400 = 609$	20. $n - 4 = 2$
7. $n - 38 = 72$	14. $n - 108 = 130$	21. $n - 18 = 3$

22. If you subtract 14 from Ruth's grade, she will have 72. What is Ruth's grade?

Solution

Let: $\qquad\qquad\qquad g$ = Ruth's grade
The equation is: $\qquad g - 14 = 72$
Adding 14: $\qquad\qquad g = 86.$
$\qquad$ Hence, Ruth's grade is 86.
Check: $\qquad\qquad 86 - 14 = 72$
$\qquad\qquad\qquad\qquad 72 = 72.$

23. What number less 41 equals 96?

24. Jack said, "I am thinking of a number; if you subtract 161 from it, the result is 316." What is the number?

25. A group of boys climbed Pike's Peak. After climbing 10,190 ft. they had 4,218 ft. to go to reach the top. What is the height of the peak?

26. The net profit of the Black Coal Co. was $2,458 and its expenses were $3,824. Find its gross income.

27. Clyde's height is $2\frac{1}{2}$ in. less than Jim's height. Jim is 61 in. tall. What is Clyde's height?

28. A farmer after selling 482 bushels of wheat had 376 bushels unsold. How many bushels did he have at first?

In the equation $\frac{1}{3}x = 4$, there is only $\frac{1}{3}$ of x in the left member. In order to have x in the left member of the equation, multiply $\frac{1}{3}x$ by 3. To keep the left and right members equal, also multiply the right member by 3.

Solution

The equation is: $\frac{1}{3}x = 4$

Multiplying by 3: $3 \cdot \frac{1}{3}x = 3 \cdot 4$

Hence: $x = 12.$

Check: $\frac{1}{3} \times 12 = 4$

$4 = 4.$

The fourth truth used in solving equations follows:

Truth IV: *If both members of an equation are multiplied by the same amount, the members remain equal.*

―――――――――――――― **EXERCISES** ――――――――――――――

Using Truth IV, solve the following equations; check results:

1. $\frac{1}{3}x = 2$

2. $\frac{1}{2}d = 5$

3. $\frac{1}{6}c = 4$

4. $\frac{1}{8}b = 7$

5. $\frac{1}{5}k = 12$

6. $\frac{1}{10}y = 8$

7. $\dfrac{n}{4} = 6$

8. $\dfrac{a}{5} = 10$

9. $\frac{1}{12}r = 6$

10. $\dfrac{m}{3} = 17$

11. $\dfrac{n}{8} = 14$

12. $\frac{1}{15}m = 8$

13. $\frac{1}{2}a = 1$

14. $\dfrac{u}{8} = 8$

15. $\frac{1}{3}a = 3$

16. $\dfrac{n}{12} = 0$

17. $\dfrac{b}{6} = 9$

18. $\dfrac{s}{2} = 5$

19. One-fourth of a certain number equals 18. Find the number.

Solution

Let: $n =$ the number

The equation is: $\dfrac{n}{4} = 18$

Multiplying by 4: $n = 72.$
Hence, the number is 72.

Check: $\frac{72}{4} = 18$

$18 = 18.$

*20. One-eighth of what number equals 16?

*21. Gerald spent one-third of his money. He spent $15. How much money had he?

*22. A school sold in one day 520 tickets to an entertainment. Those tickets represented one-third of the seating capacity of the auditorium. How many people would the auditorium seat?

*23. A motorist had car trouble 18 miles from his starting point, which was one-sixth of the distance to his destination. How far was his starting point from his destination?

*24. I saved one-twelfth of my income during the year. During this time my savings amounted to $180. How much was my income?

*25. A crew was laying a pipeline between two cities. The engineer's report showed that during the first month they had laid the pipe for a distance of 128 miles, or one-third of the distance between the cities. How far apart are the cities?

*26. A firm's report showed a sales increase of one-eighth over the preceding year. This was an increase of $28,000. What was the amount of the sales during the preceding year?

ALL PROCESSES

Solve each of the following, using the correct truth:

1. $n - 80 = 1$
2. $w + 60 = 82$
3. $\dfrac{a}{3} = 14$
4. $5k = 13$
5. $s + 2 = 18$
6. $m - 200 = 150$
7. $33y = 165$
8. $4 + b = 18$
9. $\frac{1}{2}k = 7\frac{1}{2}$
10. $w - 2\frac{1}{2} = 7\frac{1}{2}$
11. $m + 1\frac{1}{4} = 3\frac{3}{4}$
12. $n + 2.4 = 6.5$

13. $2\frac{1}{2}a = 10$
14. $\frac{1}{3}d = 2$
15. $h - 4.2 = 8.7$
16. $m - .4 = 7.2$
17. $92 + n = 183$
18. $3.1n = 9.3$
19. $s + 6 = 7$
20. $s - 7 = 6$
21. $9a = 3$
22. $16 + b = 35$
23. $\dfrac{n}{9} = 9$
24. $1\frac{1}{2}n = 3$

25. $12 + w = 21$
26. $m - 8 = 0$
27. $\dfrac{n}{17} = 2$
28. $\frac{1}{3}c = 3$
29. $18s = 6$
30. $3n = 4$
31. $s - 9 = 2$
32. $24 + a = 30$
33. $.06a = 6$
34. $.7x = 21$
35. $.001c = 1$
36. $2.8m = 5.6$

37. A square has a perimeter of 72 in. How long is one side?

38. The perimeter of a regular hexagon is 96 in. Find the length of one side.

*39. Mr. Clark bought a used car. After repairing the car, he sold it for $125 more than he paid for it. The selling price was $680. How much did he pay for the car?

*40. Cecil made doorstops to sell in order to earn money for Christmas. After selling 18, he had 24 remaining unsold. How many had he made altogether?

*41. A home room has collected one-fourth of its Red Cross quota. It has collected $2.25. What is its quota?

*42. Paul had 72 in. of wire with which to make a wire model of an equilateral triangle. How long can he make each side?

*43. Sam said, "If I earn 46 honor points this semester, I shall have 120 points." How many honor points has Sam?

*44. The sun is about 93,000,000 miles from the earth. Light travels about 186,000 miles per second. How many seconds does it take for light to reach the earth from the sun?

*45. After paying one-sixth of the cost of his bicycle, James had paid $5.75. What was the cost of his bicycle?

**46. In an isosceles triangle, each of the two equal sides is 4 inches longer than the base. If the perimeter of the triangle is 38 inches, what is the length of each side?

**47. In an isosceles triangle, each of the two equal sides is $2\frac{1}{2}$ centimeters shorter than the base. If the perimeter of this triangle is 46 centimeters, what is the length of each side?

188. Solving equations by using more than one of the preceding truths. The four truths may be combined into the following single truth: *If both members of an equation are increased, decreased, multiplied, or divided by the same amount, the members remain equal.*

When the use of more than one truth is necessary, follow the illustrated order of procedure.

EXAMPLES

A. The equation is: $3n - 2 = 10$
Adding 2: $3n = 12$
Dividing by 3: $n = 4.$
     Hence, the number is 4.
Check: $3 \cdot 4 - 2 = 10$
                 $12 - 2 = 10$
                     $10 = 10.$

B. The equation is: $\dfrac{a}{4} + 6 = 9$

Subtracting 6: $\dfrac{a}{4} = 3$

Multiplying by 4: $a = 12.$
  Hence, the number is 12.

Check: $\dfrac{12}{4} + 6 = 9$

$3 + 6 = 9$

$9 = 9.$

C. The equation is: $\tfrac{2}{5}x = 6$

Multiplying by 5: $5 \cdot \tfrac{2}{5}x = 5 \cdot 6$

$2x = 30$

Dividing by 2: $x = 15.$
  Hence, the number is 15.

Check: $\tfrac{2}{5} \cdot 15 = 6$

$6 = 6.$

EXERCISES

Solve and check each of the following equations:

1. $3n + 4 = 19$

2. $4n + 2 = 18$

3. $8n + 6 = 30$

4. $5x + 3 = 23$

5. $7x + 1 = 36$

6. $6x - 3 = 15$

7. $2a - 5 = 19$

8. $3a - 12 = 9$

9. $4a - 8 = 20$

10. $5a - 7 = 13$

*11. $\dfrac{n}{2} + 4 = 5$

*12. $\dfrac{n}{4} + 7 = 10$

*13. $\dfrac{n}{3} - 5 = 9$

*14. $\dfrac{a}{5} - 6 = 15$

*15. $\dfrac{a}{6} + 2 = 11$

*16. $4a + 2 = 10$

*17. $5 + 3a = 14$

*18. $7n - 1 = 13$

*19. $\dfrac{k}{3} - 4 = 16$

*20. $\dfrac{m}{10} + 8 = 14$

*21. $3y + 7 = 22$

*22. $\tfrac{2}{3}n = 12$

*23. $\tfrac{3}{4}n = 15$

*24. $\tfrac{2}{5}k = 8$

*25. $3n + 2n = 15$
  Hint: $5n = 15$

*26. $4a + 2a = 24$

*27. $8x - 3x = 20$

*28. $7n - n = 18$

*29. $\tfrac{1}{2}n + \tfrac{1}{4}n = 6$

*30. $2.5n + 3.5n = 12$

*31. $1.4n + 1.1n = 10$

*32. $.1y + .5y = 7.2$

*33. $.3a + .4a = 70$

*34. $.02b + .03b = 2$

*35. $2.3n + 1.3n = 72$

*36. $4.2x - 1.2x = 9$

*37. One-third of Sam's age plus 8 equals 14 years. How old is Sam? $\left(\textit{Hint:} \text{ Let } a = \text{Sam's age. Then, } \dfrac{a}{3} + 8 = 14.\right)$

*38. Three times Albert's money plus 12¢ is 60¢. How much money has Albert?

*39. Edna said, "I am thinking of a number. Four times this number plus 8 is 20." What is the number?

*40. Helen said, "Subtract 6 from two times a certain number and the result is 22." What is the number?

*41. Majorie said, "One-half of my money increased by $75 is $120." How much money had she?

*42. Four times my age increased by 3 times my age is 84 years. How old am I?

**43. One-half of a number less one-third of the number equals 20. Find the number.

**44. Mr. Karr bought a piece of land. After improving it, he sold it for $80 more than twice what he paid for it. He sold it for $2,600. What did Mr. Karr pay for the land?

**45. A graduating class of 165 pupils decided to make a class gift costing $44. The class had $11 in the treasury. How much should each member contribute in order to pay for the gift?

**46. After the last cutting of a field of alfalfa, a farmer had 90 tons of alfalfa. This was 12 tons more than one-half of last year's yield. How many tons of alfalfa did he have last year?

**47. Fred sold 76 papers today, which was 9 less than one-third of yesterday's sales. How many papers did he sell yesterday?

**48. Clark's arithmetic grade is 84 today. This is seven-eighths of yesterday's grade. What was Clark's grade yesterday?

**49. The length of Larry's step is $\frac{4}{7}$ as long as his father's step. Larry's step is 24 inches long. What is the length of his father's step?

189. Difficult arithmetic problems made easy by the use of equations. Most of the preceding problems could have been as easily solved by arithmetic as by equations. However, many problems are very difficult to solve by arithmetic but easy to solve by equations. Let us consider some of them.

EXAMPLES
---

1. A class of 36 pupils has twice as many girls as boys. How many of each are there in the class? (If more than one unknown number is to be found, it is usually better to let n, or some other symbol, represent the smallest number and express the others in terms of n, or whatever symbol is used.)

Solution

Let: n = number of boys in class
Then: $2n$ = number of girls in class
Total in class is: $n + 2n = 36$
Adding the n's: $3n = 36$
Dividing by 3: $n = 12$
                                          $2n = 24.$

Hence, there are 12 boys and 24 girls in the class.

Check: (a) $12 + 24 = 36$ (number of pupils in the class)
             (b) $12 \times 2 = 24$ (There are twice as many girls as boys.)

2. In a school election, 45 votes were cast.   Of these Don received 5 more than Richard.   How many votes did each receive?

Solution

Let: n = number of Richard's votes
Then: $n + 5$ = number of Don's votes
Total votes are: $n + n + 5 = 45$
Adding the n's: $2n + 5 = 45$
Subtracting 5: $2n = 40$
Dividing by 2: $n = 20$
                                      $n + 5 = 25.$

Hence, Richard received 20 votes and Don 25 votes.

Check: (a) $20 + 25 = 45$ (number of votes cast)
             (b) $25 - 20 = 5$ (Don received 5 more votes than Richard.)

3. Emily, Norma, and Lorene's ages are one year apart.   Emily is the youngest, Norma is a year older, and Lorene is a year older than Norma. How old is each girl if their ages total 33 years?

Solution

Let: n = Emily's age
Then: $n + 1$ = Norma's age
And: $n + 1 + 1$ = Lorene's age
Total ages: $n + n + 1 + n + 1 + 1 = 33$
Adding the n's and the 1's: $3n + 3 = 33$
Subtracting 3: $3n = 30$
Dividing by 3: $n = 10$
                                          $n + 1 = 11$
                                      $n + 1 + 1 = 12.$

Hence, Emily is 10 years old, Norma is 11, and Lorene is 12.

Check: (a) $10 + 11 + 12 = 33$ (total ages of the girls)
     (b) $10 + 1 = 11$ (Norma is one year older than Emily.)
     (c) $11 + 1 = 12$ (Lorene is one year older than Norma.)

EXERCISES

*1. Kenneth gave twice as much money to the Red Cross as did Clarence. The sum of their gifts was 63¢. How much did each give?

*2. Charles worked three times as many days during the summer as Paul. If they worked a total of 92 days, how many days did each work?

*3. Louise picked 8 more boxes of strawberries than Norene. They picked a total of 52 boxes. How many boxes did each pick?

*4. May's age is three times Jane's age. The sum of their ages is 24 years. Find the age of each girl.

*5. A certain recipe calls for 4 times as much flour as sugar. If 10 cups of the mixture are to be made, how many cups of each should be used?

*6. A mixture calls for crushed stone, sand, and cement in the ratio of 4, 3, and 1, respectively. If a total of 24 barrels of this mixture is to be used, how many barrels of each are needed?

*7. Nell sold two books at a total profit of 60¢. The profit on one book was 30¢ more than that on the other. What was the profit on each?

*8. One-third of a number equals 3. What is the number?

*9. In one month Fred earned three times as much as Bill. Together they earned $2.80. How much did each earn?

*10. Mary bought a bathing suit and a bathing cap for $3.84. The suit cost fifteen times as much as the cap. What did each cost?

*11. A hat and cap cost $8.50. The hat cost $6 more than the cap. What did each cost?

*12. Two castings weigh 46 lb. One casting weighs 1 lb. more than twice the other casting. What does each weigh?

*13. A large airplane weighs 17,600 lb. If the plane weighs four times the weight of the engine, what does each weigh?

*14. An arithmetic book and a history book together cost $3.50. The history costs $1 more than the arithmetic. Find the cost of each.

*15. The sum of the ages of Nancy, Kathleen, and Natalie is 27 years. Nancy is the youngest, Kathleen is one year older than Nancy, and Natalie is one year older than Kathleen. How old is each girl?

*16. George had 75¢ to spend. He spent four times as much of it for a game as for candy. How much did he spend for each?

**17. Bertha has 39 in. of lace. She wishes to cut it so that one piece will be 5 in. longer than the other piece. How long will she cut each piece?

**18. Mr. Adams wishes to divide a 300-ft. piece of land so that one piece will be 20 ft. shorter than the other. How shall he divide it?

**19. Allen wishes to divide a 17-in. line into three parts so that the second part will be 3 in. longer than the first part and the third part will be 5 in. longer than the first part. How long will he make each part?

**20. Grace drew a triangle so that $\angle B$ was 10° more than $\angle A$, and $\angle C$ was 20° more than $\angle A$. How many degrees did she make each angle of the triangle?

**21. Bob drew a triangle so that $\angle B$ was three times as large as $\angle A$, and $\angle C$ was twice as large as $\angle B$. How many degrees were there in each angle?

**22. Mr. Carlson sold his farm for $4,500. He gained one-fifth of its cost. Find the cost.

**23. Ben sold his bicycle for $18. He lost one-third of its cost. What was the cost?

**24. There are 2 more than twice as many girls as boys in a class of 41 pupils. How many girls and how many boys are in the class?

**25. The length of a rectangular field is three times its width. Its perimeter is 480 rods. What are the dimensions of the field?

**26. Mr. Coe told his church friends that for every dollar they contributed toward church repairs he would give two dollars. The total fund amounted to $2,100. How much of this amount was contributed by Mr. Coe?

190. Finding the value of a symbol in the right member of an equation. If the symbol of unknown value is on the right-hand side of the equality sign, solve as follows:

(a) Substitute for the known values as usual.

(b) Exchange the left member of the equation for the right

member. (This exchange can be made, for, if $3 + 5 = 6 + 2$, it is also true that $6 + 2 = 3 + 5$. And if $A = lw$, it is just as correct to write $lw = A$.)

——————— EXAMPLES ———————

1. The area of a rectangular lot is 120 sq. rd. Its length is 24 rd. Find its width.

Solution

Formula:	$A = lw$
Substituting:	$120 = 24w$
Exchanging sides:	$24w = 120$
Dividing by 24:	$w = 5$

Hence, the width of the rectangular lot is 5 rd.

2. A circular lot contains 15,400 sq. ft. Find its radius.

Solution

Formula:	$A = \pi r^2$
Substituting:	$15,400 = \frac{22}{7}r^2$
Exchanging sides:	$\frac{22}{7}r^2 = 15,400$
Dividing by $\frac{22}{7}$:	$r^2 = 4,900$
Finding square root:	$r = 70$

Hence, the radius of the circular lot is 70 ft.

3. The perimeter of a triangle is 16 in. Sides a and b are 4 and 5 in., respectively. What is the length of the third side?

Solution

Formula:	$P = a + b + c$
Substituting:	$16 = 4 + 5 + c$
Adding:	$16 = 9 + c$
Exchanging sides:	$9 + c = 16$
Subtracting 9:	$c = 7$

Hence, the length of the third side of the triangle is 7 in.

——————— EXERCISES ———————

1. A rectangular lot contains 4,800 sq. ft. It has a length of 60 ft. What is its width?

2. The area of a square playground is 6,400 sq. ft. Find the length of one side.

*3. The perimeter of a rectangle is 56 in. The length is 20 in. Find the width.

*4. What principal at 6% will yield $180 interest in 2 yr.? $(i = prt)$

*5. In what time will $500 yield $40 interest at 4%?

*6. At what rate will $1,200 yield $90 interest in $1\frac{1}{2}$ yr.?

*7. The class average in a test is 82. If 35 pupils took the test, find the sum of their grades. $\left(a = \dfrac{s}{n} \right)$

*8. Find the value of the symbol in each of the following:

(a) $27 = 18k$

(b) $168 = 4x + 32$

(c) $45 = 9 + 2a + 17$

(d) $48 = \dfrac{w}{9}$

(e) $175 = 25 + 10b$

(f) $9 + 4 = \frac{1}{3}x - 3$

(g) $1 = 6a$

(h) $16 = 3s - 2$

(i) $6 = 9h - 39$

(j) $0 = 3w - 39$

(k) $32 = 18p + 14$

(l) $3 = \dfrac{n}{9}$

(m) $27 + 19 = 12 + 2c$

(n) $\frac{1}{4}a + 1 = 5$

—————————— *REVIEW OF CHAPTER XVII* ——————————

Solve and check the results:

1. $7y = 63$

2. $4b = 18$

3. $k + 7 = 19$

4. $y + 15 = 24$

5. $n - 8 = 6$

6. $a - 18 = 21$

7. $\frac{1}{2}r = 6$

8. $\frac{1}{3}y = 5$

9. $6a = 2,100$

10. $2m = 1$

11. $9 + w = 15$

12. $a + 161 = 235$

13. $x - 119 = 221$

14. $w - 84 = 76$

15. $\frac{1}{5}k = 20$

16. $\frac{1}{8}w = 6$

17. $6b = 8$

18. $.2c = 8$

19. $12 + a = 12$

20. $r - 28 = 76$

21. $\frac{1}{2}k = 2\frac{1}{2}$

22. $w + 1\frac{3}{4} = 4\frac{1}{4}$

23. $n + 3.6 = 4.5$

24. $k - 2.4 = 8.9$

25. $2.3x = 9.2$

26. $2n + 6 = 18$

27. $3w - 4 = 8$

28. $\dfrac{a}{2} + 3 = 7$

29. $2.1y - 1.1y = 24$

30. $.2y + .3y = 5.5$

*31. Sixty is 4 times a certain number. Find the number.

*32. What number added to 146 equals 351?

*33. If you subtract 9 from Mae's grade, you will have 78. What is Mae's grade?

*34. A club had 39 present at a meeting. This number represented one-fifth of the members. How many members belonged to the club?

*35. Four times Jane's money plus $6 equals $34. How much money had Jane?

*36. Jerry's age is $\frac{2}{5}$ of his father's age. Jerry is 15 years old. How old is Jerry's father?

**37. Five times Henry's money decreased by $12 equals Joe's money, which is $68. How much money has each boy?

**38. One week John earned twice as much money as Carl. Together they earned $63. How much did each earn?

**39. Charles and Tom weigh 181 pounds together. Charles weighs 37 pounds more than twice Tom's weight. What is the weight of each?

**40. Jack and Bill have $8.10 together. Bill has $2 more than Jack. How much money has each?

———————— PLAYOFF FOR CHAPTER XVII ————————

1. The following game may be played by a class divided into small, equal-sized groups, as by rows. Each row selects a leader, who stands in front of his row. Pin on the back of each leader a formula—all formulas of equal difficulty.

The pupils of each group are told the answer to their formula. They must discover the formula that gives this answer. For instance, if the formula should be $x + 8 = 10$, the group would be given the answer $x = 2$. A score of 10 is given for the first group to discover its formula, 8 to the second group, and 5 to the third group.

One question that may be answered by "yes" or "no" may be allowed each contestant, as, "Is the operation division?" or "Is one of the numbers more than 6?"

It is well to limit the number of operations to one and the size of numbers from 1 to 10, inclusive.

Several formulas may be included in the game, a different leader being used each time.

It is well for pupils to hand in sets of formulas to the committee in charge a few days ahead of the time to play the game.

2. See if you can do this mentally, after reading it just once: A farmer bought a cow for $60 and sold it for $70. He then bought it back for $80 and resold it for $90. How much did he make or lose on the total transaction?

CHAPTER XVIII

SIGNED NUMBERS

VOCABULARY

1. signed numbers
2. positive number

3. negative number
4. absolute value

191. The meaning of signed numbers. Alaska has a wide range of temperatures. The excessive cold in winter has made highway construction extremely difficult. Also, the difficulty of preventing automobile engines from freezing at 60° below zero has made the dogsled and airplane popular. The highest summer temperature is 90° *above zero*. From 90° above zero to 60° below zero is a difference of 150° in temperature.

The statement of such a fact as this is frequently made more brief by the use of what are known as *signed numbers*. It has been agreed to indicate all thermometer readings above zero as *plus numbers* (numbers with a plus sign prefixed); for instance, +6° (read "plus 6°") means 6° above zero. And it has been agreed to denote all temperatures below zero as *minus numbers;* thus, −6° (read "minus 6°") means 6° below zero. The plus and minus signs as used in denoting temperatures show a difference in direction, the plus numbers extending above zero degrees and the minus numbers below zero degrees.

Numbers that are preceded by the plus or minus sign are called *signed numbers*. Those that are preceded by the plus sign, like +8, are called *positive numbers;* those preceded by the minus sign, like −8, are called *negative numbers*.

The plus sign is usually omitted before a positive number, but the minus sign is never omitted before a negative number. That is, "positive 5" may be written "5" or "+5"; but "negative 5" is always written "−5." Arithmetic deals only with positive numbers and does not prefix the plus sign. Algebra deals with both positive and negative numbers.

The plus (+) and minus (−) signs placed in front of numbers as in the preceding illustrations must not be confused with the + and − signs of addition and subtraction. Their use is entirely different.

The 0 meridian (the prime meridian at Greenwich, near London, England) is the guide line from which longitude is measured. The location of a place 40° east of the 0 meridian might be designated as being in +40° longitude; and a place west of the zero meridian as being in −40° longitude. These locations are said to be opposite in direction. One is east and the other west from the zero line until the 180th meridian is reached on the opposite side of the globe.

While the above locations are in opposite directions from the zero line, they are equally distant from this line in that each is 40° from it. These distances of +40° and −40° measure the same; that is, the *absolute values* of the plus 40° and the minus 40° are the same, namely, 40°. The *absolute value* of a signed number is the value of the number without regard to its sign.

192. Using signed numbers to indicate opposites. Bob has saved $5. Gene not only has saved no money, but has gone in debt $5. Bob's money may be represented by +$5, as he has $5 more than zero (no) dollars. Gene's money may be represented by −$5, as he has $5 less than zero (no) dollars. The plus and minus signs indicate that the numbers are *opposite* in meaning. In each case, the absolute value of the number is $5.

──────────────── *EXERCISES* ────────────────

1. Represent the following numbers as positive or negative and give the absolute value of each:

(a) Example: A $3 gain and a $3 loss.

Positive	*Negative*	*Absolute Value*
+$3 (gain)	−$3 (loss)	$3

(b) Locations of 20° N. latitude and 20° S. latitude.
(c) Temperatures of 15° above zero and 15° below zero.
(d) $25 deposited in a bank and $25 withdrawn.
(e) 6 games won and 6 games lost.
(f) 14 mi. east and 14 mi. west.
(g) 500 ft. above sea level and 500 ft. below sea level.
(h) $100 spent and $100 earned.

2. State the opposite of each of the following numbers and write each one as a signed number:

(a) Example: $10 profit.

Positive	Negative
+$10 (profit)	−$10 (loss)

(b) 4 ft. east. (e) 1000 A. D.
(c) $12 spent. (f) 30° below zero.
(d) 3 ft. up. (g) 40 points won.

3. Represent the following as signed numbers:

(a) 300 ft. above sea level and 50 ft. below sea level.
(b) 5 steps above a landing and 3 steps below a landing.
(c) 3 floors above the main floor and 1 floor below the main floor.
(d) 10 steps forward and 7 steps backward.
(e) 1492 A. D. and 30 B. C.

4. What do these signed numbers mean?

(a) A longitude of +90°.
(b) A longitude of −30°.
(c) The year −76.
(d) Points made in a game are +140.
(e) A temperature of −8°.
(f) Result of a sale is −$25.
(g) Location of an elevator is +8.

5. What does 0° mean in connection with longitude? Latitude? Temperature?

6. What does elevation 0 mean with reference to sea level?

7. What does the score 0 mean in a game?

8. Give additional examples of signed numbers derived from familiar experiences.

193. Using signed numbers to indicate changes. Signed numbers are often used to indicate various types of changes. For instance, advances and declines in stock prices from day to day are frequently designated by positive and negative numbers. If the price of the stock of a certain company was quoted as closing at 82 yesterday and 84 today, the change in closing prices would be +2, as the closing price today is $2 per share more than the closing price yesterday. On the other hand, if the price closed at 80 today, the change would be −2, as the price would then have closed today at $2 per share less than yesterday.

The average daily attendance of a certain class is $34\frac{1}{2}$. On a day when the attendance is 35, the change is indicated by $+\frac{1}{2}$, as there is present $\frac{1}{2}$ pupil more than the average attendance. An atterídance of 34 pupils shows a change of $-\frac{1}{2}$, as this is $\frac{1}{2}$ pupil less than the average attendance.

────────────── EXERCISES ──────────────

1. In the following stock quotations, the net change from the close of one day to the close of the next day is indicated by means of + and − signs:

TABLE 1

Name of Stock	Range of Stocks in New York	
	Closing Price	Net Change
Otis Elev..................	$45\frac{1}{2}$	$+1\frac{3}{4}$
Am. Airlines..............	25	$-\frac{1}{4}$
Du Pont..................	$220\frac{1}{2}$	$-\frac{1}{8}$
Braniff Airw..............	$13\frac{1}{2}$	$+\frac{1}{2}$
Allied Mills..............	$34\frac{5}{8}$	$-\frac{1}{4}$

How does the closing price of each of the above shares of stock compare with its closing price the previous day? Find the closing price on the previous day for each.

2. The average temperatures for a certain city during the first six months of the year are 20°, 28°, 34°, 45°, 50°, and 62°, respectively. During a recent year, the averages for these six months varied from the usual averages as follows: +3°, −7°, −2°, +1°, $-1\frac{1}{2}$°, +2°. Determine the average temperature for each of these months for this particular year.

3. Every home room of a certain school was asked to sell a definite number of tickets for a school benefit. Interpret the results obtained with reference to the quota in the home rooms whose final reports read as follows: +50 tickets, −80 tickets, −62 tickets, and +100 tickets.

4. The average test score made by a certain class was 82. Tom's was 88, Clara's 80, and Roy's 72. Express the variation in these scores from the class average using signed numbers.

5. By means of signed numbers, compare the following enrollment of a school from 1957 to 1963 with the enrollment for 1960:

TABLE 2

Year	1957	1958	1959	1960	1961	1962	1963
Enrollment	795	789	804	796	747	792	823

194. Using the number line with signed numbers. A straight line can be marked in equal units starting at any point. It can then be used to measure distances or simply to represent numbers that are equally spaced. After marking one point as zero, positive numbers can be represented in equally spaced units on one side of the zero, and negative numbers in the same way on the other side of the zero. Since a line extends indefinitely in either direction, we can think of the numbers extending as far as we like on either side of the zero. A line marked in this way is called a *number line* (see figure 1). A thermometer is an example of a number line on which each distance of one unit represents one degree in temperature.

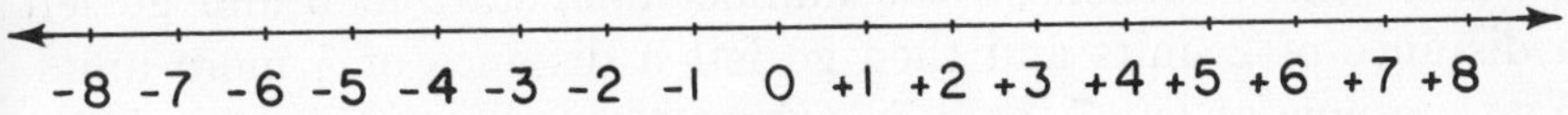

$$-8 \quad -7 \quad -6 \quad -5 \quad -4 \quad -3 \quad -2 \quad -1 \quad 0 \quad +1 \quad +2 \quad +3 \quad +4 \quad +5 \quad +6 \quad +7 \quad +8$$

Fig. 1

A number line marked as in figure 1 can help to show operations with signed numbers. Any number that you think of can be placed somewhere on this line, or an extension of it. When you are thinking of two numbers, the one that is located to the right of the other on the number line is the larger. Thus $+7$ is larger than $+3$; $+2$ is larger than -3; and -5 is larger than -9.

To add numbers by the use of the number line you start at zero and count each number in succession in the direction of its sign, to the right for $+$ and to the left for $-$. To add a $+5$ you move to the right a distance of 5 units. To add a -3 you move to the left a distance of 3 units. Adding means going in the direction the sign says, $+$ meaning to the right, and $-$ meaning to the left.

195. Adding positive and negative numbers with like signs. Ralph earned $4 and $7. How much did he earn altogether? If we add as in arithmetic, $11 is immediately seen to be the total amount earned. To add as signed numbers, think of the amount earned as $+\$4$ and $+\$7$. The sum is $+\$11$. The 11 represents the sum of the absolute values, and the plus sign indicates that it is money earned. This sum may be written in two ways:

$$\text{(a)} \ (+\$4) + (+\$7) = +\$11 \quad \text{or} \quad \text{(b)} \quad \begin{array}{r} +\$4 \\ +\$7 \\ \hline +\$11 \end{array}$$

To show this addition on the number line, start at 0 and go right 4 and then right 7 more. You are now at right 11, or $+11$. Another way to obtain this result is to add the absolute values of the numbers and prefix the plus sign to the sum.

Kate spent $2 for a game and $5 for a book. How much did she spend altogether? By arithmetic, the sum spent is seen to be $7. To add as signed numbers, think of the amounts spent as −$2 and −$5. The sum or total amount spent is −$7. The 7 represents the sum of the absolute values and the minus sign indicates that it is money spent, the opposite of money earned. This sum may be written in two ways:

$$(a)\ (-\$2) + (-\$5) = -\$7 \quad or \quad (b)\ \begin{array}{r} -\$2 \\ -\$5 \\ \hline -\$7 \end{array}$$

To show this addition on the number line, start at 0 and go left a distance of 2 units and then go left a distance of 5 more units. You are now at left 7, or −7. From these illustrations we derive the following rule:

To find the sum of numbers with like signs, add their absolute values and to the sum prefix the common sign.

――――――――――――― EXERCISES ―――――――――――――

A. Oral

State the sum of each of the following:

1. $\begin{array}{r} +3 \\ +7 \\ \hline \end{array}$	**6.** $\begin{array}{r} -10 \\ -\ 8 \\ \hline \end{array}$	**11.** $\begin{array}{r} -17 \\ -\ 4 \\ \hline \end{array}$	**16.** $\begin{array}{r} +8 \\ +7 \\ +6 \\ +2 \\ \hline \end{array}$
2. $\begin{array}{r} +4 \\ +5 \\ \hline \end{array}$	**7.** $\begin{array}{r} +9 \\ +5 \\ \hline \end{array}$	**12.** $\begin{array}{r} -40 \\ -40 \\ \hline \end{array}$	**17.** $\begin{array}{r} -4 \\ -6 \\ -8 \\ -3 \\ \hline \end{array}$
3. $\begin{array}{r} +8 \\ +8 \\ \hline \end{array}$	**8.** $\begin{array}{r} -5 \\ -8 \\ \hline \end{array}$	**13.** $\begin{array}{r} -18 \\ -10 \\ \hline \end{array}$	
4. $\begin{array}{r} -7 \\ -2 \\ \hline \end{array}$	**9.** $\begin{array}{r} -7 \\ -1 \\ \hline \end{array}$	**14.** $\begin{array}{r} -8\frac{1}{2} \\ -7\frac{1}{2} \\ \hline \end{array}$	**18.** $\begin{array}{r} -4 \\ -5 \\ -8 \\ -3 \\ \hline \end{array}$
5. $\begin{array}{r} -6 \\ -7 \\ \hline \end{array}$	**10.** $\begin{array}{r} +9 \\ +6 \\ \hline \end{array}$	**15.** $\begin{array}{r} +14\frac{1}{2} \\ +17\frac{1}{4} \\ \hline \end{array}$	

19. $(+6) + (+2)$ **22.** $(-3) + (-4)$ **25.** $(+7) + (+9)$

20. $(+5) + (+5)$ **23.** $(-8) + (-3)$ **26.** $(-4) + (-8)$

21. $(+7) + (+2)$ **24.** $(-6) + (-5)$ **27.** $(-6) + (-6)$

B. Written

28. Paul walked 12 blocks east, was overtaken by a friend in a car, and rode 16 blocks farther east with the friend. How many blocks east did Paul travel? Express the distance as the sum of two signed numbers.

29. Andy lost 25 points and 16 points in a game. What was his total loss? Express his loss in terms of signed numbers.

30. Mr. Andrews withdrew the following amounts from his bank account in one month: $50, $75, and $60. Total his withdrawals in terms of signed numbers.

Copy each of the following and add:

31. $+789$
$+156$

36. $-475\frac{3}{4}$
$-196\frac{1}{2}$

41. $+42.17$
$+16.13$

46. $-561\frac{2}{3}$
$-897\frac{3}{4}$

32. -192
-463

37. $+672\frac{1}{3}$
$+599\frac{1}{2}$

42. -48.9
-72.6

47. $+93.77$
$+49.75$

33. -198
-464

38. $+788\frac{3}{5}$
$+687\frac{3}{10}$

43. -7.48
$-.39$

48. $-4863\frac{1}{2}$
$-879\frac{3}{5}$

34. $+186$
$+782$
$+925$

39. $-148\frac{3}{8}$
$-106\frac{3}{4}$
$-58\frac{1}{2}$

44. $+1.67$
$+28.03$
$+.58$

49. $+38.19$
$+9.73$
$+26.45$

35. -784
-980
-507

40. $-700\frac{5}{6}$
$-148\frac{2}{3}$
$-905\frac{3}{4}$

45. -33.4
-72.45
-8.23

50. -4593
-609
-2846

Express every number in the following exercises as a signed number:

51. Fred's deposits for January in the school bank were $2.10, $1.85, $.78, and $.48. Find his total deposit for January.

52. Dorothy's lunch for four consecutive weeks cost her as follows: $1.20, $.90, $1.28, and $.97. What did Dorothy's lunches total for the four weeks?

53. Mr. Kirk bought two lots which he later sold, one at a loss of $176 and the other at a loss of $218. Find his total loss.

196. Adding positive and negative numbers with unlike signs. George made 12 points in a game and then lost 4 points. What was his final score? It is easily seen that George's final score was 8 points.

Writing the above facts using the plus and minus signs, we have: $+12$ points made and -4 points lost. The final score is $+8$ points, since George made 8 points more than he lost. This sum may be written in two ways:

$$\text{(a)} \quad (+12) + (-4) = +8 \quad \text{or} \quad \text{(b)} \quad \begin{array}{r} +12 \\ -4 \\ \hline +8 \end{array}$$

To show this addition on the number line, start at 0 and go right 12, and from there go left 4. You are now at right 8 or $+8$. You can also find this result by subtracting the absolute values of the numbers and prefixing the plus sign (the sign of the number having the greater absolute value).

Milton made 10 points in a game and then lost 21 points. Determine his final score. We readily see that his final score was -11 points, since he lost 11 points more than he made. This sum may be written in two ways:

$$\text{(a)} \quad (+10) + (-21) = -11 \quad \text{or} \quad \text{(b)} \quad \begin{array}{r} +10 \\ -21 \\ \hline -11 \end{array}$$

To show this addition on the number line, start at 0, go right 10, and from there go left 21. You are now at left 11, or -11. You can also obtain this result by subtracting the absolute values of the numbers and prefixing to the difference the minus sign (the sign of the number having the greater absolute value).

From these illustrations we derive the following rule:

To find the sum of numbers with unlike signs, subtract their absolute values and to the difference prefix the sign of the number having the greater absolute value.

──────────────── **EXERCISES** ────────────────

A. Oral

Using the preceding rule, state the sum of each of the following:

1. $+8$	2. $+9$	3. $+16$	4. -8	5. -7
-3	-2	$-\ 7$	$+2$	$+1$

6. $+5$	7. $+2$	8. $+4$	9. -2	10. -9
-8	-6	-4	$+8$	$+8$

11. $+3$	12. $+6$	13. $+8$	14. $+2$	15. -3
-3	-9	-7	-2	$+1$

16. -3	17. $+1$	18. $+10$	19. -12	20. -7
$+9$	-8	-8	$+7$	$+2$

21. $+56$	22. -120	23. -68	24. 36	25. 83
-32	120	-6	-26	79

26. $(+7) + (-5)$ 28. $(-6) + (+5)$ 30. $(-1) + (+1)$

27. $(+3) + (-8)$ 29. $(-4) + (+8)$ 31. $(+2) + (-9)$

32. Mr. Winn owed $5,000 and had $2,600. State his financial standing in terms of signed numbers.

33. Herbert made 18 tie racks and sold 15 of them. How many does he still own?

34. If at 6 A. M. the temperature reads 18° above zero and by 9 A. M. it has fallen 12°, what does it then register?

35. May had 170 points in a game and then lost 200 points. What was her final score?

B. Written

Copy each of the following and add:

36. $+316$	40. $+781$	44. -767	48. -7810
-477	-106	$+592$	$+3927$

37. -941	41. -401	45. -380	49. 1581
$+182$	589	$+964$	-2967

38. -158	42. $+108$	46. -868	50. -67.81
$+279$	-670	$+868$	49.33

39. 89	43. $+268$	47. $+587$	51. 170.8
-166	-942	-499	-263.5

197. Adding several positive and negative numbers. In a series of games, Clara scored as follows: won 30 points, won 25 points, lost 20 points, won 15 points, and lost 18 points. Determine Clara's final score. First add the points won (the positive numbers); next add the points lost (the negative numbers); then add the two sums.

$$
\begin{array}{ccc}
+30 & -20 & +70 \\
+25 & -18 & -38 \\
\underline{+15} & \underline{-38} & \underline{+32} \\
+70 & &
\end{array}
$$

Hence, Clara's final score is $+32$.

From the above illustration we derive the following rule:

To find the sum of several numbers with unlike signs, add the positive and negative numbers separately and then add the two sums.

―――――――――――― EXERCISES ――――――――――――

Collect the signed numbers in each of the following exercises:

*1.	+ 8	*2.	−7	*3.	−4	*4.	+6	*5.	−18
	−10		−6		−5		−8		+27
	+ 7		+2		+3		+4		−34
			+5				−3		+36

*6.	−18	*7.	−74	*8.	+148	*9.	+312	*10.	−873
	+12		+26		+263		−748		+625
	−23		−13		−152		− 69		−466
			+35				+457		+585

Use signed numbers in solving the following exercises:

*11. An airplane reached an altitude of 4,892 ft., descended 1,280 ft., ascended 460 ft., and then descended 812 ft. What was the final elevation?

*12. Two partners in a game won 150, then won 120, then lost 100, then lost 80. What was their total score?

*13. Mr. White's cash record showed the following balances for six consecutive months: −$150, −$60, +$75, −$80, −$100, and +$50. Find his gain or loss for the 6 mo.

*14. A football team was backed up to its goal line. They then made the following gains and losses: 5 yd. gain; 25 yd. gain; 4 yd. loss; 2 yd. loss; 10 yd. gain; 7 yd. gain. What yard line were they on at the end of these plays?

198. Subtraction of signed numbers. Subtraction can be thought of as finding the number which, when added to the subtrahend, gives the minuend. When you subtract 18 from 27, you are finding the number which, when added to 18, gives 27. The number is 9. This method of subtraction can help you visualize subtraction of signed numbers on the number line. Start at the number that is the subtrahend, (+18), and count the number of units from there to the minuend (+27). This distance, with its direction, + for right and − for left, gives the difference (+9).

─────────────── EXAMPLES ───────────────

1. Subtract: +11
　　　　　　 + 5
　　　　　　 ─────
　　　　　　 + 6

Starting on the number line at +5, count the number of units to +11. This is a distance of 6 units to the right. Therefore the difference is +6.

2. Subtract: +11
　　　　　　 −5
　　　　　　 ─────
　　　　　　 +16

Starting on the number line at −5 count the number of units to +11. This is a distance of 16 units to the right. Therefore the difference is +16.

3. Subtract: −11
　　　　　　 −5
　　　　　　 ─────
　　　　　　 −6

Starting on the number line at −5 count the number of units to −11. This is a distance of 6 units to the left. Therefore the difference is −6.

4. Subtract: −11
　　　　　　 +5
　　　　　　 ─────
　　　　　　 −16

Starting on the number line at +5, count the number of units to −11. This is a distance of 16 units to the left. Therefore the difference is −16.

Subtraction of signed numbers can also be done by making use of the rules of addition as follows:

To subtract signed numbers, change the sign of the subtrahend (mentally), and then add.

─────────────── EXERCISES ───────────────

A. Oral

Subtract:

1. +16	**3.** +43	**5.** −47	**7.** −81	**9.** −154	**11.** −77
−32	+31	−34	−27	− 42	−48
2. +37	**4.** 65	**6.** −36	**8.** +72	**10.** −98	**12.** +68
−18	36	45	−93	72	−91

B. Written

Solve the following:

13. $\begin{array}{r} -869 \\ -368 \\ \hline \end{array}$	**16.** $\begin{array}{r} +6.86 \\ -4.07 \\ \hline \end{array}$	**19.** $\begin{array}{r} -4.64 \\ -2.9 \\ \hline \end{array}$	**22.** $\begin{array}{r} -5386 \\ -6497 \\ \hline \end{array}$
14. $\begin{array}{r} 957 \\ 659 \\ \hline \end{array}$	**17.** $\begin{array}{r} -4037 \\ -7835 \\ \hline \end{array}$	**20.** $\begin{array}{r} 75.8 \\ -68.3 \\ \hline \end{array}$	**23.** $\begin{array}{r} -9053 \\ 6403 \\ \hline \end{array}$
15. $\begin{array}{r} -749 \\ +694 \\ \hline \end{array}$	**18.** $\begin{array}{r} 67.4 \\ 16.5 \\ \hline \end{array}$	**21.** $\begin{array}{r} -5495 \\ +4709 \\ \hline \end{array}$	**24.** $\begin{array}{r} 5219 \\ 4737 \\ \hline \end{array}$

*25. In a certain game, James had a score of -240 at the end of the first half of the game. At the close of the game, his score was $+380$. How much better off was he at the close of the game than at the end of the first half?

*26. A certain stock on the market opened at $+87$ and closed at $+78$. How much was the change?

*27. On a certain day when the temperature of a northern city was $-25°$, the temperature in a southern city was $+76°$. What was the difference in temperature of the two cities?

*28. On a certain morning the thermometer registered $-17°$. An hour later it registered $23°$. Find the difference in the two readings.

199. Graphing positive and negative numbers. The graph below shows Eloise's financial record at the close of each day

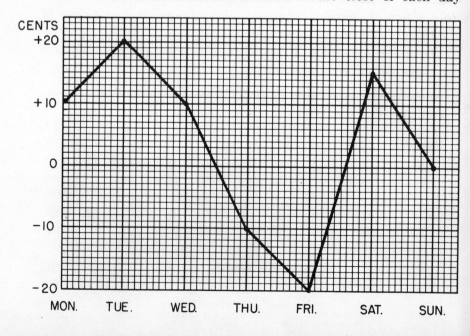

for one week. Points on the zero line represent no money on hand and no debts to be paid. Points above zero are positive and represent the amount of money on hand; points below zero are negative and denote the amount of money owed to others.

At the close of which day did Eloise have most money, and how much did she have? When was she most in debt, and how much? On which two days did she have the same amount of money? How much? What was her financial condition Thursday? Saturday? Sunday? Which day shows the greatest decrease from the preceding day?

──────────────── EXERCISES ────────────────

*1. Using squared paper, make a graph from the following facts representing Harold's financial standing:

Jan........ $10 on hand	May....... $5 in debt	Sept........ $5 on hand
Feb........ $15 on hand	June....... $15 on hand	Oct......... $5 in debt
Mar........ $5 on hand	July........ $20 on hand	Nov......... $15 in debt
April....... $10 in debt	Aug........ $25 on hand	Dec......... $5 on hand

*2. Make a graph of the following temperatures for one winter day:

6 A. M. $-10°$	9 A. M. $-6°$	Noon $+2°$	3 P. M. $+1°$
7 A. M. $-9°$	10 A. M. $-2°$	1 P. M. $+3°$	4 P. M. $-2°$
8 A. M. $-8°$	11 A. M. $0°$	2 P. M. $+5°$	5 P. M. $-4°$

*3. 80 is the normal score for a certain kind of test. Graph Frank's monthly scores as positive and negative.

September........... 70	December........... 80	March.............. 84
October............. 72	January............. 82	April............... 85
November........... 78	February........... 79	May................ 85

──────────── REVIEW OF CHAPTER XVIII ────────────

1. What is a practical use of signed numbers?

2. Indicate whether these numbers are positive or negative: (a) a space ship 30 miles above sea level; (b) a submarine 1 mile below sea level; (c) $10 spent; (d) $3 saved; (e) the year 20 B.C.; (f) the year 1492 A.D.; (g) a 25-cent increase in price of a share of stock; (h) class enrollment is 6 less than last year.

3. Add:

(a)	(b)	(c)	(d)
$+649$	-847	-6.84	$+47\frac{2}{3}$
$+176$	-980	$-.29$	$+68\frac{5}{6}$
$+238$	-306	-1.76	$+36\frac{1}{2}$

4. Add:

(a) $+872$
-488

(b) -676
$+489$

(c) -104
$+575$

(d) $+1421$
-3520

5. Add:

(a) $+213$
-628
-516
$+349$

(b) -397
-584
$+621$
-115

(c) -150
$+346$
$+524$
-82

(d) $+456$
$+398$
$+172$
-586

6. Subtract:

(a) $+124$
-356

(b) 167
489

(c) -745
-473

(d) -521.6
$+477.2$

(c) $4,216$
$7,834$

(f) -80.35
64.92

(g) $+45\frac{3}{8}$
$-77\frac{3}{4}$

(h) -723
-948

*7. Within a few hours, the temperature changed from $-4°$ to $18°$. What temperature difference was experienced in those hours?

*8. During a game, Fred scored a low of -810 and later his score rose to 165. Find the increase from Fred's low score to his high score.

*9. In May Ben deposited these amounts in his bank account: $28, $65, and $73. Total his deposits in terms of signed numbers.

*10. Clara has $800 in the bank. She owes $680. What is her financial standing in terms of signed numbers?

*11. A stock was quoted at $86 on opening. By closing time, it had dropped 1\frac{1}{4}$. What was the stock then worth?

*12. Partners in a game lost 75, won 120, lost 26, lost 60. What was their total score?

*13. In a business venture, Mr. All gained $1,500 the first month, but lost $950 the second month, then gained $860 the third month. Find Mr. All's gain or loss for the three months.

**14. Using sea level as zero, make a graph showing the outline of the land near the shore at points A, B, C, and so on, which are equidistant and have elevations as follows:

TABLE 4

Point............	A	B	C	D	E	F	G	H
Elevation.........	100'	80'	20'	Sea Level	−20'	−10'	−20'	−60'

**15. (optional) Bring to class and explain any graphs found in books or magazines that illustrate a practical use of signed numbers.

——————— PLAYOFF FOR CHAPTER XVIII ———————

(1) This game may be played by a whole class which has been divided into small groups. Each group selects a leader. A different but equally difficult exercise in *signed numbers* is given each group. Each leader, with his group, decides upon the correct answer. At a designated time, the leaders go to the chalk tray in which all the correct answers plus as many incorrect answers are arranged. The first leader to locate his answer and pin it on the bulletin board scores 10 points, the second 8 points, and the third 5 points.

Select new leaders and solve more such exercises. Total the scores to decide the winning group.

A few days ahead of playing the game, it is well for each pupil to make out and hand in to the committee in charge a set of exercises to be used in the game.

(2) *A dangerous way to buy shoes. A man went into a store and purchased a pair of shoes worth $5, handing over a $50 bill to pay for them. The merchant, not being able to make the change, crossed the street and asked a friend to give him change. He then returned and gave the stranger the shoes and his change. After the purchaser of the boots had been gone a few hours, the friend, finding the bill to be a counterfeit, returned and demanded $50 in good money from the merchant. Of course, the merchant gave it to him. How much did he lose by the operation?

(3) *Put down four vertical marks. Now put down five more straight marks and make ten.

(4) *Figure it out. (a) Two-thirds of six is nine. (b) One-half of twelve is seven. (c) One-half of five is four. (d) Six is one-half of eleven.

---

* Courtesy of Burroughs Corp.

REMEDIAL PROGRAM—PRACTICE

EXERCISES

ADDITION OF INTEGERS

PRACTICE EXERCISE 1a

Study these combinations until you *know* them so well that you can give the correct sums quickly.   Add:

7	5	6	2	8	4	3	8	7	9	
5	4	7	5	4	0	7	2	2	8	**(10)**
6	7	3	9	7	5	7	6	6	7	
5	0	5	6	7	5	9	0	3	8	
5	3	8	3	7	9	7	2	6	5	
9	4	9	6	6	0	4	7	4	3	**(30)**
3	4	5	7	2	7	9	8	4	5	
3	2	7	1	6	3	2	6	4	0	
3	5	9	8	4	0	5	8	6	4	
9	8	3	5	7	8	6	3	9	3	**(50)**
6	4	9	6	5	3	4	1	2	0	
2	9	1	8	2	8	5	6	9	0	
2	8	9	6	9	4	9	4	8	9	
8	7	7	6	5	6	9	8	8	4	**(70)**

PRACTICE EXERCISE 1b

Horizontal Addition by Endings

The exercise 24 + 8 should cause you to see "32" without saying "8 + 4 = 12, put down the two and carry the one," and so forth. Study these exercises till you can give the sums quickly. Add:

16 + 8 =	17 + 6 =	19 + 8 =	16 + 9 =	12 + 3 =	
25 + 6 =	29 + 6 =	24 + 7 =	22 + 9 =	23 + 8 =	(10)
39 + 9 =	39 + 3 =	38 + 8 =	39 + 4 =	37 + 4 =	
45 + 9 =	44 + 8 =	43 + 7 =	47 + 6 =	42 + 9 =	(20)
56 + 8 =	59 + 4 =	58 + 5 =	59 + 7 =	57 + 8 =	
69 + 8 =	63 + 6 =	66 + 9 =	69 + 0 =	66 + 7 =	(30)
74 + 8 =	77 + 6 =	72 + 9 =	71 + 7 =	74 + 5 =	
89 + 4 =	86 + 5 =	82 + 6 =	87 + 7 =	88 + 3 =	(40)

PRACTICE EXERCISE 1c

Single Columns

Add and prove:

7	6	1	7	9	8	1	7	
3	5	7	6	8	9	9	8	
8	9	6	9	7	2	7	5	
4	3	4	4	2	6	2	3	
5	8	5	8	3	4	6	9	
8	7	9	3	5	5	8	7	(8)
5	7	1	7	5	8	2	4	
8	6	0	4	3	7	6	7	
2	3	9	3	2	4	6	6	
6	4	8	8	6	3	8	5	
4	8	6	6	9	2	8	7	
3	7	4	7	4	8	3	9	(16)

PRACTICE EXERCISE 1d

Carrying

Add and prove:

497	127	264	169	183	603	
672	548	357	139	209	268	
350	266	208	108	176	529	
728	546	527	219	728	177	
549	322	140	169	323	267	
288	728	226	545	157	486	(6)

230	121	326	246	179	700
582	290	318	393	258	329
727	313	507	179	549	436
638	245	292	244	413	289
459	766	387	307	537	176
175	397	294	206	641	295 (12)

306	242	808	126	645	649
459	267	790	462	728	382
379	214	646	784	543	714
428	432	729	396	826	622
624	766	384	458	903	513
283	822	297	727	728	828
109	786	458	128	142	126 (18)

Try *Inventory Test 1* again.   You should show much improvement.

——— MULTIPLICATION OF INTEGERS ———

PRACTICE EXERCISE 2a

Important Products

Study these multiplications till you know them so well that you can give the products quickly.   Multiply:

7	5	6	2	9	7	8	3
5	9	8	5	8	2	2	7 (8)

7	6	6	7	5	7	9	3
8	3	0	9	5	7	6	5

7	6	8	0	5	6	2	7
0	5	4	4	3	4	7	4 (24)

9	7	3	8	3	5	5	4
0	6	6	9	4	4	0	4

8	9	7	2	7	5	4	3
6	2	3	6	1	7	2	3 (40)

4	6	8	5	0	4	8	9
3	9	3	6	8	7	5	3

5	3	5	2	1	4	3	5
8	9	0	9	6	5	8	2 (56)

6	9	4	6	2	8	9	6
7	1	9	2	8	7	7	6

9	8	4	9	4	9	2	0	
4	8	8	9	6	5	3	9	(72)

PRACTICE EXERCISE 2b
Zero Endings

┌─ EXAMPLE A ─┐

```
   728
  2300
 218400
1456
1674400
```

Any number times zero, or zero times any number, is zero. For example, $4 \times 0 = 0$ and $0 \times 4 = 0$ and $120 \times 20 = 2,400$.

Double zeros in the multiplier should be multiplied as illustrated in Examples A and B.

┌─ EXAMPLE B ─┐

```
   624
  2003
  1872
124800
1249872
```

Multiply and then prove the following by dividing the product by the multiplier:

450	760	180	430	590	
20	30	90	80	70	

800	700	100	900	600	
60	50	10	40	90	(10)

106	308	705	509	608	
10	40	80	90	70	

870	407	560	980	706	
60	80	90	70	90	(20)

426	716	326	612	
1500	4600	1700	2400	(24)

PRACTICE EXERCISE 2c
Center Zero

Multiply and prove by interchanging the multiplier and the multiplicand:

102	206	309	105	704
305	504	902	408	309

708	308	608	209	605
105	707	109	307	605 (10)
507	709	208	404	707
208	606	802	808	908
607	908	207	508	101
706	908	704	708	101 (20)

PRACTICE EXERCISE 2d
Large Numbers

Multiply and prove:

328	428	547	719
76	77	68	83 (4)
627	516	818	137
37	59	61	80 (8)
726	293	188	356
58	86	27	46 (12)
427	185	6257	3657
1000	308	67	82 (16)
802	58	9134	7503
27	706	64	24 (20)

Try *Inventory Test 2* again.   You should show much improvement.

———— SUBTRACTION OF INTEGERS ————
PRACTICE EXERCISE 3a

Study these exercises until you can give the remainders quickly.   Subtract:

7	5	8	4	8	7	9	6	7	9
5	4	4	0	2	2	8	5	0	6 (10)
7	5	6	6	7	9	7	6	5	3
7	5	0	3	6	0	4	4	3	3 (20)

4	7	7	9	8	4	5	9	8	8	
2	1	3	2	6	4	0	3	5	3	**(30)**

4	6	9	5	3	8	9	6	9	9	
3	2	4	2	0	7	7	6	5	9	**(40)**

9	8	8	0	7	6	1	5	4	8	
1	0	8	0	6	1	0	1	1	1	**(50)**

PRACTICE EXERCISE 3b

Subtract and prove:

27	37	44	54	19	15	
7	5	2	3	1	4	

25	17	26	18	28	36	
5	1	2	0	4	0	**(12)**

47	29	18	29	15	17	
3	4	8	3	2	0	

19	29	37	18	49	32	
6	5	6	8	0	2	**(24)**

11	10	12	14	15	11	
7	6	5	6	7	4	

26	37	11	46	24	11	
8	8	9	7	7	5	**(36)**

55	62	17	23	21	11	
8	7	9	8	8	3	

10	10	20	12	22	14	
3	1	8	7	6	8	**(48)**

33	81	42	54	24	73	
7	9	6	8	8	6	**(54)**

PRACTICE EXERCISE 3c
Zero in Minuend

Subtract and prove:

306	107	290	720	103	102	
28	34	156	264	86	35	**(6)**

408	610	105	200	100	300
29	70	28	18	45	102

404	202	101	400	304	500	
107	27	88	72	108	101	**(18)**

620	310	204	510	706	104
188	47	68	34	309	83

180	120	308	503	200	300	
77	46	21	18	87	75	**(30)**

PRACTICE EXERCISE 3d
Large Numbers

Subtract and prove:

74026	16924	35496	50628	
15634	8795	18728	13978	

24104	51807	33333	72222	
13726	21426	16666	10948	**(8)**

15213	26104	31110	17961	
8764	18702	28794	3948	

56728	33101	45202	50925	
17438	28064	17606	18628	**(16)**

63956	98646	65232	44200	
51787	19584	47111	26741	

18505	23666	47142	57128	
2487	18999	21847	9072	**(24)**

If you scored well on this test, try *Inventory Test 3* again.

DIVISION OF INTEGERS

PRACTICE EXERCISE 4a

One-figure Divisors

Divide:

$9\overline{)63}$	$8\overline{)32}$	$9\overline{)36}$	$8\overline{)0}$
$8\overline{)16}$	$9\overline{)72}$	$7\overline{)56}$	$6\overline{)18}$ **(8)**
$7\overline{)28}$	$6\overline{)24}$	$9\overline{)18}$	$8\overline{)40}$
$9\overline{)27}$	$8\overline{)64}$	$7\overline{)63}$	$7\overline{)49}$ **(16)**
$8\overline{)48}$	$6\overline{)30}$	$9\overline{)0}$	$9\overline{)54}$
$9\overline{)45}$	$7\overline{)14}$	$8\overline{)56}$	$6\overline{)0}$ **(24)**
$8\overline{)72}$	$6\overline{)12}$	$7\overline{)42}$	$7\overline{)35}$
$6\overline{)36}$	$8\overline{)24}$	$5\overline{)0}$	$6\overline{)42}$ **(32)**
$5\overline{)25}$	$4\overline{)36}$	$6\overline{)48}$	$5\overline{)15}$
$4\overline{)24}$	$3\overline{)27}$	$4\overline{)28}$	$3\overline{)18}$ **(40)**

PRACTICE EXERCISE 4b

Divide and then prove by multiplying the quotient and the divisor and adding the remainder to the product:

$4\overline{)840}$	$5\overline{)705}$	$7\overline{)714}$	$8\overline{)404}$	$9\overline{)1000}$
$6\overline{)846}$	$5\overline{)600}$	$8\overline{)912}$	$6\overline{)624}$	$7\overline{)8248}$ **(10)**
$4\overline{)728}$	$6\overline{)635}$	$9\overline{)684}$	$5\overline{)206}$	$8\overline{)8080}$
$8\overline{)645}$	$6\overline{)304}$	$7\overline{)645}$	$8\overline{)724}$	$4\overline{)4090}$ **(20)**
$6\overline{)582}$	$8\overline{)928}$	$2\overline{)505}$	$9\overline{)806}$	$7\overline{)9177}$
$3\overline{)725}$	$9\overline{)906}$	$4\overline{)325}$	$9\overline{)459}$	$6\overline{)6274}$ **(30)**

$4\overline{)726}$ $8\overline{)909}$ $7\overline{)626}$ $6\overline{)542}$ $9\overline{)5648}$

$2\overline{)101}$ $4\overline{)301}$ $8\overline{)604}$ $9\overline{)248}$ $7\overline{)5386}$ (**40**)

PRACTICE EXERCISE 4c
Long Division

Copy these exercises on paper. Divide and then prove by using the quotient as the divisor:

$18\overline{)450}$ $33\overline{)891}$ $21\overline{)1596}$ $38\overline{)3116}$

$16\overline{)384}$ $32\overline{)896}$ $52\overline{)2496}$ $23\overline{)2162}$ (**8**)

$19\overline{)418}$ $17\overline{)306}$ $45\overline{)3645}$ $67\overline{)2278}$

$16\overline{)304}$ $35\overline{)525}$ $28\overline{)2016}$ $34\overline{)1768}$ (**16**)

$18\overline{)288}$ $81\overline{)972}$ $90\overline{)3240}$ $25\overline{)1250}$

$69\overline{)966}$ $17\overline{)714}$ $37\overline{)2368}$ $73\overline{)2482}$ (**24**)

PRACTICE EXERCISE 4d
Long Division

Copy these exercises on paper. Divide and then prove:

$42\overline{)15036}$ $36\overline{)72036}$ $72\overline{)84509}$

$63\overline{)45089}$ $24\overline{)37426}$ $18\overline{)17258}$ (**6**)

$51\overline{)64145}$ $35\overline{)28696}$ $90\overline{)80603}$

$38\overline{)42122}$ $16\overline{)32048}$ $27\overline{)28972}$ (**12**)

$23\overline{)16560}$ $29\overline{)11484}$ $17\overline{)44710}$

$132\overline{)16848}$ $182\overline{)72056}$ $124\overline{)36746}$ (**18**)

Try *Inventory Test 4* again. You should pass it now.

How do you score in the four processes with integers since solving the *Practice Exercises* and retaking the *Inventory Tests*?

You no doubt show a much improved skill. However, if your skill is not satisfactory, you should make it *your* job to continue your practice until you do master these processes.

ADDITION OF COMMON FRACTIONS

You can add common fractions if you first change them to a common denominator. The examples show the fractions changed to their *least common denominator*. The example at the left shows the addition of fractions arranged vertically. The example at the right shows the fractions arranged horizontally.

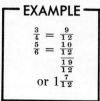

EXAMPLE

$$\frac{3}{4} = \frac{9}{12}$$
$$\frac{5}{6} = \frac{10}{12}$$
$$\frac{19}{12}$$
$$\text{or } 1\frac{7}{12}$$

EXAMPLE

$$\frac{3}{4} + \frac{5}{6} =$$
$$\frac{9}{12} + \frac{10}{12} =$$
$$\frac{19}{12} \text{ or } 1\frac{7}{12}$$

PRACTICE EXERCISE 5a

Add these fractions:

$$\frac{4}{5} + \frac{3}{10} \qquad \frac{7}{8} + \frac{3}{4} \qquad \frac{1}{3} + \frac{1}{4} \qquad \frac{1}{8} + \frac{1}{6} \quad (4)$$

$$\frac{1}{2} + \frac{1}{4} \qquad \frac{5}{6} + \frac{2}{3} \qquad \frac{2}{3} + \frac{1}{2} \qquad \frac{1}{5} + \frac{1}{3} \quad (8)$$

$\frac{1}{3}$	$\frac{3}{8}$	$\frac{1}{5}$	$\frac{2}{3}$	$\frac{2}{5}$	$\frac{1}{2}$	$\frac{3}{4}$
$\frac{3}{4}$	$\frac{1}{4}$	$\frac{3}{10}$	$\frac{3}{4}$	$\frac{1}{3}$	$\frac{2}{9}$	$\frac{1}{2}$ (15)

$\frac{5}{6}$	$\frac{7}{16}$	$\frac{9}{10}$	$\frac{6}{7}$	$\frac{7}{12}$	$\frac{15}{16}$	$\frac{4}{9}$
$\frac{7}{8}$	$\frac{3}{8}$	$\frac{4}{15}$	$\frac{5}{6}$	$\frac{5}{8}$	$\frac{7}{8}$	$\frac{7}{12}$ (22)

$$\frac{3}{4} + \frac{7}{8} + \frac{1}{2} \qquad\qquad \frac{7}{9} + \frac{2}{3} + \frac{5}{6} \qquad\qquad \frac{3}{8} + \frac{4}{5} + \frac{7}{20} \quad (25)$$

PRACTICE EXERCISE 5b

Vertical Addition

Add and express each sum in lowest terms:

$\frac{1}{4}$	$\frac{3}{8}$	$\frac{2}{5}$	$\frac{1}{3}$	$\frac{3}{8}$	$\frac{5}{6}$	$\frac{7}{10}$
$\frac{1}{6}$	$\frac{1}{2}$	$\frac{5}{8}$	$\frac{7}{8}$	$\frac{7}{12}$	$\frac{2}{3}$	$\frac{4}{5}$ (7)

$\frac{3}{16}$	$\frac{1}{2}$	$\frac{1}{4}$	$\frac{1}{4}$	$\frac{5}{12}$	$\frac{3}{8}$	$\frac{1}{3}$
$\frac{7}{8}$	$\frac{2}{3}$	$\frac{5}{6}$	$\frac{7}{8}$	$\frac{3}{4}$	$\frac{1}{6}$	$\frac{11}{12}$ (14)

$\frac{2}{5}$	$\frac{1}{8}$	$\frac{1}{4}$	$\frac{3}{4}$	$\frac{7}{10}$	$\frac{2}{3}$	$\frac{7}{12}$
$\frac{1}{2}$	$\frac{1}{4}$	$\frac{1}{3}$	$\frac{2}{3}$	$\frac{1}{4}$	$\frac{5}{6}$	$\frac{1}{2}$
$\frac{7}{10}$	$\frac{1}{2}$	$\frac{5}{12}$	$\frac{5}{7}$	$\frac{1}{2}$	$\frac{1}{4}$	$\frac{5}{6}$ (21)

$\frac{5}{8}$	$\frac{3}{5}$	$\frac{1}{12}$	$\frac{1}{4}$	$\frac{2}{3}$	$\frac{3}{4}$	$\frac{5}{9}$
$\frac{2}{3}$	$\frac{2}{3}$	$\frac{3}{5}$	$\frac{5}{7}$	$\frac{1}{4}$	$\frac{1}{3}$	$\frac{2}{3}$
$\frac{7}{8}$	$\frac{1}{5}$	$\frac{2}{3}$	$\frac{1}{2}$	$\frac{5}{6}$	$\frac{5}{8}$	$\frac{5}{6}$ (28)

PRACTICE EXERCISE 5c
Horizontal Addition

Add and express all sums in lowest terms:

$\frac{2}{3} + \frac{5}{6}$ $\frac{3}{4} + \frac{1}{2}$ $\frac{7}{8} + \frac{2}{3}$ $\frac{4}{5} + \frac{3}{8} + \frac{3}{20}$ **(4)**

$\frac{6}{7} + \frac{1}{2}$ $\frac{4}{9} + \frac{5}{6}$ $\frac{1}{2} + \frac{1}{12}$ $\frac{1}{3} + \frac{3}{4} + \frac{1}{6}$

$\frac{3}{14} + \frac{2}{7}$ $\frac{1}{12} + \frac{5}{8}$ $\frac{9}{10} + \frac{5}{6}$ $\frac{3}{4} + \frac{1}{2} + \frac{1}{4}$ **(12)**

$\frac{3}{5} + \frac{5}{6}$ $\frac{1}{9} + \frac{1}{3}$ $\frac{3}{4} + \frac{5}{8}$ $\frac{1}{5} + \frac{7}{10} + \frac{2}{15}$

$\frac{7}{12} + \frac{5}{6} + \frac{1}{2}$ $\frac{9}{12} + \frac{3}{8} + \frac{4}{4}$ $\frac{5}{12} + \frac{3}{5} + \frac{2}{3}$ **(19)**

$\frac{3}{10} + \frac{3}{4} + \frac{2}{5}$ $\frac{5}{8} + \frac{2}{5} + \frac{1}{10}$ $\frac{15}{16} + \frac{5}{8} + \frac{3}{4}$

$\frac{4}{9} + \frac{2}{3} + \frac{1}{9}$ $\frac{1}{2} + \frac{1}{8} + \frac{7}{16}$ $\frac{7}{12} + \frac{1}{6} + \frac{2}{3}$ **(25)**

PRACTICE EXERCISE 5d
Addition of Mixed Numbers

Add and write each sum in its lowest terms:

$3\frac{2}{3}$ $4\frac{3}{5}$ $7\frac{5}{9}$ $8\frac{4}{5}$ $7\frac{1}{8}$ $8\frac{3}{4}$
$7\frac{1}{2}$ $8\frac{2}{3}$ $6\frac{2}{3}$ $9\frac{1}{2}$ $9\frac{2}{3}$ $7\frac{1}{3}$ **(6)**

$9\frac{1}{2}$ $6\frac{5}{8}$ $9\frac{3}{7}$ $8\frac{5}{12}$ $7\frac{1}{3}$ $8\frac{4}{5}$
$8\frac{1}{3}$ $7\frac{3}{4}$ $9\frac{1}{2}$ $7\frac{3}{4}$ $7\frac{2}{9}$ 3 **(12)**

$3\frac{1}{4}$ $6\frac{5}{6}$ $2\frac{3}{16}$ 9 $5\frac{2}{5}$ $9\frac{7}{8}$
$2\frac{1}{3}$ $6\frac{1}{12}$ $8\frac{3}{4}$ $8\frac{4}{9}$ $7\frac{3}{5}$ $5\frac{1}{16}$ **(18)**

$5\frac{1}{8} + 2\frac{1}{3}$ $7\frac{1}{2} + 6\frac{2}{3}$ $4\frac{1}{4} + 6\frac{1}{6}$ $7\frac{1}{8} + 6\frac{1}{4}$ **(22)**

$7\frac{1}{9} + 6\frac{2}{9}$ $2\frac{1}{5} + 6\frac{4}{5}$ $3\frac{1}{3} + 5\frac{1}{5}$ $1\frac{1}{2} + 1\frac{1}{2}$ **(26)**

$9\frac{1}{3} + 7\frac{2}{5}$ $4\frac{11}{12} + 5\frac{1}{2}$ $2\frac{3}{4} + 7\frac{1}{8}$ $5\frac{1}{4} + 5\frac{2}{3}$ **(30)**

PRACTICE EXERCISE 5e
Addition of Mixed Numbers

Add and reduce all fractions to lowest terms:

$17\frac{1}{4}$ $43\frac{5}{6}$ $74\frac{1}{2}$ $69\frac{2}{5}$ $86\frac{7}{9}$
$24\frac{1}{12}$ $28\frac{2}{3}$ $82\frac{1}{3}$ $73\frac{1}{4}$ $23\frac{2}{3}$ **(5)**

$87\frac{1}{8}$ $47\frac{3}{8}$ $66\frac{1}{2}$ $94\frac{2}{5}$ $29\frac{1}{6}$
$33\frac{2}{3}$ $26\frac{1}{8}$ $38\frac{1}{4}$ $76\frac{1}{3}$ $46\frac{2}{3}$ **(10)**

$28\frac{1}{16}$ $13\frac{11}{12}$ $28\frac{3}{5}$ $55\frac{7}{8}$ $29\frac{1}{8}$
$5\frac{5}{8}$ $96\frac{3}{4}$ $77\frac{4}{5}$ $66\frac{2}{3}$ $45\frac{5}{24}$ **(15)**

$$18\frac{1}{4} + 16\frac{1}{3} \qquad\qquad 24\frac{1}{2} + 16\frac{1}{4} \qquad\qquad 38\frac{1}{5} + 17\frac{1}{8}$$
$$26\frac{3}{7} + 18\frac{4}{7} \qquad\qquad 39\frac{2}{3} + 16\frac{1}{4} \qquad\qquad 47 + 18\frac{5}{6} \qquad (21)$$

$124\frac{3}{5}$	$167\frac{1}{2}$	$343\frac{3}{5}$	$189\frac{4}{5}$	$172\frac{2}{9}$
$173\frac{1}{4}$	$238\frac{1}{3}$	$196\frac{1}{2}$	$276\frac{2}{5}$	$188\frac{2}{3}$ (26)

$724\frac{1}{6}$	$485\frac{1}{7}$	$168\frac{1}{5}$	$450\frac{2}{3}$	$276\frac{5}{6}$
$823\frac{2}{3}$	$317\frac{1}{14}$	$728\frac{1}{3}$	$706\frac{1}{2}$	$488\frac{3}{4}$ (31)

If you have scored well on this exercise, you should have no trouble passing *Inventory Test 5*.   Try it again.

——— SUBTRACTION OF COMMON FRACTIONS ———

You can subtract common fractions if you first change them to a common denominator. As in the addition of fractions, the arrangement of the fractions may be horizontal or vertical.

EXAMPLE A
$$\frac{7}{8} - \frac{3}{4}$$
$$\frac{7}{8} - \frac{6}{8} = \frac{1}{8}$$

EXAMPLE B
$$\frac{2}{3} = \frac{4}{6}$$
$$-\frac{1}{6} = \frac{1}{6}$$
$$\frac{3}{6} = \frac{1}{2}$$

PRACTICE EXERCISE 6a
Vertical Subtraction of Fractions

Subtract:

$\frac{1}{2}$	$\frac{1}{3}$	$\frac{3}{4}$	$\frac{3}{4}$	$\frac{2}{3}$	$\frac{3}{4}$
$\frac{1}{4}$	$\frac{1}{5}$	$\frac{1}{2}$	$\frac{3}{5}$	$\frac{1}{2}$	$\frac{3}{8}$

$\frac{7}{8}$	$\frac{5}{6}$	$\frac{4}{5}$	$\frac{7}{9}$	$\frac{6}{7}$	$\frac{7}{12}$
$\frac{1}{4}$	$\frac{1}{3}$	$\frac{1}{3}$	$\frac{2}{3}$	$\frac{1}{2}$	$\frac{3}{16}$ (12)

$\frac{11}{12}$	$\frac{3}{4}$	$\frac{2}{3}$	$\frac{3}{4}$	$\frac{1}{2}$	$\frac{5}{8}$
$\frac{1}{6}$	$\frac{1}{8}$	$\frac{1}{2}$	$\frac{1}{3}$	$\frac{1}{6}$	$\frac{1}{3}$

$\frac{3}{5}$	$\frac{11}{16}$	$\frac{7}{10}$	$\frac{5}{12}$	$\frac{5}{6}$	$\frac{7}{8}$
$\frac{1}{6}$	$\frac{3}{8}$	$\frac{2}{5}$	$\frac{3}{8}$	$\frac{7}{12}$	$\frac{3}{16}$ (24)

PRACTICE EXERCISE 6b
Horizontal Subtraction of Fractions

Subtract:

$$\frac{3}{4} - \frac{1}{4} \qquad\qquad \frac{7}{8} - \frac{1}{2} \qquad\qquad \frac{4}{5} - \frac{1}{5} \qquad\qquad \frac{5}{6} - \frac{1}{3}$$
$$\frac{3}{8} - \frac{1}{6} \qquad\qquad \frac{3}{4} - \frac{1}{2} \qquad\qquad \frac{9}{16} - \frac{1}{4} \qquad\qquad \frac{7}{8} - \frac{5}{16} \qquad (8)$$

$$\frac{7}{12} - \frac{5}{12} \qquad \frac{1}{2} - \frac{1}{10} \qquad \frac{2}{3} - \frac{1}{4} \qquad \frac{3}{4} - \frac{1}{3}$$
$$\frac{7}{9} - \frac{2}{3} \qquad \frac{3}{5} - \frac{1}{4} \qquad \frac{2}{3} - \frac{3}{8} \qquad \frac{9}{10} - \frac{1}{2} \quad \textbf{(16)}$$

$$\frac{7}{8} - \frac{2}{3} \qquad \frac{8}{9} - \frac{1}{6} \qquad \frac{6}{8} - \frac{1}{3} \qquad \frac{4}{5} - \frac{1}{4}$$
$$\frac{1}{2} - \frac{1}{3} \qquad \frac{1}{8} - \frac{1}{16} \qquad \frac{7}{8} - \frac{3}{4} \qquad \frac{11}{12} - \frac{3}{8} \quad \textbf{(24)}$$

——— SUBTRACTION OF MIXED NUMBERS ———

If the fraction in the minuend is less than the fraction in the subtrahend, add 1 to the fraction in the minuend; then subtract as usual. In Example A, the 1 that is to be taken from 9 and added to the fraction $\frac{3}{9}$ is expressed as $\frac{9}{9}$. The result is $\frac{12}{9}$. The $\frac{5}{9}$ subtracted from $\frac{12}{9}$ is $\frac{7}{9}$. The remainder is then $1\frac{7}{9}$.

┌─ **EXAMPLE A** ─┐
$$8 \, \cancel{9}\frac{1}{3} \quad \frac{3}{9} \quad \frac{12}{9}$$
$$-7\frac{5}{9} \quad \frac{5}{9} \quad \frac{5}{9}$$
$$\overline{1\frac{7}{9}} \qquad \overline{\frac{7}{9}}$$

┌─ **EXAMPLE B** ─┐
$$7 \, \cancel{8} \quad \frac{7}{7}$$
$$-3\frac{5}{7} \quad \frac{5}{7}$$
$$\overline{4\frac{2}{7}} \quad \overline{\frac{2}{7}}$$

In Example B, there is no fraction in the minuend. Express the 1 that is to be taken from the 8 as $\frac{7}{7}$. Then change the 8 to a 7, and proceed as usual.

PRACTICE EXERCISE 6c

Subtract:

$$\begin{array}{cccccc}
8\frac{2}{3} & 9\frac{1}{6} & 7\frac{3}{5} & 5\frac{2}{3} & 6 & 7\frac{1}{3} \\
2\frac{1}{3} & 3\frac{1}{8} & 1\frac{9}{10} & 2\frac{3}{4} & 5\frac{1}{5} & 2\frac{4}{5}
\end{array}$$

$$\begin{array}{cccccc}
8\frac{7}{8} & 9\frac{1}{2} & 7\frac{3}{8} & 5\frac{3}{16} & 8 & 7\frac{1}{4} \\
2 & 4\frac{7}{8} & 1\frac{7}{8} & \frac{3}{8} & 2\frac{5}{7} & 3\frac{3}{4} \quad \textbf{(12)}
\end{array}$$

$$\begin{array}{cccccc}
5 & 7\frac{1}{8} & 9\frac{2}{5} & 9\frac{4}{7} & 7\frac{5}{12} & 4\frac{2}{3} \\
1\frac{3}{5} & 2\frac{1}{6} & 1\frac{1}{2} & 5 & 3\frac{3}{4} & 1\frac{2}{3}
\end{array}$$

$$\begin{array}{cccccc}
6\frac{11}{12} & 7 & 1\frac{1}{4} & 6\frac{1}{5} & 8 & 7\frac{3}{5} \\
1\frac{1}{5} & 2\frac{1}{12} & \frac{7}{8} & 2\frac{1}{10} & 2\frac{3}{16} & 1\frac{3}{4} \quad \textbf{(24)}
\end{array}$$

PRACTICE EXERCISE 6d

Subtract:

$$\begin{array}{cccccc}
18\frac{2}{5} & 26\frac{1}{3} & 37\frac{1}{2} & 45\frac{1}{8} & 48\frac{1}{4} & 76 \\
7\frac{1}{5} & 9\frac{1}{3} & 16\frac{7}{8} & 28\frac{1}{4} & 19\frac{1}{3} & 18\frac{4}{5}
\end{array}$$

$$\begin{array}{cccccc}
38\frac{1}{16} & 94\frac{5}{6} & 76\frac{8}{9} & 46\frac{2}{3} & 11\frac{3}{4} & 20\frac{1}{4} \\
10\frac{1}{2} & \frac{3}{8} & 19 & 8\frac{5}{6} & 8\frac{7}{10} & 7\frac{3}{8} \quad \textbf{(12)}
\end{array}$$

$$\begin{array}{cccccc}
47\frac{1}{6} & 29\frac{1}{5} & 40\frac{1}{2} & 127 & 208\frac{1}{3} & 480\frac{1}{6} \\
19\frac{1}{2} & 18\frac{1}{2} & 16\frac{5}{8} & 88\frac{4}{7} & 194\frac{2}{3} & 89\frac{3}{4}
\end{array}$$

$$185\tfrac{7}{9} \qquad 181\tfrac{2}{3} \qquad 707\tfrac{1}{3} \qquad 398\tfrac{4}{5} \qquad 161\tfrac{1}{8} \qquad 101$$
$$\underline{110} \qquad \underline{79\tfrac{1}{8}} \qquad \underline{109\tfrac{1}{5}} \qquad \underline{109\tfrac{1}{2}} \qquad \underline{97\tfrac{3}{4}} \qquad \underline{89\tfrac{3}{8}} \quad (24)$$

If you scored well on these exercises, you should be able to pass *Inventory Test 6* now. Try it.

─────── MULTIPLICATION OF FRACTIONS ───────

In general, we find the product of two or more fractions by multiplying their numerators together for the numerator of the product and the denominators together for the denominator of the product.

EXAMPLE: $\tfrac{4}{5} \times \tfrac{3}{7} = \tfrac{12}{35}$

EXAMPLE: $\dfrac{\cancel{2}^{1}}{\cancel{3}_{1}} \times \dfrac{\cancel{6}^{1}}{5} \times \dfrac{7}{\cancel{8}_{2}}^{\;1} = \dfrac{7}{10}$

If there is a common factor in the numerator and the denominator, cancel before multiplying. To cancel, divide both numerator and denominator by the common factor.

If there are one or more mixed numbers in the multiplication, they are usually changed to improper fractions.

EXAMPLE: $\dfrac{4}{5} \times 3\tfrac{1}{3} = \dfrac{4}{\cancel{5}_{1}} \times \dfrac{\cancel{10}^{2}}{3} = \dfrac{8}{3} = 2\tfrac{2}{3}$

PRACTICE EXERCISE 7a
Multiplication of Two or More Fractions

Multiply:

$\tfrac{2}{3} \times \tfrac{2}{3}$	$\tfrac{4}{5} \times \tfrac{3}{5}$	$\tfrac{7}{8} \times \tfrac{4}{7}$	$\tfrac{6}{7} \times \tfrac{7}{9}$
$\tfrac{2}{5} \times \tfrac{15}{22}$	$\tfrac{1}{2} \times \tfrac{1}{2}$	$\tfrac{4}{9} \times \tfrac{6}{11}$	$\tfrac{1}{4} \times \tfrac{1}{4}$ (8)
$\tfrac{5}{9} \times \tfrac{6}{7}$	$\tfrac{1}{2} \times \tfrac{2}{3}$	$\tfrac{2}{3} \times \tfrac{1}{4}$	$\tfrac{15}{16} \times \tfrac{28}{25}$
$\tfrac{21}{25} \times \tfrac{10}{21}$	$\tfrac{2}{3} \times \tfrac{7}{8}$	$\tfrac{3}{8} \times \tfrac{3}{8}$	$\tfrac{4}{9} \times \tfrac{27}{28}$ (16)
$\tfrac{1}{3} \times \tfrac{2}{5} \times \tfrac{9}{10}$	$\tfrac{2}{3} \times \tfrac{2}{5} \times \tfrac{3}{4}$		$\tfrac{5}{6} \times \tfrac{1}{10} \times \tfrac{8}{21}$
$\tfrac{17}{18} \times \tfrac{4}{5} \times \tfrac{20}{51}$	$\tfrac{7}{8} \times \tfrac{1}{2} \times 4$		$6 \times \tfrac{2}{3} \times \tfrac{1}{5}$ (22)

PRACTICE EXERCISE 7b
Multiplication of Integer and Fraction

Multiply:

$6 \times \tfrac{3}{4}$	$7 \times \tfrac{3}{14}$	$8 \times \tfrac{5}{6}$	$9 \times \tfrac{2}{3}$ (4)
$\tfrac{7}{8} \times 4$	$\tfrac{5}{6} \times 9$	$2\tfrac{2}{3} \times 6$	$\tfrac{5}{9} \times 12$
$\tfrac{7}{9} \times 15$	$\tfrac{4}{5} \times 4$	$\tfrac{3}{8} \times 6$	$2\tfrac{4}{9} \times 15$ (12)

$24 \times 1\frac{3}{8}$ $72 \times \frac{5}{9}$ $78 \times \frac{1}{2}$ $45 \times 3\frac{5}{6}$

$\frac{3}{4}$ of 50 $\frac{7}{8}$ of 60 $\frac{3}{7}$ of 42 $\frac{5}{12}$ of 84   **(20)**

PRACTICE EXERCISE 7c
Multiplication of Mixed Numbers

Multiply:

$2\frac{1}{3} \times 3\frac{1}{7}$	$4\frac{1}{2} \times 3\frac{1}{3}$	$1\frac{1}{2} \times 1\frac{1}{4}$	$1\frac{1}{2} \times 1\frac{1}{2}$	
$7\frac{1}{3} \times 2\frac{1}{11}$	$3\frac{3}{4} \times 3\frac{1}{5}$	$7\frac{1}{2} \times 3\frac{1}{3}$	$2\frac{1}{4} \times 2\frac{1}{4}$	**(8)**
$4\frac{1}{5} \times 2\frac{1}{2}$	$8\frac{1}{3} \times 1\frac{7}{8}$	$8\frac{3}{4} \times 2\frac{1}{7}$	$3\frac{1}{3} \times 3\frac{1}{8}$	
$4\frac{1}{6} \times 1\frac{1}{5}$	$3\frac{2}{3} \times 4\frac{1}{2}$	$1\frac{1}{8} \times 1\frac{1}{3}$	$1\frac{1}{2} \times 3\frac{1}{3}$	**(16)**
$1\frac{4}{5} \times 2\frac{1}{2}$	$1\frac{5}{6} \times 1\frac{1}{2}$	$12\frac{1}{2} \times 12\frac{1}{2}$	$7\frac{1}{2} \times 7\frac{1}{2}$	
$1\frac{2}{3} \times 4\frac{3}{8}$	$16\frac{2}{3} \times 7\frac{3}{5}$	$18\frac{3}{4} \times 2\frac{2}{5}$	$4\frac{3}{8} \times 2\frac{4}{7}$	**(24)**

If your products are correct, try *Inventory Test 7* again.

——————DIVISION OF FRACTIONS——————

To divide with fractions, invert the divisor and multiply.

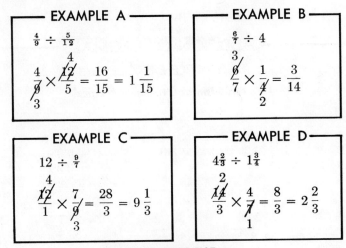

EXAMPLE A

$\frac{4}{9} \div \frac{5}{12}$

$$\frac{4}{\cancel{9}_{3}} \times \frac{\cancel{12}^{4}}{5} = \frac{16}{15} = 1\frac{1}{15}$$

EXAMPLE B

$\frac{6}{7} \div 4$

$$\frac{\cancel{6}^{3}}{7} \times \frac{1}{\cancel{4}_{2}} = \frac{3}{14}$$

EXAMPLE C

$12 \div \frac{9}{7}$

$$\frac{\cancel{12}^{4}}{1} \times \frac{7}{\cancel{9}_{3}} = \frac{28}{3} = 9\frac{1}{3}$$

EXAMPLE D

$4\frac{2}{3} \div 1\frac{3}{4}$

$$\frac{\cancel{14}^{2}}{3} \times \frac{4}{\cancel{7}_{1}} = \frac{8}{3} = 2\frac{2}{3}$$

PRACTICE EXERCISE 8a
Division of a Fraction by a Fraction

Divide; then reduce all fractions in quotients to lowest terms:

$\frac{7}{9} \div \frac{2}{3}$	$\frac{8}{15} \div \frac{1}{5}$	$\frac{5}{6} \div \frac{2}{3}$	$\frac{8}{9} \div \frac{1}{6}$	
$\frac{7}{12} \div \frac{3}{4}$	$\frac{8}{9} \div \frac{1}{2}$	$\frac{5}{9} \div \frac{5}{9}$	$\frac{3}{4} \div \frac{1}{8}$	**(8)**
$\frac{1}{2} \div \frac{2}{3}$	$\frac{7}{8} \div \frac{3}{4}$	$\frac{1}{3} \div \frac{1}{6}$	$\frac{2}{3} \div \frac{3}{4}$	
$\frac{2}{3} \div \frac{4}{9}$	$\frac{5}{8} \div \frac{1}{2}$	$\frac{1}{2} \div \frac{1}{2}$	$\frac{3}{5} \div \frac{3}{4}$	**(16)**
$\frac{1}{2} \div \frac{3}{8}$	$\frac{1}{4} \div \frac{1}{8}$	$\frac{7}{9} \div \frac{5}{6}$	$\frac{3}{16} \div \frac{7}{8}$	
$\frac{1}{9} \div \frac{1}{6}$	$\frac{1}{3} \div \frac{1}{4}$	$\frac{1}{2} \div \frac{5}{7}$	$\frac{2}{3} \div \frac{4}{7}$	**(24)**

PRACTICE EXERCISE 8b
Division of Fractions and Integers

Divide; then reduce all fractions in quotients to lowest terms:

$3 \div \frac{1}{12}$	$4 \div \frac{4}{7}$	$6 \div \frac{8}{9}$	$\frac{11}{12} \div 3$ (4)
$12 \div \frac{1}{6}$	$18 \div \frac{2}{3}$	$20 \div \frac{4}{5}$	$24 \div \frac{1}{2}$
$\frac{2}{3} \div 2$	$\frac{5}{6} \div 8$	$\frac{7}{9} \div 14$	$\frac{6}{7} \div 12$ (12)
$\frac{7}{8} \div 21$	$\frac{4}{9} \div 6$	$\frac{5}{8} \div 15$	$\frac{5}{16} \div 12$
$\frac{4}{5} \div 12$	$\frac{5}{8} \div 10$	$16 \div \frac{8}{9}$	$26 \div \frac{13}{15}$ (20)

PRACTICE EXERCISE 8c
Division of Mixed Numbers

Divide; then reduce all fractions in quotients to lowest terms:

$2\frac{1}{3} \div 4\frac{1}{2}$	$2\frac{1}{2} \div 3\frac{1}{3}$	$6\frac{1}{4} \div 1\frac{2}{3}$	$1\frac{1}{8} \div 1\frac{1}{4}$ (4)
$7\frac{1}{2} \div 2$	$6\frac{2}{3} \div 4$	$3\frac{3}{4} \div 3$	$4\frac{2}{5} \div 2\frac{1}{5}$
$8 \div 1\frac{1}{4}$	$4\frac{2}{3} \div 1\frac{1}{3}$	$9 \div 1\frac{1}{8}$	$7\frac{2}{3} \div 1\frac{2}{3}$ (12)
$12 \div 3\frac{3}{4}$	$16 \div 2\frac{1}{4}$	$6\frac{1}{2} \div \frac{7}{8}$	$9\frac{1}{3} \div 4\frac{2}{3}$
$5\frac{1}{2} \div 3\frac{2}{3}$	$21 \div 1\frac{7}{8}$	$10\frac{2}{3} \div 2\frac{2}{3}$	$12\frac{4}{5} \div 2\frac{1}{8}$ (20)

If you have a good score on this test, try *Inventory Test 8* again.

——— ADDITION OF DECIMALS ———

PRACTICE EXERCISE 9a
Addition of Decimals—Vertical

Add:

1. .4	2. 1.6	3. 4.56	4. 18.167	5. .7$\frac{1}{4}$
.6	2.3	9.	2.95	2.6
.3	7.8	7.2	3.08	3.9
.5	9.	.8	.9	.45

6. 48.67	7. 29.6	8. .83	9. 29.7	10. .85
4.38	7.4	2.9	83.$\frac{1}{2}$	2.6
7.9	.92	.7	7.64	.325
.36	3.1	4.857	.234	8.1$\frac{1}{2}$
1.7$\frac{1}{2}$	.675	.3$\frac{1}{4}$	6.$\frac{1}{8}$	7.45

PRACTICE EXERCISE 9b
Addition of Decimals—Horizontal

Add:

1. $.6 + 1.8 + 3.24$

2. $.02 + 3.7 + 7.8 + 12.78$

3. $3.86 + 4.027 + 9$

4. $.002 + 1.076 + .25 + 1.6$

5. .9 + .8 + .7 + .6

6. .82 + .9 + .74 + 8

7. 1.6 + 2.9 + $1\frac{1}{2}$

8. 32.8 + 67 + .92 + $2\frac{1}{4}$

9. 241.6 + 9.075

10. 203.8 + 24.07 + 645

11. .767 + 14.9

12. 6.7 + .406 + 30.9 + .8

13. 10.25 + $16\frac{1}{5}$

14. 27.8 + $52\frac{1}{3}$ + $46.2\frac{1}{4}$

15. 7.5 + $8\frac{2}{3}$ + 6.4

16. 1.9 + $7\frac{1}{8}$ + $2.93\frac{1}{2}$ + $.7\frac{1}{4}$

17. 2.6 + 3.7 + 27 + .9

18. .97 + 1.09 + 3 + 97.948

SUBTRACTION OF DECIMALS

PRACTICE EXERCISE 9c
Subtraction of Decimals—Vertical

Subtract:

1. .87
   .45

2. 7.6
   3.8

3. 5.1
   2.8

4. 26.85
   18.79

5. 7.871
   1.792

6. 1.06
   .78

7. 3.191
   1.06

8. 9.01
   1.872

9. 24.1
   9.27

10. 75.
    18.23

11. 33.
    9.176

12. 7.
    .1

13. 18.
    .018

14. 3.03
    .86

15. 1.
    .39

16. 17.06
    7.0848

17. .213
    .018

18. 761.8
    4.76

19. .8
    .148

20. 1.2
    .8745

PRACTICE EXERCISE 9d
Subtraction of Decimals—Horizontal

Subtract:

1. 9.6 − 1.4

2. .38 − .07

3. 4.8 − 3.27

4. 18.8 − 1.9

5. 1.76 − .39

6. 8 − 1.4

7. 8.7 − 3.9

8. 7.87 − $6.3\frac{1}{4}$

9. 24 − .8

10. $62.7\frac{1}{2}$ − 3.9

11. 35.18 − .719

12. 721.32 − 146.7

13. $82\frac{1}{2}$ − 2.4

14. 12.6 − $8\frac{1}{3}$

15. 100 − .37

16. 7.14 − 3.872

17. 200 − 4.5

18. 150 − .368

You should be able to pass *Inventory Test 9* now.

MULTIPLICATION OF DECIMALS

PRACTICE EXERCISE 10a

Multiply:

1. .067
   8
	2. 1.7
	  .9
		3. 2.68
		   .01
			4. 8.4
			   .001
				5. 7.8
				  100

6. 60.1
   .1
	7. 39.2
	  1000
		8. 1.865
		    .08
			9. 6.7
			  .04
				10. 7.57
				   .09

11. 8.64
   .28
	12. .723
	   .46
		13. 9.36
		   .83
			14. 45.72
			   7.2
				15. 7.03
				  2.08

16. .175
  400
	17. .0675
	   8.2
		18. .004
		  .002
			19. 1.725
			   .28
				20. 7.86
				   10

21. 7.48
  100
	22. .764
	  3.7
		23. 1.04
		  20.7
			24. 72.5
			  4.9
				25. 6.78
				  3.7

PRACTICE EXERCISE 10b

Multiply:

1. $10 \times .74$	**2.** $42 \times .001$	**3.** 3.15×1000
4. $8 \times .082$	**5.** $.125 \times .01$	**6.** $7.8 \times .8$
7. 3.9×10	**8.** $1.9 \times .1$	**9.** $74 \times .001$
10. $.65 \times 1000$	**11.** $100 \times .1$	**12.** 16.16×100
13. $30 \times .3$	**14.** $78 \times .44$	**15.** 2.5×2.5
16. $.6 \times 6$	**17.** $.139 \times 100$	**18.** $1.08 \times .2$
19. 1.02×10.2	**20.** $80 \times .80$	**21.** $.006 \times 10$
22. 1000×7.2	**23.** 18×1.8	**24.** 2.3456×100
25. $.009 \times .08$	**26.** $1.05 \times .105$	**27.** $.11 \times .11$
28. $.127 \times .06$	**29.** $10 \times .867$	**30.** $52.64 \times .08$

You should pass *Inventory Test 10* now.

DIVISION OF DECIMALS

PRACTICE EXERCISE 11a
Short Division of Decimals

Estimate each quotient and then divide:

1. $4\overline{)7.2}$ 2. $.3\overline{)8.4}$ 3. $.04\overline{)6.4}$ 4. $20\overline{)8}$

5. $.03\overline{).6}$ 6. $.003\overline{).06}$ 7. $.3\overline{).006}$ 8. $300\overline{).6}$

9. $.04\overline{)8}$ 10. $.4\overline{).8}$ 11. $40\overline{).8}$ 12. $4\overline{).08}$

13. $400\overline{)8}$ 14. $400\overline{).8}$ 15. $4000\overline{).8}$ 16. $.004\overline{).8}$

17. $5\overline{).1}$ 18. $.5\overline{).01}$ 19. $.05\overline{).1}$ 20. $.05\overline{)1}$

PRACTICE EXERCISE 11b
Short Division of Decimals

Estimate the quotient and then divide:

1. $.6\overline{)2526}$ 2. $.02\overline{)846}$ 3. $.7\overline{)7.49}$ 4. $.1\overline{).09}$

5. $.200\overline{).0938}$ 6. $.9\overline{)24.016}$ 7. $.04\overline{)1.124}$ 8. $.2\overline{).8}$

9. $9\overline{)708.3}$ 10. $300\overline{).012}$ 11. $30\overline{)4.62}$ 12. $.3\overline{).009}$

13. $.6\overline{)12.12}$ 14. $20\overline{).08}$ 15. $.3\overline{)4.62}$ 16. $.06\overline{).2418}$

17. $8\overline{)88.8}$ 18. $.005\overline{).02}$ 19. $.09\overline{)27.27}$ 20. $.4\overline{)288}$

PRACTICE EXERCISE 11c
Long Division of Decimals

Point off the quotients.   Prefix or annex zeros if needed.   Divide:

1. $.034\overline{)9.316}$ 274   2. $2.12\overline{)2.6924}$ 127   3. $41.2\overline{)141.316}$ 343

4. $7.17\overline{)1792.5}$ 25   5. $162\overline{)5.508}$ 34   6. $2.12\overline{)68.688}$ 324

$$
\begin{array}{lll}
& 509 & 128 & 286 \\
\textbf{7.}\ 23.2\overline{)1180.88} & \textbf{8.}\ 38.1\overline{)4876.8} & \textbf{9.}\ .723\overline{)206.778}
\end{array}
$$

$$
\begin{array}{lll}
1283 & 3107 & 91 \\
\textbf{10.}\ 8.4\overline{)1077.72} & \textbf{11.}\ .72\overline{)22.3704} & \textbf{12.}\ .86\overline{).7826}
\end{array}
$$

$$
\begin{array}{lll}
78 & 101 & 674 \\
\textbf{13.}\ 8.8\overline{)68.64} & \textbf{14.}\ 7.3\overline{)737.3} & \textbf{15.}\ .023\overline{)1.5502}
\end{array}
$$

16. $7.98 \div 10$ **17.** $469 \div 100$ **18.** $.06 \div 10$

19. $34.6 \div 1000$ **20.** $.5 \div 100$ **21.** $56.78 \div 100$

22. $.05 \div 100$ **23.** $7.4 \div 100$ **24.** $500 \div 1000$

You should be able to pass *Inventory Test 11* now.

--- PERCENTAGE ---

PRACTICE EXERCISE 12a
Changing Decimal Fractions to Per Cents

Change these decimal fractions to per cents:

1. .18	**2.** .75	**3.** .42	**4.** .64	**5.** .03
6. .05	**7.** .01	**8.** .08	**9.** .175	**10.** .256
11. .625	**12.** .5625	**13.** .8	**14.** .1	**15.** .7275
16. 1.35	**17.** 1.18	**18.** 2.0625	**19.** 3.125	**20.** 4.0
21. 1.3	**22.** 2.5	**23.** $.9\frac{1}{2}$	**24.** $.6\frac{1}{4}$	**25.** $1.3\frac{1}{3}$
26. $.14\frac{1}{2}$	**27.** $.3\frac{1}{8}$	**28.** 2.2	**29.** .002	**30.** 1.005
31. .166	**32.** 1.08	**33.** 1.15	**34.** .2	**35.** $.12\frac{1}{2}$
36. .375	**37.** 1.625	**38.** 1.5	**39.** .025	**40.** 2.25

PRACTICE EXERCISE 12b
Changing Common Fractions to Per Cents

Change each of these common fractions and mixed numbers to a per cent:

1. $\frac{1}{2}$	**2.** $\frac{3}{4}$	**3.** $\frac{1}{5}$	**4.** $\frac{3}{10}$	**5.** $\frac{7}{20}$
6. $\frac{1}{8}$	**7.** $\frac{6}{25}$	**8.** $\frac{1}{3}$	**9.** $\frac{4}{9}$	**10.** $\frac{1}{6}$
11. $\frac{3}{16}$	**12.** $\frac{7}{8}$	**13.** $\frac{4}{15}$	**14.** $\frac{1}{50}$	**15.** $\frac{1}{7}$
16. $\frac{2}{3}$	**17.** $\frac{4}{7}$	**18.** $\frac{5}{8}$	**19.** $\frac{5}{6}$	**20.** $\frac{7}{10}$
21. $\frac{3}{8}$	**22.** $\frac{3}{5}$	**23.** $\frac{3}{7}$	**24.** $\frac{1}{9}$	**25.** $1\frac{1}{2}$
26. $2\frac{2}{5}$	**27.** $1\frac{1}{4}$	**28.** $1\frac{5}{16}$	**29.** $2\frac{1}{3}$	**30.** $1\frac{2}{3}$
31. $1\frac{3}{4}$	**32.** $1\frac{2}{5}$	**33.** $1\frac{7}{9}$	**34.** $\frac{5}{12}$	**35.** $\frac{7}{16}$
36. $\frac{5}{7}$	**37.** $2\frac{2}{3}$	**38.** $\frac{1}{30}$	**39.** $\frac{4}{25}$	**40.** $1\frac{1}{8}$

PRACTICE EXERCISE 12c
Changing Per Cents to Decimal Fractions

Change these per cents to decimal fractions:

1. 50%	2. 75%	3. 18%	4. 20%
5. 10%	6. 2%	7. 9%	8. 7%
9. $2\frac{1}{2}$%	10. $3\frac{1}{4}$%	11. $1\frac{3}{4}$%	12. $12\frac{1}{2}$%
13. $18\frac{3}{4}$%	14. 6%	15. 1%	16. $16\frac{2}{3}$%
17. $17\frac{1}{2}$%	18. $8\frac{1}{3}$%	19. $6\frac{1}{4}$%	20. $83\frac{1}{3}$%
21. $62\frac{1}{2}$%	22. $37\frac{1}{2}$%	23. $\frac{1}{2}$%	24. $\frac{3}{4}$%
25. 140%	26. 250%	27. 180%	28. 235%
29. $6\frac{2}{3}$%	30. 4.5%	31. 3%	32. 1.5%
33. $28\frac{4}{7}$%	34. $1\frac{1}{2}$%	35. $\frac{3}{8}$%	36. 1.85%
37. .8%	38. .01%	39. $166\frac{2}{3}$%	40. 325%
41. 125%	42. 36%	43. 4.5%	44. .9%
45. $\frac{1}{4}$%	46. $3\frac{1}{3}$%	47. $1\frac{1}{4}$%	48. 160%

PRACTICE EXERCISE 12d
Changing Per Cents to Common Fractions

Change these per cents to common fractions and reduce to lowest terms:

1. 20%	2. 15%	3. 75%	4. 55%
5. 5%	6. 2%	7. 1%	8. 7%
9. $3\frac{1}{2}$%	10. $4\frac{1}{4}$%	11. $5\frac{3}{4}$%	12. $1\frac{1}{8}$%
13. $\frac{1}{2}$%	14. $\frac{1}{5}$%	15. $\frac{3}{8}$%	16. $\frac{4}{5}$%
17. .6%	18. 8%	19. .1%	20. .5%
21. $\frac{1}{7}$%	22. $\frac{4}{9}$%	23. $\frac{2}{3}$%	24. $\frac{5}{6}$%
25. $\frac{1}{4}$%	26. 2.8%	27. 2.5%	28. 1.25%
29. 5.3%	30. $3.2\frac{1}{2}$%	31. $15.6\frac{1}{4}$%	32. 24.5%
33. 250%	34. 180%	35. 160%	36. 200%
37. 375%	38. 225%	39. 175%	40. $212\frac{1}{2}$%
41. 45%	42. 18%	43. 150%	44. $2\frac{1}{2}$%
45. 240%	46. $\frac{1}{8}$%	47. .3%	48. $2\frac{1}{4}$%

PRACTICE EXERCISE 12e

Common fractions and their equivalent per cents to be memorized. Certain common fractions are used so frequently that it is important to memorize their equivalent per cents. See Appendix D.

Express each of the following as a common fraction, as a decimal fraction, and as a per cent:

	Common Fraction	Decimal Fraction	Per Cent
1.	$\frac{9}{12}$	--------	--------
2.	$\frac{3}{5}$	--------	--------
3.	--------	.16	--------
4.	--------	.09	--------
5.	--------	--------	4%
6.	--------	--------	12%
7.	--------	$.87\frac{1}{2}$	--------
8.	$1\frac{1}{2}$	--------	--------
9.	--------	--------	130%
10.	--------	.045	--------
11.	--------	$.14\frac{2}{7}$	--------
12.	--------	--------	$83\frac{1}{3}\%$
13.	--------	--------	$12\frac{1}{2}\%$
14.	$\frac{7}{9}$	--------	--------
15.	--------	1.25	--------
16.	--------	.175	--------
17.	$\frac{8}{25}$	--------	--------
18.	--------	--------	175%
19.	$\frac{1}{100}$	--------	--------
20.	--------	--------	$\frac{2}{5}\%$

PRACTICE EXERCISE 12f

Write the common fraction, or the per cent, whichever is missing:

1. $\frac{2}{5} = ?$
2. $? = 30\%$
3. $? = 87\frac{1}{2}\%$
4. $\frac{1}{12} = ?$
5. $? = 16\frac{2}{3}\%$
6. $? = 12\frac{1}{2}\%$

7. $3\frac{1}{2} = ?$
8. $\frac{1}{16} = ?$
9. $\frac{7}{9} = ?$
10. $? = 66\frac{2}{3}\%$
11. $? = 14\frac{2}{7}\%$
12. $\frac{5}{8} = ?$

13. $\frac{1}{3} = ?$
14. $\frac{4}{5} = ?$
15. $? = 70\%$
16. $? = 83\frac{1}{3}\%$
17. $\frac{2}{7} = ?$
18. $? = 2\frac{1}{2}\%$

You should now be able to pass *Inventory Test 12*. Try it.

PRACTICE EXERCISE 13a

Finding a Per Cent of a Number

Solve these exercises:

1. 5% of 36
2. 20% of 85

3. 17% of 60
4. 51% of 79

5. 73% of 12
6. 11% of 150

7. 9% of 40
8. 8% of 24
9. 40% of 15
10. 45% of 20
11. 20% of 72
12. 25% of 400
13. 1% of 50
14. $\frac{1}{2}$% of 400

15. 2% of 80
16. .1% of 60
17. 150% of 400
18. 175% of 200
19. 2.5% of 300
20. 200% of 82
21. 48% of 35
22. 18% of 65

23. $\frac{1}{4}$% of 200
24. .6% of 50
25. 17% of 120
26. 180% of 90
27. 79% of 500
28. $2\frac{1}{2}$% of 40
29. $7\frac{1}{4}$% of 80
30. $1\frac{3}{4}$% of 60

PRACTICE EXERCISE 13b
Finding a Per Cent of a Number

Using the equivalent fraction, solve each of these exercises:

1. $33\frac{1}{3}$% of 36
2. $12\frac{1}{2}$% of 48
3. 20% of 60
4. $87\frac{1}{2}$% of 16
5. $66\frac{2}{3}$% of 75
6. $83\frac{1}{3}$% of 42
7. $37\frac{1}{2}$% of 56
8. 60% of 25
9. $14\frac{2}{7}$% of 21
10. $62\frac{1}{2}$% of 160

11. 10% of 800
12. $8\frac{1}{3}$% of 24
13. 25% of 420
14. $16\frac{2}{3}$% of 18
15. 40% of 35
16. 75% of 12
17. $28\frac{4}{7}$% of 28
18. $11\frac{1}{9}$% of 18
19. $41\frac{2}{3}$% of 24
20. 90% of 270

21. 30% of 60
22. $6\frac{1}{4}$% of 480
23. $22\frac{2}{9}$% of 270
24. $42\frac{6}{7}$% of 14
25. $18\frac{3}{4}$% of 64
26. 110% of 70
27. 125% of 16
28. $137\frac{1}{2}$% of 80
29. $133\frac{1}{3}$% of 36
30. 120% of 45

PRACTICE EXERCISE 13c
Finding What Per Cent One Number Is of Another Number

Solve these exercises:

1. 8 = ?% of 8
2. 8 = ?% of 12
3. ?% of 100 = 5
4. ?% of 50 = 25
5. 75% of ? = 150
6. 20% of ? = 80
7. 9 = ?% of 3
8. 12 = ?% of 36
9. 10 = ?% of 40
10. ?% of 80 = 50
11. ?% of 50 = 7

12. 15% of ? = 30
13. 8% of ? = 2
14. 3% of ? = 126
15. 2% of ? = 88
16. ?% of 8 = 16
17. 15 = ?% of 45
18. 40% of ? = 32
19. 150% of ? = 90
20. 200% of ? = 72
21. $\frac{1}{2}$% of ? = 45
22. ?% of 16 = 3

23. 8 = ?% of 200
24. 20 = ?% of 8
25. ?% of 25 = 75
26. ?% of 20 = 6
27. 1 = ?% of 8
28. $\frac{1}{2}$ = ?% of 2
29. 16 = ?% of 24
30. ?% of 5 = 3
31. 9 = ?% of 15
32. 10 = ?% of 14
33. 105% of ? = 420

34. $3 = ?\%$ of 3   **38.** $2 = ?\%$ of 14   **42.** $\frac{1}{3} = ?\%$ of 1

35. 21% of $? = 42$ **39.** 100% of $? = 22$ **43.** 100% of $? = 70$

36. $?\%$ of $20 = 45$ **40.** $?\%$ of $16 = 1$ **44.** $7 = ?\%$ of 50

37. 125% of $? = 36$ **41.** $?\%$ of $12 = 1$ **45.** $\frac{1}{4}\%$ of $? = 8$

PRACTICE EXERCISE 13d

Per Cent Exercises

Fill in the missing numbers:

1. 30% of $25 = ?$ **11.** $2 = ?\%$ of 10   **21.** $5 = ?\%$ of 2

2. $?\%$ of $30 = 5$ **12.** $\frac{1}{2}\%$ of $800 = ?$ **22.** $6 = ?\%$ of 300

3. 10% of $? = 6$ **13.** 60% of $? = 12$ **23.** $62\frac{1}{2}\%$ of $64 = ?$

4. $33\frac{1}{3}\%$ of $186 = ?$ **14.** $33\frac{1}{3}\%$ of $? = 9$ **24.** $?\%$ of $18 = 12$

5. $?\%$ of $50 = 15$ **15.** 2.5% of $8 = ?$ **25.** 250% of $40 = ?$

6. $18 = ?\%$ of 45   **16.** $3\frac{1}{2}\%$ of $6 = ?$ **26.** $37\frac{1}{2}\%$ of $24 = ?$

7. $15 = ?\%$ of 60   **17.** 12% of $? = 18$ **27.** $?\%$ of $12 = 2$

8. 7% of $50 = ?$ **18.** 140% of $? = 28$ **28.** $.1\%$ of $? = 10$

9. 28% of $100 = ?$ **19.** $?\%$ of $20 = 16$ **29.** $16\frac{2}{3}\%$ of $72 = ?$

10. 125% of $60 = ?$ **20.** $?\%$ of $32 = 8$ **30.** $112\frac{1}{2}\%$ of $32 = ?$

If you have done well on these *Practice Exercises,* you should be able to pass *Inventory Test 13.* Try it again.

The present business world demands a thorough mastery of percentage. Are you prepared to meet such a demand? If not, consult your teacher about any part of percentage that you do not clearly understand, and then continue your practice.

———— DENOMINATE NUMBERS ————

PRACTICE EXERCISE 14a

Reduction to Lower Units

Change these measures to the specified units:

1. 2 ft. 8 in. $=$ _____ in.   **10.** 2 hr. 15 min. $=$ _____ min.

2. 3 yd. $=$ _____ ft.   **11.** 8 min. $=$ _____ sec.

3. 3 qt. $=$ _____ pt.   **12.** 3 sq. ft. $=$ _____ sq. in.

4. 5 gal. $=$ _____ qt.   **13.** 2 sq. yd. $=$ _____ sq. ft.

5. 3 lb. 6 oz. $=$ _____ oz.   **14.** 2 cu. yd. $=$ _____ cu. ft.

6. 2 bu. $=$ _____ pk.   **15.** 5 cu. yd. $=$ _____ cu. ft.

7. 2 yd. $=$ _____ in.   **16.** 2 sq. mi. $=$ _____ acres

8. 2 T. $=$ _____ lb.   **17.** 3 gal. $=$ _____ cu. in.

9. 15 doz. $=$ _____ articles   **18.** 3 pk. 2 qt. $=$ _____ qt.

13. 18 mi. 96 rd.	14. 52 min. 45 sec.	15. 5 yd. 10 ft.
5	10	7

Try *Inventory Test 16* again.

PRACTICE EXERCISE 17a

Denominate Numbers—Subtraction

Subtract these units of measure:

1. 12 ft. 6 in. 8 ft. 8 in.	6. 8 ft. 2 ft. 7 in.	11. 31 hr. 30 min. 18 hr. 42 min.
2. 4 pk. 1 qt. 1 pk. 3 qt.	7. 45 pk. 3 qt. 16 pk. 7 qt.	12. 1900 yr. 9 mo. 5 da. 1879 yr. 6 mo. 18 da.
3. 10 T. 1,000 lb. 7 T. 1,800 lb.	8. 21 T. 800 lb. 16 T. 1,000 lb.	13. 18 hr. 10 min. 20 sec. 17 hr. 42 sec.
4. 40 min. 10 sec. 10 min. 20 sec.	9. 70 min. 18 sec. 32 min. 35 sec.	14. 13 gal. 1 qt. 5 gal. 2 qt. 1 pt.
5. 3 pk. 1 pk. 3 qt.	10. 32 yd. 17 yd. 1 ft.	15. 1943 yr. 6 mo. 20 da. 1908 yr. 8 mo. 25 da.

Try *Inventory Test 17* again.

PRACTICE EXERCISE 18a

Division of Denominate Numbers

```
┌──────────────── EXAMPLE ────────────────┐
│              0 yd. 2 ft. 6 in.           │
│              4)3 yd. 1 ft.               │
│  (a) 3 yd. ÷ 4 = 0 yd. and 3 yd. remainder. │
│  (b) 3 yd. = 9 ft. (changed to next lower unit) │
│  (c) 9 ft. + 1 ft. = 10 ft. (added to like unit) │
│  (d) 10 ft. ÷ 4 = 2 ft. and 2 ft. remainder │
│  (e) 2 ft. = 24 in. (remainder changed to lower unit) │
│  (f) 24 in. ÷ 4 = 6 in.                  │
│      Quotient is 2 ft. 6 in.             │
└──────────────────────────────────────────┘
```

Divide these units of measure:

1. 5)10 hr. 30 min.	2. 4)8 pk. 5 qt.	3. 6)24 min. 10 sec.

4. 3)18 ft. 8 in.   8. 4)18 yd. 2 ft.   12. 3)8 bu. 1 pk.

5. 2)5 qt. 1 pt.   9. 5)21 ft. 5 in.   13. 3)8 ft. 7 in.

6. 3)4 yd. 2 ft.   10. 3)17 mi. 100 rd.   14. 5)1 qt. 1 pt.

7. 5)1 yd. 2 ft.   11. 4)42 min. 4 sec.   15. 4)6 mi. 180 rd.

Now try *Inventory Test 18* again if you have done well with this *Practice Exercise*. If you *have not* done well, practice more before attempting the test.

GLOSSARY OF MATHEMATICAL TERMS*

A

Absolute value: the value of a number without regard to the plus or minus sign preceding it.

Accuracy: amount of error in measurement compared with the size of the measurement; the smaller the relative error, the greater being the accuracy.

Acute angle: an angle that contains less than 90 degrees.

Acute triangle: a triangle all of whose angles are acute angles.

Adjacent side: adjoining side.

Altitude: vertical height.

Amount: the new value of a given principal after adding the interest it has earned for a given period of time at a given rate.

Angle: opening between two intersecting lines at the point where they meet.

Angle of elevation: See paragraph 175.

Annual: occurring every year.

Annuity: an assured income paid by an insurance company.

Approximate: nearly accurate.

Arc: any section of a curve.

Area: the number of square units in the surface of a plane figure.

Assessed value: the worth that is assigned to property for the purpose of taxation.

Associative Law for Addition: when adding a set of numbers, we can group together any numbers we wish.

B

Balanced equation: one in which the left and right members are equal.

Bank discount: the interest on a loan that is taken from the face of the loan at the time the loan is made.

Base: the line or surface upon which a plane or a solid figure rests.

Beneficiary: the person who is to receive the proceeds from an insurance policy.

Bisect: to cut into two equal parts.

Brokerage: the commission paid for the buying and selling of stocks and bonds.

Budget: a statement of probable expenses based on an expected income.

* The definitions apply to the use of the words in this book.

C

Canceled check: a check that has been paid by the bank and is so indicated on the check.

Capital stock: the amount of money represented by the total face value of the shares of a corporation.

Check: a depositor's written order on a bank for the payment of a certain sum of money on demand.

Circle: a plane bounded by a curved line all points of which are equidistant from the center.

Circumference: the line that bounds a circle; the length of the line that bounds the circle.

Coefficient: a number placed as a multiplier of another quantity.

Collateral: personal property given to be held as security for the payment of a debt.

Common stock: stock that does not pay the holder a stated amount of dividend.

Commutative Law for Addition: in adding two numbers, it does not matter in what order we add them.

Commutative Law for Multiplication: in multiplying two numbers, it does not matter in what order we multiply them.

Compasses: an instrument used to draw circles and arcs of circles.

Compound interest: interest on both the principal and the accrued interest.

Concentric circles: two or more circles with the same center.

Cone: a solid figure with a curved surface reaching a point at one end and a circular base at the other.

Consumer: one who consumes or uses a product or service.

Corporation: a group of persons who have been granted a charter to manufacture or sell certain merchandise.

Credit: sold on trust; charged.

Cube: the product obtained when a number is multiplied twice by itself; a solid figure with 6 equal square faces.

Currency: paper money.

Cylinder: a solid figure with a curved surface on the side and two equal circles for bases.

D

Day of maturity: the day on which an obligation becomes due.

Decagon: a plane figure having ten straight sides and ten angles.

Decimal fraction: a part of a unit that is expressed by the use of a decimal point.

Deduction: the amount subtracted.

Deposit: money placed in a bank and subject to withdrawal by the depositor.

Depositor: one who puts money in a bank subject to withdrawal.

Diagonal: a straight line drawn across a plane figure from one vertex to another vertex, the vertices being not consecutive.

Diameter: a straight line through the center of a circle dividing the circle into halves.

Difference: the result obtained by subtracting one number from another.

Digit: any one of the ten numerals, as, 1, 2, 3, and so on.

Dimension: extension in a single line or direction, as length, width, and thickness or depth.

Discount: a reduction from the list price of an article or an invoice; a deduction made as an interest charge for the loan of money.

Dissimilar terms: terms whose combinations of letters and exponents are not alike.

Dividend: the amount of the profits paid by a corporation to its stockholders; the amount of the earnings paid by a life insurance company to the holders of its participating policies.

Drawee: the person or organization on which an order is written.

Drawer: the person who writes a check or other demand for payment.

E

Employee: a person who works for another.

Equation: the statement that two quantities are equal in value.

Equilateral triangle: a triangle whose sides are equal in length.

Equity: amount paid on the principal when buying a home.

Equivalent: equal in value.

Estimate: to form an opinion as to certain values.

Evaluate: to find the numerical value of a quantity.

Exemption: a release from some obligation or payment of money.

Extremes: the two outside quantities of a proportion.

F

Face of note: amount stated on a note.

Face of policy: the amount of insurance stated in the policy.

Factor: one of two or more numbers which, when multiplied together, give a certain product.

Formula: the expression of a rule by means of letters and numbers.

Frustum: the remainder of a pyramid or cone after the top has been cut off by a plane parallel to the base.

G

Gauge: a measuring device.

Graph: a representation by means of lines showing relationships.

Gross: whole; twelve dozen.

Gross income: entire receipts without any deductions.

H

Height: the vertical distance from the base to the top of an object.

Hemisphere: one half of a sphere.

Hexagon: a plane figure having six straight sides and six angles.

Horizontal: a position parallel to the horizon.

Hypotenuse: that side of a right-angle triangle that is opposite the right angle.

I

Income: earnings, profit, or interest, coming in regularly.

Income tax: a tax levied upon the yearly receipts or profits.

Indirect measurement: a method of finding the size of an object without applying a measuring instrument directly.

Indorsement: the writing on the back of a check that transfers the ownership of the paper.

Inheritance tax: a charge or duty levied upon the amount of money or property received by an heir.

Installment buying: paid for in a number of stated payments.

Insurance: a system by means of which one may protect himself or his family against a specific loss or damage.

Insured: the person whose life or property is protected from loss or damage.

Integer: a whole number.

Interest: money paid for the use of money.

Internal revenue: the Bureau of Internal Revenue is the department of the government which collects the tax on certain articles manufactured in the United States; a tax on articles manufactured (within the United States).

Inventory: an itemized list of merchandise on hand.

Investment: placing of money so as to receive income or profit.

Isosceles triangle: a triangle that has two equal sides.

L

Lateral area: the sum of the areas of the sides, not including the base or bases, of a solid figure.

Lateral face: one of the sides of a solid figure.

Latitude: the number of degrees, on the surface of the earth, that lie between a given place and the equator.

Left member (of an equation): the terms to the left of the equals sign.

Length: the measure of an object from end to end.

Levy: an amount to be raised; to assess a certain amount.

License: a legal permit or right, usually issued upon the payment of a fee.

Line of sight: See paragraph 175.

Literal factor: any letter in an algebraic term.

Longitude: the number of degrees on the earth's surface that lie between a given place and the prime meridian.

Luxury tax: a duty levied by the government on the purchase price of nonessential articles.

M

Market value: the price that a property will bring when offered for sale.

Maximum: greatest quantity or degree attainable.

Means: the two inside quantities of a proportion.

Measurement: dimension.

Meridian: an imaginary circle extending around the earth through both poles.

Minimum: least quantity or degree possible.

Mortgage: assignment of property as security for debt.

Multiple: a number that can be divided exactly by a given number.

N

Negative number: a number preceded by a minus sign, expressing a quantity less than zero.

Negotiable: capable of being transferred from one owner to another.

Net income: the amount of money derived from labor, business, property, or capital remaining after all deductions have been subtracted.

Non-participating policy: a life insurance policy stating that the insured receives no dividends, that is, does not share in the profits of the insurance company.

Note or **promissory note:** a written promise to pay back the amount of a loan.

Numerical factor: in an algebraic term, the number that is a multiplier of the letters following it.

O

Obtuse angle: an angle that contains more than 90 degrees and less than 180 degrees.

Obtuse triangle: a triangle one of whose angles is obtuse.

Octagon: a plane figure having 8 straight sides and 8 angles.

Opposite side: in a triangle, the side that connects the two sides of the angle being considered.

Original: not copied.

Overhead: the operating expenses of a firm.

P

Parallel: lines an equal distance apart no matter how far extended.

Parallelogram: a 4-sided plane figure whose opposite sides are straight, equal, and parallel.

Participating policy: a life insurance policy stating that the insured receives dividends and so shares in the profits of the insurance company.

Par value: the original price stated on a bond or share of stock.

Payee: the person who receives or is to receive a sum of money.

Pentagon: a plane figure having 5 straight sides and 5 angles.

Per capita: for each person in a group.

Per cent: a value expressed in hundredths by means of the words *per cent* or a per cent (%) sign.

Perfect square: a product formed when a number is multiplied by itself.

Perimeter: the sum of the lengths of the sides of a plane figure.

Perpendicular: at right angles to a line or surface.

Pi ($\pi = 3.1416$): the ratio of the circumference of a circle to its diameter.

Plane: a flat surface—if any two points on it are joined by a straight line, the line will lie wholly in the surface.

Plane figure: a shape, drawn on a flat surface, that has length and width but no thickness.

Policy: a written agreement of insurance issued by an insurance company to the insured.

Polygon: a closed figure having any number of straight sides and angles.

Position: the arrangement of an object when in place.

Positive number: a number, sometimes preceded by a plus sign, expressing a quantity greater than zero.

Preferred stock: stock that pays the holder a stated amount of dividends.

Premium: the price of insurance for a stated period.

Principal: an amount of money that is invested or borrowed.

Proceeds: the amount of money received from a sale.

Promissory note: a written promise to pay a certain sum of money on a stated day to a certain person.

Property tax: a charge or duty based on the assessed value of a certain piece of property.

Protractor: instrument for measuring angles.

Pyramid: a solid figure having triangles for faces.

Q

Quadrilateral: any 4-sided plane figure having straight sides.

R

Radical sign: a mark ($\sqrt{}$) placed before a number to indicate that its square root is to be found.

Radii: (plural of *radius*).

Radius: a straight line from the center of a circle to its circumference.

Rate: the percent of a given principal that is to be paid as interest for one year.

Reconciliation: the act of making the balance of the checkbook stubs and the balance of the bank statement agree.

Rectangle: a plane figure having 4 straight sides and 4 right angles.

Rectangular prism: a solid figure which has 6 sides, all of which are rectangles.

Registered bond: a bond on which the owner's name is recorded by the company.

Regular figure: a plane figure in which all sides are equal in length.

Remainder: in subtraction, the result obtained by subtracting one number from another; in division, the number remaining after a given number has been divided exactly by another number.

Retail: the sale of merchandise by a shopkeeper to a consumer.

Revenue: income.

Right angle: an angle that contains exactly 90 degrees.

Right member (of an equation): the terms to the right of the equals sign.

Right triangle: a triangle containing one right angle.

Ruler fractions: fractions usually marked off on a ruler, as $\frac{1}{2}$, $\frac{1}{4}$, $\frac{1}{8}$, and so forth.

S

Salability: ease with which the item can be sold.

Sales tax: a tax collected by a state or city government from the seller and paid by the customer at the time of the sale.

Scale: a straight edged instrument marked with equal units of measure; also a ratio used to show comparison of measurements.

Scale drawing: a drawing reduced in size with lines in the same proportion as in the original object.

Signature: the name of a person written by his own hand.

Signed number: a number preceded by a plus or minus sign.

Similar terms: two or more terms having the same combination of letters.

Similar triangles: triangles that have the same size angles and the same shape.

Slanting: in a position neither horizontal nor vertical.

Social Security tax: a per cent of a worker's salary added to a like amount paid by the employer and sent to the government, to be paid to retired workers as a pension.

Solid figure: a figure that has length, width, and thickness.

Sphere: a circular solid all points of whose surface are equally distant from the center.

Square: a rectangle all of whose sides are equal; the product obtained by multiplying a number by itself.

Square root: a number which, when multiplied by itself, gives a certain product; one of the two equal factors of a product.

Square unit: a square of a certain size that is used to determine the area of a surface.

Stockholder: owner of stock in a corporation.

Straight angle: an angle of 180 degrees.

Subdivision: a smaller part.

Symbol: representation by a sign or letter.

T

Tangent: See paragraph 176.

Tax: a compulsory charge or duty on income or property levied for the support of the government.

Tax rate: a fixed standard used to compute the tax to be paid by any individual.

Terms: quantities connected by plus or minus signs.

Thickness: the distance between two parallel sides of a solid figure.

Total area: the sum of the areas of the sides and bases of a solid figure.

Trapezoid: a plane figure with 4 straight sides only 2 of which are parallel.

Triangle: a plane figure having 3 straight sides and 3 angles.

Triangular prism: a solid figure with 3 rectangular faces and 2 parallel triangles for bases.

U

Unit of area: the measurement used to determine the amount of space in a plane figure.

Unknown number: the quantity to be found.

V

Valuation: estimated value.

Vertex: the point where the two sides of an angle meet.

Vertical: a position at right angles to the horizon.

Volume: the number of cubic units in a solid figure.

W

Width: the measure of an object from side to side.

Withdrawal: money taken from a depositor's bank account.

BRAIN TEASERS

1. These "figureheads" are made from the digits, 0, 1, 2, 3, 4, 5, 6, 7, 8, 9. Design several different "figureheads."

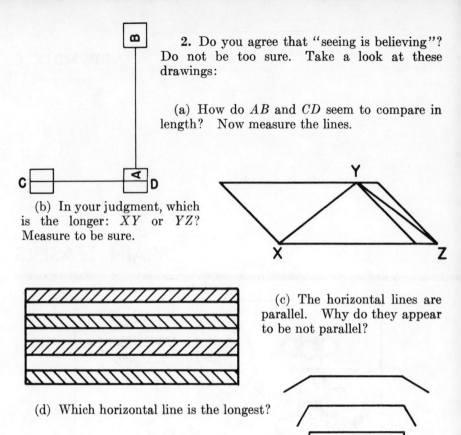

2. Do you agree that "seeing is believing"? Do not be too sure. Take a look at these drawings:

(a) How do *AB* and *CD* seem to compare in length? Now measure the lines.

(b) In your judgment, which is the longer: *XY* or *YZ*? Measure to be sure.

(c) The horizontal lines are parallel. Why do they appear to be not parallel?

(d) Which horizontal line is the longest?

3. Add 1 to 11 and make it 20.

4. Four sheep ahead of a sheep, four sheep behind a sheep, and a sheep in the middle. How many sheep are there?

5. How can you take one-half of eleven and get six?

6. Draw a square. Divide it into 9 equal squares. In these squares arrange the digits 1 to 9, inclusive, so as to add to 15 in every straight line.

7. If a speeder going 45 miles per hour has a two-minute start on a police car traveling 60 miles per hour, show by a straight-line graph how many minutes are required and how far each car will travel before the police car overtakes the speeder.

8. If a pup in a box weighs 2 pounds 10 ounces, and the box alone weighs 10 ounces, what does the pup weigh?

9. How far can you continue to multiply the digits 1 to 9, exclusive of the 8, by 9 or multiples of 9, and get like digits in the product, as:

12345679	12345679	12345679
9	18	27
111111111	222222222	333333333

10. Two fishermen, each weighing 200 pounds, and their two sons, weighing 100 pounds each, cross a river in a small boat that will carry only 200 pounds. How do they all manage to get across?

11. What is the difference between a two-foot square and two square feet?

12. Arrange the digits 1 to 9, inclusive, in any order. Try dividing the result by 9.

13. Which is correct to say: "12 and 9 *is* 20" or "12 and 9 *are* 20"?

14. An old Indian offered to divide his 23 ponies among his three sons. The oldest was to receive one-half the ponies, the second son one-third, and the youngest one-eighth. How was the division made?

15. Prove that 960 = 1000.

16. Can you determine the sum of the numbers 1 to 40, inclusive, without adding them?

17. Take one from nine and get ten.

18. How many half-inch blocks will it take to fill an inch hole?

19. A $\frac{1}{2}$-mile square is what part of $\frac{1}{2}$ square mile?

20. How can you place three 9's so that they will exactly equal ten?

21. A pan and a lid cost $1.20. The pan cost $1 more than the lid. What is the cost of each?

22. How far can you continue to multiply 37 by multiples of 3 and have like digits in the products, as:

37	37	37
3	6	9
111	222	333

23. Select any number. Reverse the order of its digits and subtract the two numbers. Try dividing the remainder by 9.

24. Write 20 with two equal figures.

25. John has 36 ears of corn in a box. How many trips will it take a squirrel to carry out all the corn, if it carries out 3 ears each trip?

26. Tom wishes to take his cat, his bird, and his dog across the river to his home. He can take but one at a time. The cat will eat the bird and the dog will kill the cat if they are left together. How can he get them all safely across?

27. A girl went to the pantry with a 5-cup and a 3-cup measure to get exactly 4 cups of sugar. How did she measure it?

28. If it takes 6 minutes to saw a log into 3 pieces, how long will it take to saw the same log into 4 pieces?

29. How many minutes will it take to cut 10 yards of cloth into one-yard towels, if one yard is cut off per minute?

30. Jack bought a bicycle for $30, sold it for $35, and then bought it back for $25. How much is his profit?

31. How much dirt is there in a hole 3 ft. by 2 ft. by 1 ft.?

3. In XI cross the I with another I and the result is XX.

4. 5 sheep.

5. The upper half of XI is vi.

6.

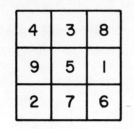

There are other solutions to **6**; however, the numbers will always be in the same relative positions.

7.

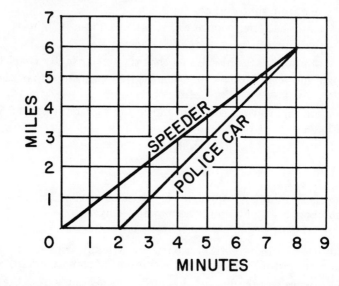

8. 2 pounds 10 ounces.

9. Up through 81.

10. Two sons cross, and one son rows back. One man crosses, and other son rows back. Both sons cross, and one son rows back. Other man rows over, and other son rows back. Both sons cross.

11. A two-foot square is a square 2 feet on an edge. Two square feet is an area of any shape that contains 2 square feet.

12. The result will always be divisible by 9.

13. Neither is correct, for 12 and 9 are *21*.

14. The father borrowed a pony from a friend and placed it in the pen, making 24 ponies. The oldest son took one-half the ponies, or 12; the second son took 8, and the third son took 3. The father returned the borrowed pony, and all were satisfied.

15. In counting time, 9:60 = 10:00.

16. The sum of each pair of end numbers, as 1 and 40, 2 and 39, and so forth, is 41 in each case. The 20 pairs of these numbers would add the same as 20 × 41 = 820.

17. Take I away from IX and X remains.

18. 8.   **19.** $\frac{1}{2}$.   **20.** $9\frac{9}{9}$.

21. The pan cost $1.10 and the lid $.10.   **22.** Up through 27.

23. The remainder will always be divisible by 9. This is used as a test by bookkeepers to locate mistakes in copying in correct order the numbers on the books.

24. XX.   **25.** 36 trips. He carries his own 2 ears each trip.

26. Tom takes the cat across; returns and takes the dog across; brings the cat back and takes the bird across. He leaves the bird with the dog and returns for the cat.

27. She fills the 3-cup measure and pours the sugar into the 5-cup measure. The 3-cup measure is filled again and enough of it is poured into the 5-cup measure to fill it, leaving 1 cup of sugar in the 3-cup measure. The 5-cup measure is emptied and the one cup of sugar is poured into it. The 3-cup measure is filled and poured into the 5-cup measure, making 4 cups of sugar.

28. 9 minutes.   **29.** 9 minutes.   **30.** $10.00.   **31.** No dirt.

USEFUL TABLES

BUSINESS COUNTING UNITS

12 units = 1 dozen (doz.)
12 dozen = 1 gross (gr.)
144 units = 1 gross

BUSINESS WEIGHT UNITS

16 ounces (oz.) = 1 pound (lb.)
100 pounds (lb.) = 1 hundredweight (cwt.)
2,000 pounds   = 1 ton (T.)

LINEAR MEASURE

12 inches (in. *or* '') = 1 foot (ft. *or* ')
3 feet = 1 yard (yd.)
$16\frac{1}{2}$ feet = 1 rod (rd.)
$5\frac{1}{2}$ yards = 1 rod
5,280 feet = 1 mile (mi.)
320 rods = 1 mile

SQUARE MEASURE

144 square inches (sq. in.) = 1 square foot (sq. ft.)
9 square feet = 1 square yard (sq. yd.)
$272\frac{1}{4}$ square feet = 1 square rod (sq. rd.)
$30\frac{1}{4}$ square yards = 1 square rod
160 square rods = 1 acre (A.)
640 acres = 1 square mile (sq. mi.)

CUBIC MEASURE

1,728 cubic inches (cu. in.) = 1 cubic foot (cu. ft.)
27 cubic feet = 1 cubic yard (cu. yd.)

DRY MEASURE

2 pints (pt.) = 1 quart (qt.)
8 quarts   = 1 peck (pk.)
4 pecks   = 1 bushel (bu.)

LIQUID MEASURE

4 gills (gi.) = 1 pint (pt.)
2 pints   = 1 quart (qt.)
4 quarts   = 1 gallon (gal.)
$31\frac{1}{2}$ gallons   = 1 barrel (bbl.)
2 barrels   = 1 hogshead (hhd.)

ANGLES AND ARCS

$$60 \text{ seconds } ('') = 1 \text{ minute } (')$$
$$60 \text{ minutes } = 1 \text{ degree } (°)$$
$$90 \text{ degrees } = 1 \text{ right angle}$$
$$360 \text{ degrees } = 1 \text{ circle}$$

EQUIVALENTS

1 bushel	= 2,150 cu. in. or $1\frac{1}{4}$ cu. ft. (approximately,
1 gallon	= 231 cu. in.
1 cubic foot	= $7\frac{1}{2}$ gallons
1 cubic foot water	= $62\frac{1}{2}$ pounds
1 cubic foot ice	= $57\frac{1}{2}$ pounds
π	= 3.1416 or $3\frac{1}{7}$ (approximately)
1 meter	= 39.37 inches or 1.1 yd.
1 centimeter	= .4 inch (approximately)
1 decimeter	= 4 inches
1 kilometer	= .6 mile or $\frac{5}{8}$ mile (approximately)
1 yard	= .914 meter
1 mile	= 1.609 kilometers

FORMULAS

$A = bh$, area of a rectangle.

$A = s^2$, area of a square.

$A = bh$, area of a parallelogram.

$A = \frac{1}{2}bh$, area of a triangle.

$A = \frac{1}{2}h(b + b')$, area of a trapezoid.

$A = \pi r^2$, area of a circle.

$C = \pi d$ or $2\pi r$, circumference of a circle.

$A = 4\pi r^2$, area of the surface of a sphere.

$S = Ph$, lateral area of a rectangular prism.

$S = Ch$, or $2\pi rh$, lateral area of a cylinder.

$V = Bh$ or lwh, volume of a rectangular prism.

$V = Bh$ or $\pi r^2 h$, volume of a cylinder.

$V = \frac{1}{3}Bh$ or $\frac{1}{3}\pi r^2 h$, volume of a cone.

$V = \frac{1}{3}Bh$, volume of a pyramid.

$V = \frac{4}{3}\pi r^3$, volume of a sphere.

$A + B + C = 180°$, sum of the angles of a triangle.

$P = 2b + 2h$, perimeter of a rectangle.

$P = 4s$, perimeter of a square.

$P = a + b + c$, perimeter of a triangle.

$D = 16t^2$, distance covered by a falling object.

$a = \dfrac{S}{n}$, average of a sum.

$S = a \times n$, sum of numbers.

$p = .0005V^3$, pounds of pressure of air exerted upon wings of a moving airplane.

$C = \dfrac{F - 32°}{9} \times 5$, Fahrenheit to Centigrade.

$$F = \frac{C}{5} \times 9 + 32°, \text{ Centigrade to Fahrenheit.}$$

$$p = \frac{2wh}{s+1}, \text{ an engineer's formula.}$$

$$d = \frac{v^2}{2r}, \text{ a mechanic's formula.}$$

$$L = d + \frac{2r^2}{5d}, \text{ a pendulum formula.}$$

$$h = \frac{V}{b^2}, \text{ height of a square prism.}$$

COMMON PER CENTS AND THEIR EQUIVALENT FRACTIONS

$*\frac{1}{2} = .50 = 50\%$	$\frac{2}{7} = .28\frac{4}{7} = 28\frac{4}{7}\%$	$*\frac{1}{12} = .08\frac{1}{3} = 8\frac{1}{3}\%$
$*\frac{1}{3} = .33\frac{1}{3} = 33\frac{1}{3}\%$	$\frac{3}{7} = .42\frac{6}{7} = 42\frac{6}{7}\%$	$\frac{5}{12} = .41\frac{2}{3} = 41\frac{2}{3}\%$
$*\frac{2}{3} = .66\frac{2}{3} = 66\frac{2}{3}\%$	$\frac{4}{7} = .57\frac{1}{7} = 57\frac{1}{7}\%$	$\frac{7}{12} = .58\frac{1}{3} = 58\frac{1}{3}\%$
$*\frac{1}{4} = .25 = 25\%$	$*\frac{1}{8} = .12\frac{1}{2} = 12\frac{1}{2}\%$	$\frac{11}{12} = .91\frac{2}{3} = 91\frac{2}{3}\%$
$*\frac{3}{4} = .75 = 75\%$	$*\frac{3}{8} = .37\frac{1}{2} = 37\frac{1}{2}\%$	$*\frac{1}{16} = .06\frac{1}{4} = 6\frac{1}{4}\%$
$*\frac{1}{5} = .20 = 20\%$	$*\frac{5}{8} = .62\frac{1}{2} = 62\frac{1}{2}\%$	$\frac{3}{16} = .18\frac{3}{4} = 18\frac{3}{4}\%$
$*\frac{2}{5} = .40 = 40\%$	$*\frac{7}{8} = .87\frac{1}{2} = 87\frac{1}{2}\%$	$\frac{7}{16} = .43\frac{3}{4} = 43\frac{3}{4}\%$
$*\frac{3}{5} = .60 = 60\%$	$*\frac{1}{10} = .10 = 10\%$	$*\frac{1}{15} = .06\frac{2}{3} = 6\frac{2}{3}\%$
$*\frac{1}{6} = .16\frac{2}{3} = 16\frac{2}{3}\%$	$*\frac{2}{10} = .20 = 20\%$	$\frac{2}{15} = .13\frac{1}{3} = 13\frac{1}{3}\%$
$*\frac{5}{6} = .83\frac{1}{3} = 83\frac{1}{3}\%$	$*\frac{3}{10} = .30 = 30\%$	$\frac{4}{15} = .26\frac{2}{3} = 26\frac{2}{3}\%$
$*\frac{1}{7} = .14\frac{2}{7} = 14\frac{2}{7}\%$	$*\frac{4}{10} = .40 = 40\%$	$\frac{7}{15} = .46\frac{2}{3} = 46\frac{2}{3}\%$

ANSWERS TO PRACTICE EXERCISES*

Practice Exercise 1a (page 403)

12	9	13	7	12	4	10	10	9	17	(10)
11	7	8	15	14	10	16	6	9	15	
14	7	17	9	13	9	11	9	10	8	(30)
6	6	12	8	8	10	11	14	8	5	(40)

Practice Exercise 1b (page 404)

24	23	27	25	15	
31	35	31	31	31	(10)
48	42	46	43	41	
54	52	50	53	51	(20)
64	63	63	66	65	(25)

Practice Exercise 1c (page 404)

35 38 32 37 34 34 33 39   (8)

Practice Exercise 1d (page 404)

| 3,084 | 2,537 | 1,722 | 1,349 | 1,776 | 2,330 | (6) |
| 2,811 | 2,132 | 2,124 | 1,575 | 2,577 | 2,225 | (12) |

Practice Exercise 2a (page 405)

35	45	48	10	72	14	16	21	(8)
56	18	0	63	25	49	54	15	
0	30	32	0	15	24	14	28	(24)
0	42	18	72	12	20	0	16	
48	18	21	12	7	35	8	9	(40)

Practice Exercise 2b (page 406)

9,000	22,800	16,200	34,400	41,300	
48,000	35,000	1,000	36,000	54,000	(10)
1,060	12,320	56,400	45,810	42,560	(15)

Practice Exercise 2c (page 406)

| 31,110 | 103,824 | 278,718 | 42,840 | 217,536 | |
| 74,340 | 217,756 | 66,272 | 64,163 | 366,025 | (10) |

Practice Exercise 2d (page 407)

24,928	32,956	37,196	59,677	(4)
23,199	32,214	49,898	10,960	
42,108	25,198	5,076	16,376	(12)

* The answers to the last half of the problems are in *The Teacher's Manual.*

Practice Exercise 3a (page 407)

2 1 4 4 6 5 1 1 7 3 (10)

0 0 6 3 1 9 3 2 2 0 (20)

Practice Exercise 3b (page 408)

20	32	42	51	18	11	
20	16	24	18	24	36	(12)
44	25	10	26	13	17	
13	24	31	10	49	30	(24)
4	4	7	8	8	7	(30)

Practice Exercise 3c (page 409)

278 73 134 456 17 67 (6)

379 540 77 182 55 198 (12)

Practice Exercise 3d (page 409)

58,392	8,129	16,768	36,650	
10,378	30,381	16,667	61,274	(8)
6,449	7,402	2,316	14,013	
39,290	5,037	27,596	32,297	(16)

Practice Exercise 4a (page 410)

7	4	4	0		3	8	9	7	(16)
2	8	8	3	(8)	6	5	0	6	
4	4	2	5		5	2	7	0	(24)

Practice Exercise 4b (page 410)

210	141	102	$50\frac{1}{2}$	$111\frac{1}{9}$	
141	120	114	104	$1178\frac{2}{7}$	(10)
182	$105\frac{5}{6}$	76	$41\frac{1}{5}$	1010	
$80\frac{5}{8}$	$50\frac{2}{3}$	$92\frac{1}{7}$	$90\frac{1}{2}$	$1022\frac{1}{2}$	(20)

Practice Exercise 4c (page 411)

25	27	76	82	
24	28	48	94	(8)
22	18	81	34	(12)

Practice Exercise 4d (page 411)

358	2001	$1173\frac{53}{72}$	
$715\frac{44}{63}$	$1559\frac{5}{12}$	$958\frac{7}{9}$	(6)
$1257\frac{38}{51}$	$819\frac{31}{35}$	$895\frac{53}{90}$	(9)

Practice Exercise 5a (page 412)

$1\frac{1}{10}$		$1\frac{5}{8}$		$\frac{7}{12}$		$\frac{7}{24}$	
$\frac{3}{4}$		$1\frac{1}{2}$		$1\frac{1}{6}$		$\frac{8}{15}$	(8)
$1\frac{1}{12}$	$\frac{5}{8}$	$\frac{1}{2}$	$1\frac{5}{12}$	$\frac{11}{15}$	$\frac{13}{18}$	$1\frac{1}{4}$	(15)

Practice Exercise 5b (page 412)

$\frac{5}{12}$	$\frac{7}{8}$	$1\frac{1}{40}$	$1\frac{5}{24}$	$\frac{23}{24}$	$1\frac{1}{2}$	$1\frac{1}{2}$	(7)
$1\frac{1}{16}$	$1\frac{1}{6}$	$1\frac{1}{12}$	$1\frac{1}{8}$	$1\frac{1}{6}$	$\frac{13}{24}$	$1\frac{1}{4}$	(14)

Practice Exercise 5c (page 413)

$1\frac{1}{2}$		$1\frac{1}{4}$		$1\frac{13}{24}$		$1\frac{13}{40}$	(4)
$1\frac{5}{14}$		$1\frac{5}{18}$		$\frac{7}{12}$		$1\frac{1}{4}$	
$\frac{1}{2}$		$\frac{17}{24}$		$1\frac{11}{15}$		$1\frac{1}{2}$	(12)

APPENDIX E

Practice Exercise 5d (page 413)

$11\frac{1}{6}$	$13\frac{4}{15}$	$14\frac{2}{9}$	$18\frac{3}{10}$	$16\frac{19}{24}$	$16\frac{1}{12}$	(6)
$17\frac{5}{6}$	$14\frac{3}{8}$	$18\frac{13}{14}$	$16\frac{1}{6}$	$14\frac{5}{9}$	$11\frac{4}{5}$	(12)
$5\frac{7}{12}$	$12\frac{11}{12}$	$10\frac{15}{16}$	$17\frac{4}{9}$	13	$14\frac{15}{16}$	(18)

Practice Exercise 5e (page 413)

$41\frac{1}{3}$	$72\frac{1}{2}$	$156\frac{5}{6}$	$142\frac{13}{20}$	$110\frac{4}{9}$	(5)
121	$73\frac{1}{2}$	$104\frac{3}{4}$	$170\frac{11}{15}$	$75\frac{5}{6}$	(10)
$33\frac{11}{16}$	$110\frac{2}{3}$	$106\frac{2}{5}$	$122\frac{13}{24}$	$74\frac{1}{3}$	(15)

Practice Exercise 6a (page 414)

$\frac{1}{4}$	$\frac{2}{15}$	$\frac{1}{4}$	$\frac{3}{20}$	$\frac{1}{6}$	$\frac{3}{8}$
$\frac{5}{8}$	$\frac{1}{2}$	$\frac{7}{15}$	$\frac{1}{9}$	$\frac{5}{14}$	$\frac{19}{48}$ (12)

Practice Exercise 6b (page 414)

$\frac{1}{2}$	$\frac{3}{8}$	$\frac{3}{5}$	$\frac{1}{2}$
$\frac{5}{24}$	$\frac{1}{4}$	$\frac{5}{16}$	$\frac{9}{16}$ (8)
$\frac{1}{6}$	$\frac{2}{5}$	$\frac{5}{12}$	$\frac{5}{12}$ (12)

Practice Exercise 6c (page 415)

$6\frac{1}{3}$	$6\frac{1}{24}$	$5\frac{7}{10}$	$2\frac{11}{12}$	$\frac{4}{5}$	$4\frac{8}{15}$
$6\frac{7}{8}$	$4\frac{5}{8}$	$5\frac{1}{2}$	$4\frac{13}{16}$	$5\frac{2}{7}$	$3\frac{1}{2}$ (12)

Practice Exercise 6d (page 415)

$11\frac{1}{5}$	17	$20\frac{5}{8}$	$16\frac{7}{8}$	$28\frac{11}{12}$	$57\frac{1}{5}$
$27\frac{9}{16}$	$94\frac{11}{24}$	$57\frac{8}{9}$	$37\frac{5}{6}$	$3\frac{1}{20}$	$12\frac{7}{8}$ (12)

Practice Exercise 7a (page 416)

$\frac{4}{9}$	$\frac{12}{25}$	$\frac{1}{2}$	$\frac{2}{3}$
$\frac{3}{11}$	$\frac{1}{4}$	$\frac{8}{33}$	$\frac{1}{16}$ (8)
$\frac{10}{21}$	$\frac{1}{3}$	$\frac{1}{6}$	$1\frac{1}{20}$ (12)

Practice Exercise 7b (page 416)

$4\frac{1}{2}$	$1\frac{1}{2}$	$6\frac{2}{3}$	6 (4)
$3\frac{1}{2}$	$7\frac{1}{2}$	16	$6\frac{2}{3}$
$11\frac{2}{3}$	$3\frac{1}{5}$	$2\frac{1}{4}$	$36\frac{2}{3}$ (12)

Practice Exercise 7c (page 417)

$7\frac{1}{3}$	15	$1\frac{7}{8}$	$2\frac{1}{4}$
$15\frac{1}{3}$	12	25	$5\frac{1}{16}$ (8)
$10\frac{1}{2}$	$15\frac{5}{8}$	$18\frac{3}{4}$	$11\frac{1}{9}$ (12)

Practice Exercise 8a (page 417)

$1\frac{1}{6}$	$2\frac{2}{3}$	$1\frac{1}{4}$	$5\frac{1}{3}$
$\frac{7}{9}$	$1\frac{7}{9}$	1	6 (8)
$\frac{3}{4}$	$1\frac{1}{6}$	2	$\frac{8}{9}$ (12)

Practice Exercise 8b (page 418)

36	7	$6\frac{3}{4}$	$\frac{11}{36}$ (4)
72	27	25	48
$\frac{1}{3}$	$\frac{5}{48}$	$\frac{1}{18}$	$\frac{1}{14}$ (12)

Practice Exercise 8c (page 418)

$\frac{14}{27}$	$\frac{3}{4}$	$3\frac{3}{4}$	$\frac{9}{10}$ (4)
$3\frac{3}{4}$	$1\frac{2}{3}$	$1\frac{1}{4}$	2
$6\frac{2}{5}$	$3\frac{1}{2}$	8	$4\frac{3}{5}$ (12)

Practice Exercise 9a (page 418)

1. 1.8   **2.** 20.7   **3.** 21.56   **4.** 25.097   **5.** 7.675   **6.** 63.06

Practice Exercise 9b (page 418)

1. 5.64   **2.** 24.30   **3.** 16.887   **4.** 2.928   **5.** 3.0

6. 10.46   **7.** 6.0   **8.** 102.97   **9.** 250.675   **10.** 872.87

ANSWERS TO PRACTICE EXERCISES

Practice Exercise 9c (page 419)

1. .42	2. 3.8	3. 2.3	4. 8.06	5. 6.079
6. .28	7. 2.131	8. 7.138	9. 14.83	10. 56.77

Practice Exercise 9d (page 419)

1. 8.2	2. .31	3. 1.53	4. 16.9	5. 1.37
6. 6.6	7. 4.8	8. 1.545	9. 23.2	10. $58.8\frac{1}{2}$

Practice Exercise 10a (page 420)

1. .536	2. 1.53	3. .0268	4. .0084	5. 780
6. 6.01	7. 39,200	8. .14920	9. .268	10. .6813
11. 2.4192	12. .33258	13. 7.7688	14. 329.184	15. 14.6224

Practice Exercise 10b (page 420)

1. 7.4	2. .042	3. 3150	4. .656	5. .00125
6. 6.24	7. 39	8. .19	9. .074	10. 650
11. 10	12. 1616	13. 9	14. 34.32	15. 6.25

Practice Exercise 11a (page 421)

1. 1.8	2. 28	3. 160	4. .4	5. 20
6. 20	7. .02	8. .002	9. 200	10. 2

Practice Exercise 11b (page 421)

1. 4210	2. 42300	3. 10.7	4. .9	5. .469
6. $26.68\frac{4}{9}$	7. 28.1	8. 4	9. 78.7	10. .00004

Practice Exercise 11c (page 421)

1. 274	2. 1.27	3. 3.43	4. 250	5. .034	6. 32.4
7. 50.9	8. 128	9. 286	10. 128.3	11. 31.07	12. .91

Practice Exercise 12a (page 422)

1. 18%	2. 75%	3. 42%	4. 64%	5. 3%
6. 5%	7. 1%	8. 8%	9. $17\frac{1}{2}$%	10. 25.6%
11. $62\frac{1}{2}$%	12. $56\frac{1}{4}$%	13. 80%	14. 10%	15. $72\frac{3}{4}$%
16. 135%	17. 118%	18. $206\frac{1}{4}$%	19. $312\frac{1}{2}$%	20. 400%

Practice Exercise 12b (page 422)

1. 50%	2. 75%	3. 20%	4. 30%	5. 35%
6. $12\frac{1}{2}$%	7. 24%	8. $33\frac{1}{3}$%	9. $44\frac{4}{9}$%	10. $16\frac{2}{3}$%
11. $18\frac{3}{4}$%	12. $87\frac{1}{2}$%	13. $26\frac{2}{3}$%	14. 2%	15. $14\frac{2}{7}$%
16. $66\frac{2}{3}$%	17. $57\frac{1}{7}$%	18. $62\frac{1}{2}$%	19. $83\frac{1}{3}$%	20. 70%

Practice Exercise 12c (page 423)

1. .50	2. .75	3. .18	4. .20	5. .10	6. .02
7. .09	8. .07	9. .025	10. .0325	11. .0175	12. .125
13. .1875	14. .06	15. .01	16. $.16\frac{2}{3}$	17. .175	18. $.08\frac{1}{3}$
19. .0625	20. $.83\frac{1}{3}$	21. .625	22. .375	23. .005	24. .0075

APPENDIX E

Practice Exercise 12d (page 423)

1. $\frac{1}{5}$ 2. $\frac{3}{20}$ 3. $\frac{3}{4}$ 4. $\frac{11}{20}$ 5. $\frac{1}{20}$ 6. $\frac{1}{50}$

7. $\frac{1}{100}$ 8. $\frac{7}{100}$ 9. $\frac{7}{200}$ 10. $\frac{17}{400}$ 11. $\frac{23}{400}$ 12. $\frac{9}{800}$

13. $\frac{1}{200}$ 14. $\frac{1}{500}$ 15. $\frac{3}{800}$ 16. $\frac{1}{125}$ 17. $\frac{3}{500}$ 18. $\frac{2}{25}$

19. $\frac{1}{1000}$ 20. $\frac{1}{200}$ 21. $\frac{1}{700}$ 22. $\frac{1}{225}$ 23. $\frac{1}{150}$ 24. $\frac{1}{120}$

Practice Exercise 12e (pages 423–424)

Common Fraction	Decimal Fraction	Per Cent	Common Fraction	Decimal Fraction	Per Cent
1. $\frac{9}{10}$	.9	90%	6. $\frac{3}{25}$	.12	12%
2. $\frac{3}{5}$	.6	60%	7. $\frac{7}{8}$	$.87\frac{1}{2}$	$87\frac{1}{2}$%
3. $\frac{4}{25}$	.16	16%	8. $1\frac{1}{2}$	1.5	150%
4. $\frac{9}{100}$	.09	9%	9. $1\frac{3}{10}$	1.3	130%
5. $\frac{1}{25}$	.04	4%	10. $\frac{9}{200}$	.045	$4\frac{1}{2}$%

Practice Exercise 12f (page 424)

1. 40%   2. $\frac{3}{10}$ 3. $\frac{7}{8}$ 4. $8\frac{1}{3}$%   5. $\frac{1}{6}$

6. $\frac{1}{8}$ 7. 350%   8. $6\frac{1}{4}$%   9. $77\frac{7}{9}$%

Practice Exercise 13a (page 424)

1. 1.8   2. 17   3. 10.2   4. 40.29   5. 8.76   6. 16.5   7. 3.6   8. 1.92

9. 6   10. 9   11. 14.4   12. 100   13. .5   14. 2   15. 1.6   16. .06

Practice Exercise 13b (page 425)

1. 12   2. 6   3. 12   4. 14   5. 50   6. 35   7. 21   8. 15

9. 3   10. 100   11. 80   12. 2   13. 105   14. 3   15. 14   16. 9

Practice Exercise 13c (page 425)

1. 100%   2. $66\frac{2}{3}$%   3. 5%   4. 50%   5. 200   6. 400   7. 300%

8. $33\frac{1}{3}$%   9. 25%   10. $62\frac{1}{2}$%   11. 14%   12. 200   13. 25   14. 4200

15. 4400   16. 200%   17. $33\frac{1}{3}$%   18. 80   19. 60   20. 36   21. 9000

Practice Exercise 13d (page 426)

1. 7.5   2. $16\frac{2}{3}$%   3. 60   4. 62   5. 30%   6. 40%   7. 25%

8. 3.5   9. 28   10. 75   11. 20%   12. 4   13. 20   14. 27

Practice Exercise 14a (page 426)

1. 32 in.   2. 9 ft.   3. 6 pt.   4. 20 qt.   5. 54 oz.

6. 8 pk.   7. 72 in.   8. 4,000 lb.   9. $1\frac{1}{4}$ doz.   10. 135 min.

11. 480 sec.   12. 432 sq. in.   13. 18 sq. ft.   14. 54 cu. ft.   15. 135 cu. ft.

16. 1280 acres   17. 693 cu. in.   18. 26 qt.   19. 9 in.   20. 45 min.

ANSWERS TO PRACTICE EXERCISES

Practice Exercise 14b (page 427)

1. 1 ft. 10 in. **2.** 2 yd. 1 ft. **3.** 1 hr. 30 min. **4.** $2\frac{1}{2}$ gal.
5. $7\frac{1}{2}$ qt. **6.** $1\frac{1}{2}$ lb. **7.** $1\frac{2}{3}$ hr. **8.** $1\frac{1}{2}$ sq. ft.
9. $1\frac{1}{4}$ min. **10.** $6\frac{1}{4}$ ft. **11.** $1\frac{1}{2}$ gal. **12.** 3 tons

Practice Exercise 14c (page 427)

1. 54 in. **2.** 88 oz. **3.** 7 pt. **4.** $1\frac{1}{4}$ lb. **5.** 45 in.
6. 8 ft. 4 in. **7.** 135 min. **8.** $2\frac{1}{2}$ min. **9.** 7 pk. **10.** 21 articles

Practice Exercise 15a (page 428)

1. 7 ft. 9 in. **2.** 10 yd. **3.** 12 yr.
4. 6 gal. **5.** 56 min. 10 sec. **6.** 14 yd. 2 ft. 11 in.
7. 1 da. 11 hr. 35 min. **8.** 42 min. 59 sec.

Practice Exercise 16a (page 428)

1. 1 bu. 2 pk. 6 qt. **2.** 1 da. 8 hr. 40 min. **3.** 18 T. 600 lb.
4. 53 yd. 1 ft. **5.** 4 gal. 2 qt. **6.** 3 yd. 2 ft.
7. 1 hr. 41 min. 20 sec. **8.** 17 mi.

Practice Exercise 17a (page 429)

1. 3' 10'' **2.** 2 pk. 6 qt. **3.** 2 T. 1200 lb.
4. 29 min. 50 sec. **5.** 1 pk. 5 qt. **6.** 5 ft. 5 in.
7. 28 pk. 4 qt. **8.** 4 T. 1800 lb.

Practice Exercise 18a (page 429)

1. 2 hr. 6 min. **2.** 2 pk. 1 qt. $\frac{1}{2}$ pt. **3.** 4 min. $1\frac{2}{3}$ sec. **4.** 6 ft. $2\frac{2}{3}$ in.
5. 2 qt. $1\frac{1}{2}$ pt. **6.** 1 yd. 1 ft. 8 in. **7.** 1 ft. **8.** 4 yd. 2 ft.

INDEX

Horizontal line, 259
Hypotenuse, 330

I

Income taxes, 245
Indirect measurement, 325
  by right triangles, 330
  by scale drawings, 120
Indorsement, 183
Installment buying, 226
Insurance:
  annuities, 161
  automobile, 170
  beneficiary, 157
  coinsurance clause, 167
  collision, 170
  dividend, 158
  endowment, 160
  fire, 167, 170
  group, 161
  kinds of, 158
  liability, 170
  life, 158
  limited payment, 159
  need for, 157
  non-participating, 158
  participating, 158
  policy, 157
  premium, 157, 158
  property damage, 170
  Social Security, 164
  straight life, 159
  terms of, 157
  theft, 170
  workmen's compensation, 163
Integer, 3
Interest:
  bonds, 199
  compound, 192
  graph, 190
  loans, 223
  simple, 187
  six per cent method, 189
  table, 194
Inventory tests (see Testing and improvement program)
Investments, 198
Isosceles triangle, 313

K

Known number, 369

L

Lateral area, 284
  of cylinder, 298
  of rectangular prism, 284
Lateral faces, 285

Latitude, 263
Law of Grouping for Addition, 9
Law of Order for Addition, 8
Law of Order for Multiplication, 14
Left member of equation, 369
Life insurance, 158–162
  annuities, 161
  benefits of, 158
  dividends, 158
  endowment, 160
  family income, 161
  group, 161
  investing in, 205
  kinds of, 159
  limited payment, 159
  premium, 158
  rates (table), 162
  straight life, 159
Limited payment life insurance, 159
Lines:
  bisector of, 315
  curved, 260
  designs, 262
  graph, 145, 146
  horizontal, 259
  of sight, 334
  parallel, 260
  perpendicular, 261
  slanting, 259
  vertical, 259
Literal factor, 347
Loans, bank, 223
Longitude, 263

M

Making change, 233
Map reading, 262–263
Mathematics, importance of, 3
Maturity, day of, 224
Measurement:
  angles, 126
  cubit, 105, 107
  digit, 105, 107
  direct, 105–130, 325
  foot, 105
  history of, 105
  inch, 106, 108
  indirect, 325, 330–331
  metric system, 113
  of angles, 126
  of diameters, 293
  of lines, 110
  origin of, 105
  rod, 106
  ruler, 108
  scale, 108
  with protractor, 126
  yard, 106, 107

4 5 6 7 8

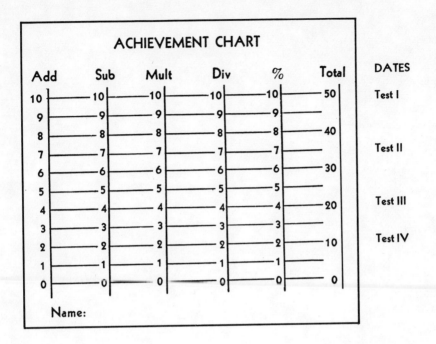

ACHIEVEMENT CHART

Add	Sub	Mult	Div	%	Total	DATES
10	10	10	10	10	50	Test I
9	9	9	9	9		
8	8	8	8	8	40	
7	7	7	7	7		Test II
6	6	6	6	6	30	
5	5	5	5	5		
4	4	4	4	4	20	Test III
3	3	3	3	3		
2	2	2	2	2	10	Test IV
1	1	1	1	1		
0	0	0	0	0	0	

Name:

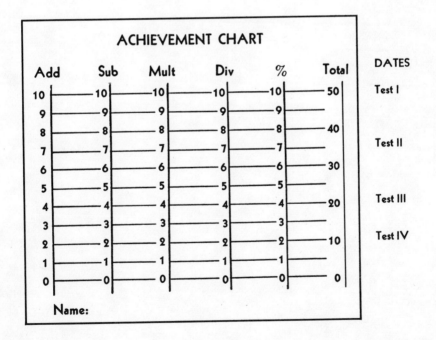

ACHIEVEMENT CHART

Add	Sub	Mult	Div	%	Total	DATES
10	10	10	10	10	50	Test I
9	9	9	9	9		
8	8	8	8	8	40	
7	7	7	7	7		Test II
6	6	6	6	6	30	
5	5	5	5	5		
4	4	4	4	4	20	Test III
3	3	3	3	3		
2	2	2	2	2	10	Test IV
1	1	1	1	1		
0	0	0	0	0	0	

Name: